STUDIES IN THE
THEORY OF NUMBERS

STUDIES IN THE
THEORY OF NUMBERS

By

LEONARD EUGENE DICKSON

Professor of Mathematics in the
University of Chicago

CHELSEA PUBLISHING COMPANY
NEW YORK, N. Y.

Printed in the United States of America

PREFACE

This book contains numerous original investigations in the theory of quadratic forms in three or four variables. These investigations are based on an extensive literature which requires numerous corrections, revisions, and extensions. It was therefore decided to start from first principles and give a systematic exposition of both old and new results in the arithmetic of quadratic forms, chiefly in three variables.

A form f is called universal if it represents all integers; and f is a zero form if $f = 0$ has integral solutions not all zero. The novel results include the following. Every universal, indefinite, ternary, quadratic form is a zero form. We determine all universal zero forms in three or four variables. We obtain three general theorems on the representation of numbers by ternary quadratic forms; a special case of one of them had been found by Arnold Meyer, but with the omission of a condition. These theorems lead us to the first complete proof of the remarkable theorem that every indefinite quadratic form f in five or more variables is a zero form, and also enable us to give necessary and sufficient conditions that $ax^2 + by^2 + cz^2 + du^2 = 0$ be solvable. We obtain the fourth, as well as the known first three, minima of real, indefinite, ternary, quadratic forms, and prove that the fifth minimum is more remote from the fourth than the latter is from the third. Here is first published Oppenheim's extension to forms without minima and his determination of the minima of indefinite, quaternary, quadratic forms. Finally, we give a complete geometrical theory of reduced, positive, ternary, quadratic forms.

Proofs of most of these new results depend upon known facts which are here developed in detail and with minute care. Previous statements of several of these facts have been erroneous and their proofs quite inadequate. It was no small task to write a satisfactory exposition. Practically no help was to be had from Bachmann's two large volumes on *Die Arithmetik der quadratischen Formen* (1898 and 1923), which contain the same errors as the original articles, and which impose very restrictive conditions on the topics treated (but without explicit mention in the theorems), so that his special results do not furnish an adequate basis for our new results.

The leading theorems are those for which the word "theorem" is printed in bold face type.

Arnold Ross was of great assistance in the revision of chapters iv, v, and vi, and the construction of the two tables. Gordon Pall rendered very valuable aid during the early stages of chapters vii and xiii. These gifted young men were aiding the author in successive years as Research Assistants in the University of Chicago. It was appropriate that the final revision of chapter xiii, dealing with Hardy's memoir on sums of squares, should be done by his former pupil, A. Oppenheim, now in his third year at Chicago as Commonwealth Fund Fellow and already an expert in number theory. The author is under still further obligations to Ross and Oppenheim for reading the proof sheets, and to Pall for reading chapters vii and xiii.

L. E. DICKSON

CONTENTS

PART I. ARITHMETIC OF TERNARY QUADRATIC FORMS

CHAPTER   PAGE

I. QUADRATIC FORMS IN n VARIABLES 3
Adjoint. Invariants. Reciprocal form. Principle of reciprocity. Primitive form represents assigned integer.

II. INTRODUCTION TO TERNARY QUADRATIC FORMS; UNIVERSAL FORMS . 9
Two fundamental identities. Definite and positive forms. Signs of Ω, Δ. Primitive sets. Simultaneous and proper representation by f and its reciprocal F. Numbers $\equiv \pm 1$ (mod 4) are represented. Every universal, indefinite, ternary, quadratic form is a zero form.

III. REPRESENTATION OF BINARY FORMS BY TERNARY FORMS 24
All solutions of $ax+by+cz=0$. A representation determines a pair of roots R and S of three congruences. Representation of numbers.

IV. EQUIVALENCE OF INDEFINITE, TERNARY, QUADRATIC FORMS . . . 35
Properties of solutions of $x^2-pqEy^2=1$. When all binary forms of a genus are represented by one indefinite ternary form. Numbers represented by binary forms. Characters of a ternary form. Cases in which every genus of ternary forms contains a single class.

V. GENERA AND REPRESENTATION OF NUMBERS 61
Gauss's celebrated theorem on duplication of binary forms. General theorems on the representation of numbers by ternary forms. Existence of genera.

VI. QUADRATIC DIOPHANTINE EQUATIONS 68
Every indefinite quadratic form in n variables is a zero form if $n \geqq 5$. Necessary and sufficient conditions that $ax^2+by^2+cz^2+du^2=0$ shall have integral solutions not all zero.

PART II. MINIMA OF INDEFINITE QUADRATIC FORMS

VII. MINIMA OF INDEFINITE, BINARY, QUADRATIC FORMS 79

VIII. MINIMA OF INDEFINITE, TERNARY, QUADRATIC FORMS 108
Associated binary form. First four minima of ternary forms. Reduced binary forms. Below the fourth minimum. Forms without minima.

IX. MINIMA OF INDEFINITE, QUATERNARY, QUADRATIC FORMS 134
Five lemmas on ternary forms. Associated ternary form.

X. TABULATION OF REDUCED, INTEGRAL, TERNARY, QUADRATIC FORMS WHICH ARE INDEFINITE, BUT NOT ZERO FORMS 147

PART III. MISCELLANEOUS INVESTIGATIONS OF QUADRATIC FORMS

CHAPTER   PAGE

XI. REDUCED, POSITIVE, QUADRATIC FORMS; THEIR MINIMA 155
Literature. All equivalent binary forms are represented by the same point lattice. Reduced fundamental parallelograms and binary forms. The hexagon. Ternary forms, lattices, reduced parallelopipeds. Minima. Seeber's inequality. Reduced, positive, ternary, quadratic forms; tables. No two reduced forms are equivalent. Automorphs. Minimum of positive quadratic forms in four variables.

XII. UNIVERSAL, ZERO, QUADRATIC FORMS 187
Normal form. Problem reduced to a congruence. Case of three variables. Four variables.

XIII. NUMBER OF REPRESENTATIONS AS A SUM OF 5, 6, 7, OR 8 SQUARES . 198
History. Outline of method. Modular and theta functions. Eighteen lemmas. Sum of singular series.

INDEX 229

PART I

ARITHMETIC OF TERNARY QUADRATIC FORMS

The first six chapters deal with general aspects of quadratic forms, chiefly in three variables, with applications to quadratic Diophantine equations in n variables.

CHAPTER I

QUADRATIC FORMS IN n VARIABLES

In this chapter we shall define certain arithmetical invariants of a quadratic form f and discuss the relations between f and two forms said to be adjoint or reciprocal to f. No previous acquaintance with the subject is expected, but full details are given. In §§ 1, 2, the coefficients may be any complex numbers.

1. Adjoint of a form. In this chapter we consider only those quadratic forms $a_{11}x_1^2+2a_{12}x_1x_2+\ldots$ in which the coefficients of all products of distinct variables are even. We denote a_{12} also by a_{21}, and in general take $a_{ji}=a_{ij}$. We can therefore express our form as a double sum

$$(1) \qquad f=f(x_1, \ldots, x_n) = \Sigma_{ij}a_{ij}x_ix_j \ ,$$

where each summation index i and j takes the values $1, \ldots, n$, and similarly throughout the chapter.

Consider the halves of the derivatives of f:

$$(2) \qquad X_i = \tfrac{1}{2}\partial f/\partial x_i = \Sigma_j a_{ij}x_j \qquad (i=1, \ldots, n) \ .$$

The determinant $d=|a_{ij}|$ of these n linear functions is called the *determinant*[1] of the form (1). We assume that $d\neq0$. To the minor of a_{ij} in d we prefix the sign $(-)^{i+j}$ and obtain the *cofactor* A_{ij} of a_{ij} in d. Hence the solved form of equations (2) is

$$(3) \qquad dx_j = \Sigma_i A_{ij}X_i \qquad (j=1, \ldots, n) \ .$$

Elimination of the X_i between (2) and (3) yields equations which show that $|A_{ij}| \cdot |a_{ij}| = d^n$. This proves

$$(4) \qquad\qquad |A_{ij}| = d^{n-1} \ .$$

By (1) and (2), we get

$$(5) \qquad\qquad \Sigma x_i X_i = f \ ,$$

$$(6) \qquad\qquad \tfrac{1}{2}\Sigma x_i \partial f/\partial x_i = f \ .$$

---

[1] When $n=2$, we shall in later chapters call $-d$ the determinant of (1).

3

From (3) and (5), we see at once that

$$(7) \qquad df = \Sigma_{ij} A_{ij} X_i X_j \equiv \phi(X_1, \ldots, X_n) \,,$$

which is called the *adjoint* of f. By (4), the determinant of ϕ is d^{n-1}. Insertion of the values (2) of the X_i yields the identity

$$(8) \qquad \phi(\tfrac{1}{2}\partial f/\partial x_1, \ldots, \tfrac{1}{2}\partial f/\partial x_n) \equiv df(x_1, \ldots, x_n) \,.$$

Let ψ be the adjoint of $\phi(X_1, , \ldots, X_n)$. Hence

$$\psi(\tfrac{1}{2}\partial\phi/\partial X_1, \ldots, \tfrac{1}{2}\partial\phi/\partial X_n) \equiv d^{n-1}\phi(X_1, \ldots, X_n) \,.$$

The left member is $\psi(dx_1, \ldots, dx_n)$ since $dx_j = \tfrac{1}{2}\partial\phi/\partial X_j$ by (3) and (7). But ψ is homogeneous and of degree 2. Hence $\psi(dx_1, \ldots, dx_n) = d^2\psi(x_1, \ldots, x_n)$. This proves that

$$\psi(x_1, \ldots, x_n) = d^{n-3}\phi(X_1, \ldots, X_n) \,.$$

Hence by (7),

$$(9) \qquad \psi(x_1, \ldots, x_n) \equiv d^{n-2}f(x_1, \ldots, x_n) \,.$$

THEOREM 1. *The adjoint of the adjoint of f is the product of f by the power $n-2$ of the determinant of f.*

The literal coefficients of ϕ in (7) are the cofactors A_{ij} of the elements a_{ij} of $|a_{ij}|$. Applying this result to ψ, we have

$$(10) \qquad \text{Cofactor of } A_{ij} \text{ in } |A_{ij}| \text{ is } d^{n-2} a_{ij} \,.$$

2. Transformation of f and its adjoint ϕ. The equations

$$(11) \qquad x_j = \Sigma_k c_{jk} y_k \qquad (j = 1, \ldots, n)$$

are said to define a linear transformation whose determinant $C = |c_{jk}|$ is assumed $\neq 0$. For f in (1), we shall write

$$(12) \qquad f_k = f(c_{1k}, \ldots, c_{nk}) \,.$$

By (2) and (11),

$$(13) \qquad \tfrac{1}{2}\partial f/\partial x_i = \Sigma_{jk} a_{ij} c_{jk} y_k \,.$$

Replacing x_i by c_{ik} in (2) for $i = 1, \ldots, n$, we get

$$(14) \qquad \tfrac{1}{2}\partial f_k/\partial c_{ik} = \Sigma_j a_{ij} c_{jk} \,.$$

Multiply this by y_k and sum as to k; we get (13), whence

(15) $$\partial f/\partial x_i = \Sigma_k y_k \partial f_k/\partial c_{ik} \ .$$

In (6) insert the values (11) and (15); thus

$$f = \tfrac{1}{2}\Sigma_{isk}c_{is}\partial f_k/\partial c_{ik}\cdot y_s y_k \ .$$

Denote this quadratic form by

(16) $$g(y_1, \ldots , y_n) = \Sigma_{sk}b_{sk}y_s y_k \ .$$

Hence transformation (11) replaces f by g, where

(17) $$b_{sk} = \tfrac{1}{2}\Sigma_i c_{is}\partial f_k/\partial c_{ik} \ .$$

Replacing x_i by c_{ik} in (6), we see that

(18) $$b_{kk} = f_k \ .$$

By (14) and (17),

(19) $$b_{sk} = \Sigma_{ij}c_{is}a_{ij}c_{jk} \ ,$$

which evidently reduces to (18) when $s = k$.
Let δ denote the determinant of g. By (19),

(20) $$\delta = C^2 d \ .$$

Write Y_s for $\tfrac{1}{2}\partial g/\partial y_s$. As in (5),

(21) $$\Sigma y_s Y_s = g \ .$$

By (16), (19), and (13),

(22) $$Y_s = \Sigma_k b_{sk}y_k = \Sigma_{ijk}c_{is}a_{ij}c_{jk}y_k = \tfrac{1}{2}\Sigma_i c_{is}\partial f/\partial x_i \ ,$$

whence

(23) $$Y_s = \Sigma_i c_{is}X_i \qquad (s = 1, \ldots , n) \ .$$

The matrix of (23) is obtained from the matrix of (11) by interchanging rows and columns. Hence transformation (23) is called the *transpose* of transformation (11).

As in (7), the adjoint of g is a quadratic form $\chi(Y_1, \ldots, Y_n)$ which becomes δg for the values (22). But $g = f = \phi/d$. Hence (23) replaces χ/δ by ϕ/d.

Let C_{is} denote the cofactor of c_{is} in $C = |c_{is}|$. Then the solved form of (23) is

$$(24) \qquad X_j = \Sigma_k C^{-1} C_{jk} Y_k \qquad (j = 1, \ldots, n) \; .$$

This must replace ϕ/d by χ/δ and hence, by (20), replace $C^2\phi$ by χ. By (5) and (21),

$$(25) \qquad \Sigma x_i X_i = \Sigma y_s Y_s$$

is another form of $f = g$ when the X_i are replaced by (2) and Y_s by $\frac{1}{2}\partial g/\partial y_s$. Also when the x_i and the X_i are all independent variables, (25) holds under transformations (11) and (24), which are therefore called *contragredient* transformations. In fact,

$$\Sigma x_j X_j = C^{-1} \Sigma_{j,s,k} c_{js} C_{jk} y_s Y_k = \Sigma y_s Y_s \; ,$$

since $\Sigma_j c_{js} C_{jk} = 0$ or C, according as $k \neq s$ or $k = s$.

Theorem 2. *Let transformation* (11) *of determinant* $C \neq 0$ *replace* f *of determinant* d *by* g. *The coefficients of* g *have the values* (18) *and* (19). *The determinant* δ *of* g *is* $C^2 d$. *If* ϕ *and* χ *are the adjoints of* f *and* g, *the contragredient transformation* (24) *replaces* $C^2\phi$ *by* χ. *Also,* (25) *holds for* (11) *and* (24).

3. Equivalence, invariants σ and τ, primitive forms. Henceforth, let transformation (11) be *integral*, i.e., have integral coefficients, and let its determinant C be unity. Solving (11), we get

$$(26) \qquad y_k = \Sigma_j C_{jk} x_j \qquad (k = 1, \ldots, n) \; ,$$

which define the *inverse* transformation. Its determinant is unity by (4), and its coefficients C_{jk} are integers. Then (11) is said to replace f by an *equivalent* form g, while (26) replaces g by the equivalent form f.

By (20), equivalent forms have the same determinant, which is therefore called an *invariant* of f. Since the coefficients of (24) are integers of determinant unity, Theorem 2 yields

Theorem 3. *The adjoints of equivalent forms are equivalent.*

Let τ denote the g.c.d. (greatest common divisor) of the literal coefficients a_{ij} of f. Let σ denote the g.c.d. of its coefficients

$$(27) \qquad a_{11}, \ldots, a_{nn}, 2a_{12}, \ldots, 2a_{n-1\,n} \; .$$

Then σ is called the *divisor* of f. The literal coefficients b_{sk} of g have the values (19). Hence any common divisor of the a_{ij} is a common divisor of the b_{sk}. The converse follows from (26). Hence τ is also the g.c.d. of the b_{sk}.

By (18), $b_{kk} = f(c_{1k}, \ldots, c_{nk})$ is a linear homogeneous function of the coefficients (27) of f with integral coefficients. By (19), every $2b_{sk}$ is such a function. Hence σ is a factor of the divisor of g. Conversely, by (26), the divisor of g is a factor of σ.

THEOREM 4. *Equivalent forms have the same determinant d, same divisor σ, and same greatest common divisor τ of their literal coefficients. In other words, d, σ, τ are invariants of the form f.*

If $\tau = 1$, f is called *primitive*. Then the g.c.d. of the $2a_{ij}$ is 2, whence $\sigma = 1$ or 2. Evidently $\sigma = 1$ if $a_{11}, \ldots, a_{nn}$ are not all even, and $\sigma = 2$ if they are all even. When $\tau = 1$, f is called *properly* or *improperly primitive*, according[1] as $\sigma = 1$ or $\sigma = 2$. Theorem 4 shows that if f is properly (improperly) primitive, any form equivalent to f is properly (improperly) primitive.

4. Invariants Ω and Δ, reciprocal form. Let Ω denote the g.c.d. of the literal coefficients A_{ij} of the adjoint ϕ of f. By Theorems 3 and 4, Ω is an invariant of f.

We write $\phi = \Omega F$ and call F the form *reciprocal* to f. Evidently F is a primitive form.

Assume that also f is primitive. Then, by (10), Ω^{n-1} divides all $d^{n-2}a_{ij}$ and hence divides d^{n-2}. Hence

$$(28) \qquad d^{n-2} = \Delta\Omega^{n-1}$$

defines an integer Δ which is an invariant of f. By its definition (7), the adjoint of $\phi = \Omega F$ is the product of Ω^{n-1} by the adjoint of F. Hence by Theorem 1 and (28),

$$(29) \qquad \text{adjoint of } F \text{ is } \Delta f \,.$$

The form reciprocal to F is therefore f. Theorem 3 now implies that *if two forms are equivalent, their reciprocals are equivalent, and conversely.*

Let D denote the determinant of F. The determinant of $\phi = \Omega F$ is evidently $\Omega^n D$, but is d^{n-1} by (4), whence

$$(30) \qquad D = d^{n-1}/\Omega^n \,.$$

From (28) and (30) we conclude that

$$(31) \qquad D^{n-2} = \Omega\Delta^{n-1} \,.$$

[1] When $\sigma = 1$, then $\tau = 1$. Of forms with $\sigma = 2$, some have $\tau = 1$ and others have $\tau = 2$; for example, $2x^2 + 2y^2 + 2mxy$ with m odd or even.

THEOREM 5. *For a primitive form f of determinant d and invariants Ω and Δ, and its reciprocal form F of determinant D and invariants Δ and Ω, there is a principle of reciprocity which permits the interchange of f with F and Ω with Δ in all relations.*

When $n=3$, (28) and (31) become $d=\Delta\Omega^2$ and $D=\Omega\Delta^2$.

5. Primitive forms represent integers prime to an assigned one.

When $x_1, \ldots, x_n$ are integers, the value of $f(x_1, \ldots, x_n)$ is said to be *represented* by the form f. It is represented *properly* in case the g.c.d. of $x_1, \ldots, x_n$ is unity.

THEOREM 6. *Any properly primitive form f represents properly an integer prime to any assigned integer m.*

Let p be any prime factor of m. Give f the notation (1).

I. Let one of the coefficients a_{ii} be prime to p. After a change of notation we may assume that a_{11} is prime to p. Assign integral values to the x_i such that x_1 is prime to p, while $x_2, \ldots, x_n$ are all divisible by p. Then the value of f is an integer prime to p.

II. Let every a_{ii} be divisible by p. Since f is properly primitive, $p>2$, and not every $a_{ij}(i\neq j)$ is divisible by p. We may assume that a_{12} is prime to p. Take x_1 and x_2 both prime to p, but $x_3, \ldots, x_n$ all divisible by p. Then the value of f is an integer prime to p.

Let $p_1, \ldots, p_k$ be the distinct prime factors of m. We just proved the existence of integers $x_{1i}, \ldots, x_{ni}$ such that $f(x_{1i}, \ldots, x_{ni})$ is prime to p_i for $i=1, \ldots, k$. If j is any one of $1, \ldots, n$, there exists an integer x_j for which simultaneously

$$x_j \equiv x_{j1} \pmod{p_1}, \ldots, x_j \equiv x_{jk} \pmod{p_k} .$$

For $i=1, \ldots, k$, $f(x_1, \ldots, x_n)$ is therefore congruent modulo p_i to $f(x_{1i}, \ldots, x_{ni})$ and hence is prime to p_i. It is therefore prime to m. Let g denote the g.c.d. of $x_1=gX_1, \ldots, x_n=gX_n$. Then $f(X_1, \ldots, X_n)$ is prime to m, and is an integer represented properly by f.

THEOREM 7. *Any improperly primitive form f represents properly the double of an odd integer prime to any assigned integer m.*

Here $a_{ii}=2\alpha_{ii}$ and the a_{ij} $(i\neq j)$ are not all even. As in the parts I and II of the proof of Theorem 6,

$$\tfrac{1}{2}f = \Sigma\alpha_{ii}x_i{}^2 + a_{12}x_1x_2 + a_{13}x_1x_3 + \ldots$$

takes a value not divisible by any given prime ≥ 2. As in the third part of that proof, there exist integers $X_1, \ldots, X_n$ whose g.c.d. is 1 such that $\tfrac{1}{2}f(X_1, \ldots, X_n)$ is prime to $2m$.

CHAPTER II

INTRODUCTION TO TERNARY QUADRATIC FORMS; UNIVERSAL FORMS

In the first half of this chapter we shall develop elementary theorems relating mainly to the simultaneous representation of integers by a form and its reciprocal. These theorems are required for the advanced theory in later chapters. Fortunately they suffice also for the proof (in the second half of this chapter) of the writer's new theorem that every universal, indefinite, ternary, quadratic form is a zero form.

In this chapter summation indices always take the values 1, 2, 3.

6. The fundamental identities. By (12), (17), and (18),

$$f(c_{11}, c_{21}, c_{31})f(c_{12}, c_{22}, c_{32}) - \tfrac{1}{4}[\Sigma c_{i1}\partial f(c_{12}, c_{22}, c_{32})/\partial c_{i2}]^2$$

is the value of $b_{11}b_{22} - b_{12}^2$. The latter is evidently the coefficient of Y_3^2 in the adjoint χ of g in (16) and may be computed as follows. We saw that transformation (24) replaces $C^2\phi$ by χ. As in (18) for $k=3$, the coefficient of Y_3^2 in the transform of ϕ by (24) is

$$\phi(C^{-1}C_{13}, \ C^{-1}C_{23}, \ C^{-1}C_{33}) \ .$$

Multiplication by C^2 deletes the factors C^{-1} and gives

$$\phi(c_{21}c_{32} - c_{22}c_{31}, \ c_{12}c_{31} - c_{11}c_{32}, \ c_{11}c_{22} - c_{12}c_{21}) \ .$$

Writing u_i for c_{i1} and v_i for c_{i2}, we get the identity

$$(32) \quad f(u_1, u_2, u_3) \cdot f(v_1, v_2, v_3) - \tfrac{1}{4}[\Sigma u_i \partial f(v_1, v_2, v_3)/\partial v_i]^2$$
$$\equiv \phi(u_2 v_3 - u_3 v_2, \ u_3 v_1 - u_1 v_3, \ u_1 v_2 - u_2 v_1) \ ,$$

where ϕ is the adjoint of f.

Let f be primitive and F its reciprocal form. In (32) we replace f by F, apply (29), and get

$$(33) \quad F(u_1, u_2, u_3) \cdot F(v_1, v_2, v_3) - \tfrac{1}{4}[\Sigma u_i \partial F(v_1, v_2, v_3)/\partial v_i]^2$$
$$\equiv \Delta f(u_2 v_3 - u_3 v_2, \ u_3 v_1 - u_1 v_3, \ u_1 v_2 - u_2 v_1) \ .$$

We call (32) the first, and (33) the second, fundamental identity.

7. Definite and indefinite forms. For real values of the variables and coefficients, f is called a *positive* form (or *negative* form) if every value of f is $\geqq 0$ (or $\leqq 0$) and if $f = 0$ only when each variable is zero. Both positive and negative forms are called *definite*. But forms which take both positive and negative values are called *indefinite*. By (7), a form and its adjoint are both definite or both indefinite. The properties of a negative form f follow from those of the positive form $-f$.

Let f be a positive form (1) with $n = 3$. Then each $a_{ii} > 0$ since $f(1, 0, 0) = a_{11}$, etc. By (32) for $v_1 = 1$, $v_2 = v_3 = 0$,

$$(34) \qquad a_{11}f(u_1,\ u_2,\ u_3) \equiv L^2 + A_{33}u_2^2 - 2A_{23}u_2u_3 + A_{22}u_3^2\ ,$$

where $L = a_{11}u_1 + a_{12}u_2 + a_{13}u_3$. Multiply by A_{33} and apply (10) for $i = j = 1$; we get

$$(35) \qquad a_{11}A_{33}f(u_1,\ u_2,\ u_3) \equiv A_{33}L^2 + (A_{33}u_2 - A_{23}u_3)^2 + da_{11}u_3^2\ .$$

When $u_1 = -a_{12}, u_2 = a_{11}, u_3 = 0$, (34) becomes $a_{11}f = A_{33}a_{11}^2$, whence $A_{33} > 0$. If $d < 0$, (35) shows that f would take negative values. Hence $d > 0$ and the adjoint is a positive form by (7). Since $-f$ has the same adjoint as f, the adjoint of a negative form is a positive form.

Conversely, let a_{11}, A_{33}, and d be all positive. Then (35) shows that $f \geqq 0$ and that $f = 0$ implies $u_3 = 0$, $u_2 = 0$, $u_1 = 0$.

THEOREM 8. *In a positive form, d, a_{ii}, A_{ii} $(i = 1, 2, 3)$ are all positive. If a_{11}, A_{33}, and d are positive, the form is positive.*

8. Conventions. Let d be the determinant of a primitive ternary form f. We continue to define Δ by (28), which is now $d = \Delta\Omega^2$.

If f is a positive form, then $d > 0$ and $\Delta > 0$. We take $\Omega > 0$. Since the adjoint of f is ΩF and is a positive form (§ 7), F is a positive form with the invariants Δ and Ω.

Let f be indefinite. If $d > 0$, then $\Delta > 0$ and we take $\Omega < 0$. But if $d < 0$, then $\Delta < 0$ and we take $\Omega > 0$. If F were definite, its adjoint would be a positive form by § 7, contrary to (29); hence F is indefinite. The determinant of F is $\Delta^2\Omega$ by § 4. Hence if f is indefinite and $d > 0$, the first and second invariants of f are $\Omega < 0$ and $\Delta > 0$, and those of F are Δ and Ω.

Hence reciprocity Theorem 5 continues to hold also for these new conventions, which aid in certain proofs.

Since the determinant of $-f$ is $-d$, we may restrict our future proofs to forms f having $d > 0$.

For example, $t = x^2 + \Omega y^2 + \Omega\Delta z^2$ has a positive determinant if $\Delta > 0$. Then t is a positive form if $\Omega > 0$ and indefinite if $\Omega < 0$. In each case, Ω and Δ are the invariants of t.

9. Primitive sets. Three integers are said to form a *primitive set* when their g.c.d. is unity.

THEOREM 9. *If a_1, a_2, a_3 and Z_1, Z_2, Z_3 are two primitive sets satisfying*

$$(36) \qquad a_1 Z_1 + a_2 Z_2 + a_3 Z_3 = 0 ,$$

there exist integers b_1, b_2, b_3 such that

$$(37) \qquad a_2 b_3 - a_3 b_2 = Z_1, \ a_3 b_1 - a_1 b_3 = Z_2, \ a_1 b_2 - a_2 b_1 = Z_3 .$$

Choose any solutions of $a_1 l + a_2 m + a_3 n = 1$ and take

$$b_1 = a_1 - mZ_3 + nZ_2, \ b_2 = a_2 - nZ_1 + lZ_3, \ b_3 = a_3 - lZ_2 + mZ_1 .$$

Write s for $a_1 l + a_2 m + a_3 n$, and t for $a_1 Z_1 + a_2 Z_2 + a_3 Z_3$. Then

$$\begin{vmatrix} a_2 & b_2 \\ a_3 & b_3 \end{vmatrix} = \begin{vmatrix} a_2 & -nZ_1 + lZ_3 \\ a_3 & -lZ_2 + mZ_1 \end{vmatrix} = sZ_1 - tl = Z_1 ,$$

$$\begin{vmatrix} a_3 & b_3 \\ a_1 & b_1 \end{vmatrix} = sZ_2 - tm = Z_2 , \qquad \begin{vmatrix} a_1 & b_1 \\ a_2 & b_2 \end{vmatrix} = sZ_3 - tn = Z_3 .$$

Remark 1. Given any primitive set Z_i, we can find a primitive set a_i satisfying (36). For example, let $Z_3 \neq 0$. Then (36) holds when

$$a_1 = a_2 = Z_3/D , \qquad a_3 = -(Z_1 + Z_2)/D ,$$

where D is chosen so that the g.c.d. of a_1, a_2, a_3 is 1.

The following interesting theorem will be used only in proving the minor Theorem 39.

Remark 2. If a_i, b_i, Z_i are given integers satisfying (37), where the Z_i have the g.c.d. unity, then all integral solutions of

$$(38) \qquad x_2 y_3 - x_3 y_2 = Z_1 , \quad x_3 y_1 - x_1 y_3 = Z_2 , \quad x_1 y_2 - x_2 y_1 = Z_3$$

are $x_i = \alpha a_i + \gamma b_i$, $y_i = \beta a_i + \delta b_i$, where α, β, γ, δ are integers such that $\alpha\delta - \beta\gamma = 1$.

Choose integers c_i so that $\Sigma c_i Z_i = 1$. In the determinant $|a_i, b_i, c_i| = 1$, let A_i and B_i denote the cofactors of a_i and b_i. By (37), Z_i is the cofactor of c_i. Write

$$\alpha = \Sigma A_i x_i , \quad \beta = \Sigma A_i y_i , \quad \gamma = \Sigma B_i x_i , \quad \delta = \Sigma B_i y_i .$$

Then

$$\begin{vmatrix} a & \gamma \\ \beta & \delta \end{vmatrix} = Z_1(A_2B_3 - A_3B_2) + Z_2(A_3B_1 - A_1B_3) + Z_3(A_1B_2 - A_2B_1)$$

is the expansion of the determinant $|A_i, B_i, Z_i| = 1$. By (38),

$$\delta x_1 - \gamma y_1 = B_2Z_3 - B_3Z_2 = a_1 , \qquad -\beta x_1 + a y_1 = A_3Z_2 - A_2Z_3 = b_1 ,$$

whose solution gives the values of x_1, y_1 in Remark 2.

10. Theorem 10. *If f represents A properly, f is equivalent to a form having A as the coefficient of y_1^2.*

By hypothesis, $f(a_1, a_2, a_3) = A$, where the a_i form a primitive set. If $a_1 = a_2 = 0$, then $a_3 = \pm 1$ and A is the coefficient of x_3^2. In the contrary case, $Z_1 = a_2/g$, $Z_2 = -a_1/g$, $Z_3 = 0$ satisfy (36) and form a primitive set by choice of g. Choose integers b_i as in Theorem 9. Employ integral solutions c_i of $Z_1c_1 + Z_2c_2 + Z_3c_3 = 1$. Then by (37) the transformation

$$(39) \qquad x_i = a_i y_1 + b_i y_2 + c_i y_3 \qquad (i = 1, 2, 3)$$

has the determinant $c_1Z_1 + c_2Z_2 + c_3Z_3 = 1$. Evidently it replaces $f(x_1, x_2, x_3)$ by $f(a_1, a_2, a_3)y_1^2 + \ldots$.

11. Simultaneous representation by reciprocal forms. Let f be a primitive form and F its reciprocal form. If

$$(40) \qquad m = f(a_1, a_2, a_3) , \qquad M = F(Z_1, Z_2, Z_3)$$

hold for integers a_i and Z_i satisfying (36), then the representations of m by f and M by F are called *simultaneous*. If also the a_i and the Z_i are both primitive sets, the representations are called simultaneous and *proper*. By (25), we have

THEOREM 11. *Let f be primitive and equivalent to g, and let G be reciprocal to g. Then m and M are represented simultaneously and properly by g and G if so represented by f and F.*

Consider the adjoint (7) of f in (1) for $n = 3$. Take $x_1 = X_3 = 1$, $x_2 = x_3 = X_1 = X_2 = 0$. Then $f = a_{11}$, $\phi = A_{33}$. But $\phi = \Omega F$. The coefficient A_{33}/Ω of X_3^2 in F is called its *third* coefficient. Similarly, a_{11} is the *first* coefficient of f. This proves

THEOREM 12. *The first coefficient of f and the third coefficient of its reciprocal F are represented simultaneously and properly by f and F.*

Hence the first coefficient of f and the third coefficient of F are represented simultaneously and properly by g and G. After interchanging f and g, and F and G, we see that the converse is

Theorem 13. *If m and M are represented simultaneously and properly by a primitive f and its reciprocal F, then f is equivalent to a form whose first coefficient is m and whose reciprocal form has M as its third coefficient.*

We employ § 10 with $A = m$. Transformation (39) has integral coefficients of determinant unity. It replaces f by $f_1 = E + H$, where H has the factor y_3, and

$$(41) \qquad E = my_1^2 + 2ry_1y_2 + ty_2^2 ,$$

$$2r = \Sigma a_i \partial f(b_1, b_2, b_3)/\partial b_i , \qquad t = f(b_1, b_2, b_3) ,$$

as shown by (17) and (18) with $s = 1$, $k = 2$. In (32) take $u_i = a_i$, $v_i = b_i$ and apply (37) and $\phi = \Omega F$. We get

$$mt - r^2 = \Omega F(Z_1, Z_2, Z_3) = \Omega M .$$

Hence, by (41), M is the third coefficient in the form reciprocal to f_1.

Theorem 14. *If m and M are represented simultaneously and properly by a primitive form f of positive determinant and its reciprocal F, and if $m > 0$, then $M > 0$.*

By Theorem 13 we may take $a_{11} = m$, $A_{33} = \Omega M$. Then $A_{33} \neq 0$ by $A_{22}A_{33} - A_{23}^2 = md > 0$. If $A_{33} > 0$, f is a positive form by Theorem 8, whence $\Omega > 0$ (§ 8), $M > 0$. If $A_{33} < 0$, f is indefinite, whence $\Omega < 0$, $M > 0$.

Second proof. Assume (40) for integers a_i and Z_i satisfying (36). In (32) take $u_i = x_i$, $v_i = a_i$; we get

$$(42) \quad mf(x_1, x_2, x_3) = \tfrac{1}{4}[\Sigma x_i \partial f(a)/\partial a_i]^2 + \Omega F(X_1, X_2, X_3) ,$$

$$X_1 = x_2a_3 - x_3a_2 , \qquad X_2 = x_3a_1 - x_1a_3 , \qquad X_3 = x_1a_2 - x_2a_1.$$

In (33) take $u_i = X_i$, $v_i = Z_i$; we get

$$MF(X_1, X_2, X_3) = \tfrac{1}{4}[\Sigma X_i \partial F(Z)/\partial Z_i]^2 + \Delta f(k_1, k_2, k_3) ,$$

$$k_1 = X_2Z_3 - X_3Z_2 , \qquad k_2 = X_3Z_1 - X_1Z_3 , \qquad k_3 = X_1Z_2 - X_2Z_1 .$$

We find that

$$k_1 = a_1(x_1Z_1 + x_2Z_2 + x_3Z_3) - x_1(a_1Z_1 + a_2Z_2 + a_3Z_3) .$$

The final sum is zero by (36). Similarly,

$$k_i = a_i(x_1Z_1 + x_2Z_2 + x_3Z_3) \qquad (i = 2, 3) .$$

Multiply (42) by M and replace MF by its foregoing value. We get

(43) $mMf(x_1, x_2, x_3) = M[\frac{1}{2}\Sigma x_i \partial f(a)/\partial a_i]^2 + \Omega[\frac{1}{2}\Sigma X_i \partial F(Z)/\partial Z_i]^2$
$$+ \Omega\Delta m(x_1Z_1 + x_2Z_2 + x_3Z_3)^2 .$$

If $m > 0$ and $M = 0$, then $x_1Z_1 + \ldots \equiv 0$ since $\Delta > 0$, $\Omega \neq 0$, whence every $Z_i = 0$, whereas the Z_i form a primitive set. Next, let $m > 0$, $M < 0$. If f is a positive form, then $\Omega > 0$ (§ 8) and the second member of (43) is an indefinite form, whereas the first member is a negative form. If f is indefinite, then $\Omega < 0$ and the second member is a negative form, whereas the first member is indefinite.

12. On numbers represented by a ternary form.

Theorem 15. *Let f be any ternary form whose determinant d is odd. Then f represents properly an integer $\equiv 1$ (mod 4) and also one $\equiv 3$ (mod 4).*

Since d is odd, the a_{ii} are not all even. We may assume that a_{11} is odd. When x_1 is replaced by $x_1 + (1 + a_{22})x_2 + (1 + a_{33})x_3$, f becomes a form in which the coefficient of each x_i^2 is odd. Hence let this be true of f itself. Then $s = a_{12} + a_{13} + a_{23}$ is even since d is odd. Write $t = a_{11} + a_{22} + a_{33}$. When $x_1 = x_2 = x_3 = 1$, the value of f is $v = t + 2s \equiv t$ (mod 4). If $a_{11} \equiv a_{22} \equiv a_{33}$ (mod 4), then $v - a_{11} \equiv 2a_{11} \not\equiv 0$ (mod 4). Hence not all of the four odd numbers a_{11}, a_{22}, a_{33}, v (each represented properly by f) are congruent modulo 4. Hence at least one of the four is $\equiv 1$ and another is $\equiv 3$ (mod 4).

Theorem 16. *If g is properly primitive, is not negative, and has determinant d, then g represents properly a positive integer k, such that k is prime to any assigned integer s and, in case d is odd, $k \equiv r$ (mod 4), where r is any assigned one of 1, 3.*

In case g is indefinite, it represents properly a positive integer and hence by Theorem 10 is equivalent to a form f whose first coefficient is positive. In case g is definite and hence positive, this is true of g itself and we write $f = g$.

By Theorem 6 there exist integers y_i such that $f(y_1, y_2, y_3)$ is prime to s. If d is even, take $\xi_i = y_i$. If d is odd, Theorem 15 shows that there exist integers z_i such that $f(z_1, z_2, z_3) \equiv r$ (mod 4). Let S be the largest odd divisor of s. Determine integers ξ_i such that

$$\xi_i \equiv y_i \pmod{S} , \quad \xi_i \equiv z_i \pmod{4} \qquad (i = 1, 2, 3) .$$

Whether d is even or odd, $f(\xi_1, \xi_2, \xi_3)$ is prime to s, and is $\equiv r$ (mod 4) if d is odd. The same is true of $f(\xi_1 + 4st, \xi_2, \xi_3)$ for every integer t. Applying (34) to this f, we see that this f is positive when t is sufficiently large numerically and of the same sign as s.

If the integers x_1, x_2, x_3 giving the corresponding representation by g have the g.c.d. D, then $k = g(x_1/D, x_2/D, x_3/D)$ has all the properties in the theorem.

13. Conclusion of simultaneous representation by f and F. By Theorems 10 and 16, any properly primitive form is equivalent to one whose third coefficient K has the properties

$$(44) \qquad \begin{cases} K > 0; \ K \text{ is prime to any assigned } n; \\ \text{when } \Omega\Delta \text{ is odd}, \ K \equiv \Omega \ (\text{mod } 4) \ . \end{cases}$$

THEOREM 17. *Let f and its reciprocal F be properly primitive, so that F may be assumed to have properties* (44), *where $n = \Omega^2 \Delta N$, N being arbitrary. Then f is equivalent to a form*

$$(45) \qquad f_1 = \psi + (\gamma\Omega\Delta + \tau n)z^2 + 2\rho nyz + 2\sigma nxz \ ,$$

where γ, τ, ρ, σ are integers and

$$(46) \qquad \psi = ax^2 + 2txy + by^2$$

is properly primitive. For $z = 0$, $f = f_1 = \psi$.

To avoid subscripts, give to f the notation

$$(47) \qquad ax^2 + by^2 + cz^2 + 2ryz + 2sxz + 2txy \ ,$$

and denote the cofactors of $a, \dots, t$ in the determinant d of f by $A, \dots, T$. Thus $K = C/\Omega$. Since K is prime to n and hence to ΩN, $K\gamma \equiv 1 \ (\text{mod } \Omega N)$ has a solution γ. We have

$$aS + tR + sC = 0 \ , \qquad tS + bR + rC = 0 \ , \qquad sS + rR + cC = d = \Omega^2\Delta \ .$$

Hence

$$a\lambda + t\mu + s \equiv 0 \ , \qquad t\lambda + b\mu + r \equiv 0$$
$$s\lambda + r\mu + c \equiv \gamma\Omega\Delta \qquad (\text{mod } n)$$

are satisfied when λ and μ are determined by

$$K\lambda \equiv S/\Omega \ , \qquad K\mu \equiv R/\Omega \qquad (\text{mod } n) \ .$$

Let f become f_1 when x is replaced by $x + \lambda z$ and y by $y + \mu z$. Evidently f and f_1 have the same terms (46) free of z. The altered coefficients are

$$r' = t\lambda + b\mu + r \equiv 0 \ , \qquad s' = a\lambda + t\mu + s \equiv 0$$
$$c' = \lambda s' + \mu r' + s\lambda + r\mu + c \equiv \gamma\Omega\Delta \qquad (\text{mod } n) \ .$$

Hence f_1 is of the form (45). We next prove that ψ is primitive. If a prime p divides a, t, and b, it divides $ab - t^2 = C = K\Omega$ and divides the determinant $d = \Omega^2\Delta$ of f. But K is prime to n and hence to d. Hence p divides Ω and thus divides the six literal coefficients of the primitive form (45), a contradiction.

Finally, ψ is properly primitive. This is evident by (45) if $\Omega\Delta$ and hence n is even, since f and f_1 are properly primitive, whence a and b are not both even. Next, let $\Omega\Delta$ be odd. Then $C = K\Omega \equiv \Omega^2 \equiv 1 \pmod 4$ by (44). But if a and b were even, then t is odd and $C = ab - t^2 \equiv -1 \pmod 4$.

In Theorems 18, 20, and 21, we assume that the determinant of f is positive.

Theorem 18. *If f and its reciprocal F are both properly primitive, there exist positive integers which are relatively prime to each other and to $2\Omega\Delta$ and are represented simultaneously and properly by f and F, respectively.*

In view of Theorem 11 the final property in our theorem is not altered by the transformation of F (and of f) used to secure (44). We have (45) and (46). The reciprocal F_1 of f_1 has the same third coefficient $K = C/\Omega$ as F. Take $N = 2$ (or the double of any product of primes dividing $\Omega\Delta$). Let the transformation

$$(48) \qquad x = ux' + vy' , \qquad y = wx' + ky' , \qquad uk - vw = 1 ,$$

which leaves z unaltered, replace f_1 by a new form g. The solved form of its transpose is

$$X = kX' - wY' , \qquad Y = -vX' + uY' ,$$

which by Theorem 2 replaces F_1 by the reciprocal G of g. The third coefficient (of Z^2) in G is evidently K. Since u and w may be chosen as any relatively prime integers, the first coefficient of g may be identified with any integer represented properly by ψ. But ψ is properly primitive. Hence by Theorem 6, ψ represents properly an integer prime to any assigned integer and hence one prime to both K and $2\Omega\Delta$.

The first coefficient of g and the third coefficient K of G are represented simultaneously and properly by g and G (Theorem 12) and hence by f and F (Theorem 11). The first coefficient of g is positive if g is positive. But if g is indefinite, $K > 0$ implies that $g(x',y',0)$, of discriminant $-4\Omega K > 0$, is indefinite. After applying transformations of type (48) and that below it, we have the same K and a new first coefficient of g which is positive and prime to $2K\Omega\Delta$.

From Theorems 13 and 18, we have the

COROLLARY. *If f and F are properly primitive, f is equivalent to a form whose first coefficient and the third coefficient of whose reciprocal are positive integers which are relatively prime to each other and to $2\Omega\Delta$.*

THEOREM 19. *Let f be improperly primitive and let δ be the largest odd factor of Δ. Write $n' = \Omega^2 \delta N$, where N is any odd integer. The reciprocal form F is properly primitive and d is even. Applying Theorem 16 with $g = F$, we may assume that the third coefficient K of F is positive and prime to $2n'$. Then f is equivalent to a form (45) with n replaced by n', where ψ is now improperly primitive.*

Here a, b, c are all even, while r, s, t are not all even. Hence A, B, C are not all even, whence Ω is odd and F is properly primitive. Since d is even, Δ is even. We proceed as in the proof of Theorem 17 with n replaced by n' and see that f is equivalent to (45) with n replaced by n', and that ψ is improperly primitive.

Theorem 20. *If f is improperly primitive, there exist positive integers m and M represented simultaneously and properly by f and its reciprocal F, respectively, such that $\frac{1}{2}m$ and M are odd integers, relatively prime to each other and to $\Omega\Delta$.*

The proof employs Theorem 19. The properly primitive form $\frac{1}{2}\psi$ represents an integer prime to any assigned integer by Theorem 6. Hence ψ is equivalent to a binary form half of whose first coefficient is odd and prime to both K and $\Omega\Delta$. Take $N = 1$ (or $\Omega\delta$) and proceed as in the proof of Theorem 18.

By reciprocity, if f is positive, Theorem 20 implies

Theorem 21. *If F is improperly primitive, there exist positive integers m and M represented simultaneously and properly by f and F, respectively, such that m and $\frac{1}{2}M$ are odd, relatively prime to each other and to $\Delta\Omega$.*

For indefinite forms we employ the proofs of Theorems 19 and 20 with f and F interchanged and note that $m = K > 0$ implies $M > 0$ by Theorem 14.

14. Every universal, indefinite, ternary form is a zero form. By applying the foregoing theory, the author has obtained the following remarkable results which are first published here. A form f is called *universal* if it represents every integer, positive, negative, or zero. In case $f = 0$ for integral values of the variables not all zero, f is called a *zero form*.

We shall first treat *classic* forms (47), and later treat *non-classic* forms in which some product of two distinct variables has an odd coefficient.

Theorem 22. *Every universal, indefinite, classic, ternary, quadratic form f is a zero form.*

Give to f the notation (47). Let $A, \ldots, T$ denote the cofactors of $a, \ldots, t$ in the determinant d of f. We take $d > 0$. By (34),

$$(49) \qquad af = u^2 + Cy^2 - 2Ryz + Bz^2, \qquad u = ax + ty + sz .$$

We readily exclude the case in which $A, \ldots, T$ have a common odd prime factor p. For, then $af \equiv u^2$ (mod p). If a is not divisible by p, f takes at most $1 + \frac{1}{2}(p-1)$ incongruent values modulo p and hence is not universal. Thus a is divisible by p. Similarly, $b \equiv c \equiv 0$ (mod p). Then $A \equiv B \equiv C \equiv 0$ imply $r \equiv s \equiv t \equiv 0$ (mod p). Then f represents only multiples of p and is not universal.

If a, b, c were all even, f would represent only even numbers. We may therefore take a odd. If $A, \ldots, T$ are all divisible by 4, then $af \equiv u^2 \equiv 0$ or 1 (mod 4), and f takes only two values modulo 4 and is not universal.

Hence f is properly primitive and $\Omega = -1$ or -2.

I. Let the form F reciprocal to f be properly primitive. By the Corollary to Theorem 18, we may assume, after applying a suitable transformation, that a and $P = C/\Omega$ are positive integers relatively prime to each other and to $2\Omega\Delta$. We have $d = \Omega^2\Delta$. By (49),

$$(50) \qquad aCf = Cu^2 + (Cy - Rz)^2 + daz^2 .$$

In the present case this becomes

$$(51) \qquad a\Omega Pf = \Omega Pu^2 + v^2 + daz^2 , \qquad v = \Omega Py - Rz .$$

I_1. Let $\Omega = -1$. We readily exclude the case $d \equiv 0$ (mod 4). Since $a\Omega P$ is odd, f and hence also $Cu^2 + v^2$ must then range over a complete set of residues modulo 4. Thus 0, 1, C, $C+1$ must be incongruent, whence $C \equiv 2$ (mod 4), whereas C is odd.

If p is any odd prime factor of d, P must be a quadratic residue of p. For, let P be a non-residue of p. We restrict x, y, z to values for which f is a multiple of p and write $f = pf_1$, $d = pd_1$. By (51), $Pu^2 \equiv v^2$ (mod p), whence $u \equiv v \equiv 0$ (mod p). Then $-aPpf_1 \equiv pd_1az^2$ (mod p^2). But a and P are prime to $\Omega\Delta$ and hence to d and p. Thus $f_1 \equiv kz^2$ (mod p), where k is a constant, and f_1 takes at most $\frac{1}{2}(p+1)$ incongruent values modulo p. Thus f represents only certain multiples of p and is not universal. It follows by induction that P is a quadratic residue of every power of p. Since d is not divisible by 4, it follows that P is a quadratic residue of d.

If q is any prime factor of a, q is odd. Since P is prime to a and since $P = -C = t^2 - ab$, P is a quadratic residue of q. As before, P is a quadratic residue of a.

Finally, if π is any prime factor of P, π is odd and $-da \equiv R^2$ (mod π) by $BC - R^2 = da$. Also, da is not divisible by π. Hence $-da$ is a quadratic residue of P.

The three italicized statements and the fact that P and da are relatively prime and $P > 0$ are sufficient conditions that $-Pu^2 + v^2 + daz^2$ be a zero form, in view of

THEOREM 23. *If a, b, c are $\neq 0$ and are relatively prime in pairs, $ax^2 + by^2 + cz^2 = 0$ has integral solutions relatively prime in pairs if and only if $-bc$, $-ca$, $-ab$ are respectively quadratic residues of a, b, c, and the latter are not all of the same sign.*[1]

From integral solutions u, v, z, not all zero, we obtain rational solutions x, y, z, not all zero, of $f = 0$ and hence integral solutions of the homogeneous equation $f = 0$.

I_2. When $\Omega = -2$, f is not universal. Since R is even, $v = 2V$, where V has integral coefficients. Deleting the factor 2 from (51), we get

$$Q = -aPf = -Pu^2 + 2V^2 + 2\Delta az^2 , \quad aP \text{ odd} .$$

The case in which Δ is a multiple of 4 is excluded since $2V^2 \equiv 0$ or 2 (mod 8), whence Q takes at most six values modulo 8.

Suppose that Δ is odd. Since Q must represent the four odd residues modulo 8, $u^2 \equiv 1$ (mod 8) and $V^2 + \Delta az^2$ must represent all residues modulo 4. Hence 0, 1, Δa, $\Delta a + 1$ must be incongruent, whence $\Delta a \equiv 2$ (mod 4), whereas Δa is odd.

Hence Δ is double an odd integer. Then Q is the case $l = 1$ of the form $h = ku^2 + 2lV^2 + 4mz^2$, where k, l, m are all odd. But no such form h is universal. For, if it represents all even residues modulo 16, then $u = 2U$ and $\frac{1}{2}h = 2kU^2 + lV^2 + 2mz^2$ must represent all residues modulo 8. To obtain the odd ones, we must have V odd, $V^2 \equiv 1$ (mod 8), whence $2kU^2 + 2mz^2$ must represent the four even residues modulo 8. In other words, $kU^2 + mz^2$ must represent all residues modulo 4. The same is true of its product by k, which is of the form $w^2 + nz^2$, where n is odd. This is impossible by the preceding paragraph.

II. Let F be improperly primitive. By Theorems 13 and 21, we may assume that a and $P = C/(2\Omega)$ are positive odd integers which are relatively prime to each other and to $\Omega\Delta$.

II_1. The case $\Omega = -1$ is excluded.[2] Since A, B, C are even, the determinant d^2 of F is even. Hence $d = 2\delta$, and (50) becomes

$$-2aPf = -2Pu^2 + v^2 + 2\delta az^2 , \quad v = -2Py - Rz .$$

Since v is even for every z, $R = 2\rho$, $v = 2V$,

$$-aPf = -Pu^2 + 2V^2 + \delta az^2 , \quad V = -Py - \rho z .$$

By $BC - R^2 = da$, d is a multiple of 4 and δ is even. As in I_2, f is not universal.

---

[1] Dickson, *Introduction to the Theory of Numbers*, p. 129 (cited as *Introd.*).

[2] Vacuous since not all of the coefficients R_1, S_1, T_1 of F are even and $A_1B_1 - T_1^2 = c\Delta$, etc., whence Δ is odd, Ω even.

II$_2$. Let $\Omega = -2$. Then $R = 2\rho$, $d = 4\Delta$, $C = -4P$. Cancellation of 4 from (50) gives

$$-aPf = -Pu^2 + V^2 + \Delta az^2 , \qquad V = -2Py - \rho z .$$

But this f is derived from f in I$_1$ by replacing v by V and d by Δ. No use was made in I$_1$ of the special form of the linear function v. Hence the same conclusion holds also here.

This completes the proof of Theorem 22.

Our next proof shows how we apply results for classic forms in the investigation of non-classic forms.

Theorem 24. *Every universal, indefinite, non-classic, ternary, quadratic form q is a zero form.*

Here $2q$ is a form f of type (47) having a, b, c all even and r, s, t not all even. Since q is universal, the g.c.d. of its coefficients $\frac{1}{2}a$, ... , t is 1. Hence the g.c.d. of a, ... , t is 1. Thus f is improperly primitive and represents all even integers.

Suppose that A, ... , T are all divisible by an odd prime p. By (49), $af \equiv u^2 \pmod{p}$. Assume that a is not divisible by p. Then there is an integer n such that an is a quadratic non-residue of p. If n is even, it is represented by f and $af = an \equiv u^2 \pmod{p}$, a contradiction. If n is odd, $n + p$ is even and is represented by f, whence

$$af = a(n+p) \equiv an \equiv u^2 \qquad \pmod{p} ,$$

a contradiction. Hence $a \equiv 0 \pmod{p}$. Similarly, $b \equiv c \equiv 0 \pmod{p}$. Then $A \equiv B \equiv C \equiv 0$ imply $r \equiv s \equiv t \equiv 0 \pmod{p}$, and q would not be universal. This contradiction shows that A, ... , T have no common odd factor > 1. They are not all even by the initial remarks concerning a, ... , t. Hence $\Omega = -1$.

By Theorems 13 and 20, we may assume that $\frac{1}{2}a$ and $P = -C$ are positive, odd, and relatively prime to each other and to $\Delta = d$. Here d is even. Write $a = 2\alpha$. Then (50) becomes

$$(52) \qquad -2\alpha Pf = -Pu^2 + v^2 + 2\alpha dz^2 , \quad u = 2\alpha x + ty + sz , \quad v = Py + Rz .$$

Here α, P, d are relatively prime in pairs, while α and P are positive and odd. Since $P = t^2 - ab \equiv t^2 \pmod{4}$,

$$(53) \qquad\qquad\qquad P \equiv 1 \qquad \pmod{4} ,$$

and t is odd. Then $R = st - ar \equiv s \pmod{2}$. Hence $u \equiv v \pmod{2}$ for all x, y, z. Conversely, if u and v are any integers which are both even or both odd, (53) implies that $v^2 - Pu^2$ is divisible by 4 and f in (52) is even.

Let 2^n be the highest power of 2 which divides $2d$, whence $n\geq 2$. Except in the case

(54) $$d\equiv 4 , \qquad P\equiv 5 \qquad (\text{mod } 8) ,$$

we shall prove that P is a quadratic residue of 2^n. This is evident from (53) if d is not divisible by 4, whence $n=2$, and also if $d\equiv 4$ (mod 8) and

(55) $$P\equiv 1 \qquad (\text{mod } 8) ,$$

since then $n=3$. There remains only the case $d\equiv 0$ (mod 8). Since f shall represent all even integers, (52) shows that $E=v^2-Pu^2$ must represent all multiples of 4 modulo 16. For v and u both even, $E\equiv 0$, 4, $-4\equiv 12$ (mod 16). The missing residue 8 must be a residue of E when v and u are both odd, whence $8\equiv 1-P$ (mod 8), which gives (55). But (55) implies that P is a quadratic residue of 2^n for every n. This is evident if $n\leq 3$. To proceed by induction on n, let $x^2=P+2^mQ$, $m\geq 3$. Then x is odd and

$$(x+2^{m-1}z)^2\equiv P+2^m(Q+xz)\equiv P \qquad (\text{mod } 2^{m+1})$$

by choice of z modulo 2. The induction is complete.

If p is any odd prime factor of d, P must be a quadratic residue of p. For, suppose that P is a non-residue. We restrict x, y, z to values for which f is a multiple of $2p$ and write $f=pf_1$, $d=p\delta$. By (52), $v^2\equiv Pu^2$, $v\equiv u\equiv 0$ (mod p), whence $-2aPf_1\equiv 2a\delta z^2$, $2aP\not\equiv 0$ (mod p). As in the second paragraph below Theorem 24, f_1 does not represent all even integers, which gives a contradiction on f.

Hence, except in case (54), P is a quadratic residue of $2d$. As in the three paragraphs preceding Theorem 23, P is a quadratic residue of $a=2\mathfrak{a}$, and $-da=-2d\mathfrak{a}$ is a quadratic residue of P, and f is a zero form.

But in case (54), q is not universal. Write $d=4e$, where e is odd. We saw that P must be a quadratic residue of e. By the preceding paragraph, P is a quadratic residue of $\mathfrak{a}$, and $-2\mathfrak{a}e$ is a quadratic residue of P. Hence

$$(-2|P)=(2|P)=-1 , \qquad (-2\mathfrak{a}e|P)=1 ,$$
$$-1=(\mathfrak{a}e|P)=(P|\mathfrak{a}e)=(P|\mathfrak{a})(P|e)=+1 ,$$

a contradiction. This completes the proof of Theorem 24.

15. Universal forms $f=ax^2+by^2+cz^2$.

Theorem 25. *If a, b, c are integers $\neq 0$, f is universal if and only if*

I. *a, b, c are not all of like sign;*

II. *No two of a, b, c have a common odd factor >1;*

III. *abc is odd or double an odd integer;*

IV. *$-bc$, $-ac$, $-ab$ are quadratic residues of a, b, c, respectively.*

We first prove that I–IV are necessary conditions. If a, b, c were all of like sign, f would not represent both positive and negative integers. This proves I.

If a and b are divisible by an odd prime p, f represents only $1+\frac{1}{2}(p-1)$ incongruent residues cz^2 modulo p. This proves II.

No one of a, b, c is divisible by 8. Let $a \equiv 0$ (mod 8). First, let $b = 2B$. Then $by^2 \equiv 0$ or $2B$, $cz^2 \equiv 0$, c, or $4c$ (mod 8), whence f has at most six residues modulo 8, while a universal form has eight. Second, let both b and c be odd, whence $4b \equiv 4c \equiv 4$ (mod 8). Then the residues of f modulo 8 are obtained by adding each of 0, 4, b to each of 0, 4, c, and hence are the seven: 0, 4, b, c, $b+4$, $c+4$, $b+c$.

No one of a, b, c is divisible by 4. Let a be divisible by 4. We saw that a is not divisible by 8. Hence $a = 4m$, m odd. Evidently $f \equiv 0$, b, c, or $b+c$ (mod 4) and these four must be incongruent. If b and c were odd, then $b \equiv c+2$, $b+c \equiv 2c+2 \equiv 0$ (mod 4). By symmetry, we may take b even, whence $b = 2l$, l odd. Since f represents odd integers, c is odd. By the proof at the end of case I_2 of § 14, f is not universal.

By the proof just cited, f is not universal if two of a, b, c are doubles of odd integers and the third is odd. This completes the proof of III.

In particular, a, b, c are relatively prime in pairs.

Suppose that $-bc$ is a quadratic non-residue of an odd prime factor p of $a = pA$. Consider values of x, y, z for which f is divisible by p. Then $-bcy^2 \equiv (cz)^2$ (mod p), whence $y \equiv 0$, $z \equiv 0$, $f = pF$, $F \equiv Ax^2$ (mod p). But Ax^2 takes at most $1+\frac{1}{2}(p-1)$ values incongruent modulo p. Hence f fails to represent certain multiples of p. This contradiction shows that $-bc$ is a quadratic residue of p and hence of a. This proves IV.

Conversely,[1] I–IV imply that f is universal. By Theorem 23 they imply that $f = 0$ has integral solutions ξ, η, ζ which are relatively prime in pairs. Then $\xi s - \eta r = 1$ has integral solutions s, r. The transformation

$$x = \xi X + rY, \qquad y = \eta X + sY, \qquad z = \zeta X + Z ,$$

has determinant unity and replaces f by

$$F = 2uXY + 2c\zeta XZ + vY^2 + cZ^2 ,$$

where $u = a\xi r + b\eta s$, $v = ar^2 + bs^2$. Then

$$u^2 - v(a\xi^2 + b\eta^2) \equiv -ab(s\xi - r\eta)^2 ,$$

---

[1] In *Bull. Amer. Math. Soc.*, XXXV (1929), 55–59, the author gave a wholly different proof of the converse which did not yield the Corollary.

identically in ξ, η. Thus

$$u^2 + cv\zeta^2 = -ab .$$

Hence no prime divides both u and c. Suppose that u and ζ have a common prime factor p. Then p divides ab. If p divides a, it divides the second term of $a\xi^2 + b\eta^2 + c\zeta^2 = 0$, whereas b is prime to a, and η to ζ. Similarly, p cannot divide b. Hence the coefficients of $y_1 = uY + c\zeta Z$ are relatively prime. Thus there exists another linear function z_1 of Y and Z such that the determinant of the coefficients in y_1 and z_1 is unity. Hence F is equivalent to $2Xy_1 + \phi$, where ϕ is quadratic in y_1 and z_1. Dropping subscripts, we have

$$2Xy + By^2 + 2Cyz - Dz^2 .$$

Replacing X by $x + ky - Cz$, we get $2xy + Ey^2 - Dz^2$, where $E = B + 2k$. By choice of the integer k, we have $E = 0$ or 1. Since this form has the same determinant as f, $D = abc$. The cases are

$$g = 2xy - Dz^2 , \qquad h = 2xy + y^2 - Dz^2 .$$

If D were even in g, the coefficients of the equivalent form f would be all even, whereas two of a, b, c are odd. Hence D is odd in g. Its values for $y = 1$, $z = 0$, 1, are $2x$, $2x - D$, which together give all integers. Hence g is universal.

If D is odd in h, we replace x by $x + Dz$ and z by $z + y$; we get $2xy + (1 - D)y^2 - Dz^2$. We now replace x by $x + \frac{1}{2}(D - 1)y$ and get g. It remains to consider h when D is double an odd integer. For $y = 1$, $z = 0$; $y = 2$, $z = 0$, 1, the values of h are $2x + 1$, $4(x + 1)$, $4(x + 1) - D$, which together give all integers.

This completes the proof of Theorem 25.

COROLLARY. *According as abc is odd or double an odd integer, a universal form $ax^2 + by^2 + cz^2$ is equivalent to $2xy - abcz^2$ or $2xy + y^2 - abcz^2$.*

CHAPTER III

REPRESENTATION OF BINARY FORMS
BY TERNARY FORMS

We shall derive the result due to Gauss that the problem to find all representations of a given integer by a given ternary quadratic form F reduces to the problem to find all representations of a given binary form by the reciprocal f of F. The latter topic is required in later chapters and is treated without the restrictions imposed by Gauss.

16. Solution of $ax+by+cz=0$.

THEOREM 26. *If a, b, c have no common factor >1, all integral solutions of $ax+by+cz=0$ are given by*

$$(56) \qquad x=bk-cn, \quad y=cs-ak, \quad z=an-bs,$$

where s, n, k are integers.

Let d be the g.c.d. of $a=dA$ and $b=dB$. Then A is prime to B, and d to c. Hence z/d is an integer. It can be expressed as a linear combination of A and B, say $AN-BM$. Hence

$$(57) \qquad z=aN-bM.$$

Then the proposed equation gives

$$A(x+cN)=B(cM-y).$$

Since A is prime to B, this gives

$$(58) \qquad x=BR-cN, \quad y=cM-AR,$$

where R is an integer. Since c and d are relatively prime, there exist integral solutions k and t of $R=dk-ct$. Then (58) become

$$x=bk-c(N+Bt), \quad y=c(M+At)-ak.$$

But these equations and (57) coincide with (56) if we write $s=M+At$, $n=N+Bt$.

17. Proper representation. Consider a transformation

$$(59) \qquad x_i=a_iy_1+b_iy_2+c_iy_3 \qquad (i=1, 2, 3)$$

having integral coefficients. Let A_j, B_j, C_j denote the cofactors of a_j, b_j, c_j in the determinant of (59). For $y_3 = 0$, (59) become

$$x_i = a_i y_1 + b_i y_2 \qquad (i = 1, 2, 3) \ .$$
(60)

When these expressions for x_i are inserted into a form $f(x_1, x_2, x_3)$, we evidently obtain a binary form

$$\phi = a y_1^2 + 2t y_1 y_2 + b y_2^2 \ ,$$
(61)

denoted by (a, t, b). Then (60) is called a *representation* of ϕ by f.

When the g.c.d. of C_1, C_2, C_3 is unity, this representation is called *proper*.

Let Ω and Δ be the invariants of f and let F be the form reciprocal to f. The proof of Theorem 13 yields

THEOREM 27. *If* (60) *is a proper representation of ϕ by f, the determinant $t^2 - ab$ of ϕ is $-\Omega C$, where $C = F(C_1, C_2, C_3)$.*

18. Representation of and by equivalent forms.

THEOREM 28. *If ϕ is represented properly by f and if ϕ becomes ψ by an integral transformation of determinant ± 1, then ψ is represented properly by f, and the C_1, C_2, C_3 for the latter representation are the products of those of the representation of ϕ by ± 1.*

Let the transformation

$$y_1 = \alpha z_1 + \beta z_2 \ , \qquad y_2 = \gamma z_1 + \delta z_2 \ , \qquad \alpha\delta - \beta\gamma = \pm 1$$
(62)

replace ϕ by ψ. Elimination of the y's from (60) gives

$$x_i = g_i z_1 + h_i z_2 \ , \qquad g_i = a_i \alpha + b_i \gamma \ , \qquad h_i = a_i \beta + b_i \delta \ .$$
(63)

Hence f becomes ψ by means of the latter equations. Also,

$$
\begin{vmatrix} g_i & h_i \\ g_j & h_j \end{vmatrix} = \begin{vmatrix} a_i & b_i \\ a_j & b_j \end{vmatrix} \cdot \begin{vmatrix} \alpha & \beta \\ \gamma & \delta \end{vmatrix} \ .
$$
(64)

Since the final factor is ± 1, the C_i are the products of those for the representation of ϕ by ± 1.

THEOREM 29. *Equivalent ternary forms represent properly the same binary forms.*

Let (60) be a proper representation of ϕ by f, whence the g.c.d. of C_1, C_2, C_3 is 1. Choose integers c_i so that $\Sigma c_i C_i = 1$. Then transformation (59) has determinant unity. It replaces f by an equivalent form $g(y_1, y_2, y_3)$ such that $g(y_1, y_2, 0) \equiv \phi$.

Let $h(z_1, z_2, z_3)$ be any form equivalent to f and hence to g. Thus $h = g$ under a transformation

(65) $$z_i = u_i y_1 + v_i y_2 + w_i y_3 \qquad (i = 1, 2, 3)$$

of determinant unity. Taking $y_3 = 0$, we see that

$$z_i = u_i y_1 + v_i y_2 \qquad (i = 1, 2, 3)$$

give a representation of ϕ by h. This representation is proper since the determinant of (65) is 1, whence the two-rowed determinants with elements from its first two columns have unity as their g.c.d.

19. A representation determines a root of (67).

THEOREM 30. *Let* (60) *be a proper representation of* $\phi = (a, t, b)$ *by* f. *Choose integers* c_i *so that* $\Sigma c_i C_i = 1$ *and write*

(66) $$R = \tfrac{1}{2} \Sigma B_i \partial F(C_1, C_2, C_3)/\partial C_i, \qquad S = \tfrac{1}{2} \Sigma A_i \partial F(C)/\partial C_i.$$

Then if C *is not[1] divisible by 4 and* f *is primitive and has the invariants* Ω *and* Δ,

(67) $$R^2 + \Delta a \equiv 0, \qquad RS - \Delta t \equiv 0, \qquad S^2 + \Delta b \equiv 0 \qquad (mod \; C).$$

Write

$$u = a_1 x_1 + a_2 x_2 + a_3 x_3, \qquad v = b_1 x_1 + b_2 x_2 + b_3 x_3.$$

Then

$$a_1 v - b_1 u = x_2 C_3 - x_3 C_2, \qquad a_2 v - b_2 u = x_3 C_1 - x_1 C_3, \qquad a_3 v - b_3 u = x_1 C_2 - x_2 C_1.$$

We have $f(x_1, x_2, x_3) = \phi(y_1, y_2)$ in view of (60). Insert the values (60) and replace y_1 by v, and y_2 by $-u$. Then $x_1 = a_1 v - b_1 u$, etc. Hence

$$f(x_2 C_3 - x_3 C_2, \; x_3 C_1 - x_1 C_3, \; x_1 C_2 - x_2 C_1) = av^2 - 2tvu + bu^2.$$

In the second fundamental identity (33) take $u_i = x_i$, $v_i = C_i$, and apply Theorem 27, and the preceding relation. Hence

$$[\tfrac{1}{2} \Sigma x_i \partial F(C_1, C_2, C_3)/\partial C_i]^2 + \Delta(av^2 - 2tvu + bu^2) \equiv 0 \; (\text{mod } C).$$

First, take $x_i = B_i$, whence $u = 0, v = 1$; we get (67_1). Second, take $x_i = A_i$, whence $u = 1, v = 0$; we get (67_3). Third, take $x_i = A_i + B_i$, whence $u = v = 1$. We get

$$(R + S)^2 + \Delta(a - 2t + b) \equiv 0 \qquad (\text{mod } C).$$

[1] True also if C is divisible by 4 by the shorter proof at the end of §19.

By the first and third parts of (67), this gives $2(RS - \Delta t) \equiv 0$ (mod C). If C is odd, we get (67$_2$).

Finally, let $C = 2N$, where N is odd.

If Δ is even, then R is even by (67$_1$). Since $RS - \Delta t$ is even and divisible by N, it is divisible by C.

Let Δ be odd. By Theorem 27, $t^2 - ab = -\Omega C$ is even. If a or b is even, then t is even, while R or S is even by (67$_1$) or (67$_3$), whence $RS - \Delta t$ is even. But if a and b are odd, then t, R, S are all odd and $RS - \Delta t$ is again even and hence divisible by C.

There are infinitely many ways to choose the c_i. The effect on R and S by a new choice is described in

THEOREM 31. *When the solution c_i of $\Sigma c_i C_i = 1$ is replaced by another solution c_i', then R and S are replaced by integers congruent to them modulo C.*

Evidently $d_i = c_i' - c_i$ satisfy $\Sigma d_i C_i = 0$, whose complete solution in integers is given by Theorem 26. Hence

$$c_1' = c_1 + C_2 k - C_3 n , \qquad c_2' = c_2 + C_3 s - C_1 k , \qquad c_3' = c_3 + C_1 n - C_2 s .$$

Write

$$(68) \qquad h = a_1 s + a_2 n + a_3 k , \qquad j = b_1 s + b_2 n + b_3 k .$$

Using $\Sigma b_i C_i = 0$ and $\Sigma a_i C_i = 0$, we see that A_i becomes $A_i + j C_i$, and B_i becomes $B_i - h C_i$. Hence R and S in (66) are replaced by $R - hC$ and $S + jC$, respectively, as shown by (6) and Theorem 27. This proves Theorem 31.

If R and S satisfy congruences (67), the infinitely many solutions $R + uC$ and $S + vC$, in which u and v take all integral values, are said to give the same *root* of (67), while R and S give a *representative* of that root.

By Theorems 30 and 31, we have the first statement in

Theorem 32. *Let the determinant of $\phi = (a, t, b)$ be $-\Omega C \neq 0$, where C is not divisible by 4. Let f be a primitive ternary form having the invariants Ω and Δ. To any proper representation of ϕ by f corresponds a definite root of congruences (67). We can choose integers c_i so that the determinant of (59) is unity and so that R and S in (66) coincide with any preassigned representative of that root. Then (59) replaces f by a form g such that $g(y_1, y_2, 0) = \phi$ and such that the reciprocal of g is*

$$(69) \qquad A y_1^2 + B y_2^2 + C y_3^2 + 2R y_2 y_3 + 2S y_1 y_3 + 2T y_1 y_2 ,$$

in which the integers A, B, T are determined by

$$(70) \qquad BC - R^2 = \Delta a , \quad RS - TC = \Delta t , \quad AC - S^2 = \Delta b .$$

If we annex equation $l = c_1 s + c_2 n + c_3 k$ to (68), we obtain three equations the determinant of whose coefficients is $\Sigma c_i C_i = 1$. Hence they serve to express s, n, k as linear functions of h, j, l with integral coefficients. Hence if h and j are any assigned integers, there exist infinitely many triples of integers, s, n, k, which satisfy the two equations (68). Select such a triple and determine c_1', c_2', c_3' by the formulas preceding (68).

By choice of h and j, the values $R - hC$ and $S + jC$, obtained below (68), coincide with any preassigned representative of the root of (67) in question. Dropping the accents on c_i', we have the second statement in Theorem 32.

It remains to show that the reciprocal G of g is (69). Give to (59) the notation (11). Its contragredient transformation (24) with $C = 1$ replaces the adjoint ΩF of f by the adjoint ΩG of g by Theorem 2. Hence $C_{i1} = A_i$, $C_{i2} = B_i$, $C_{i3} = C_i$. By (17) written in capital letters, G has as coefficient of $2y_s y_3$ or $y_s y_3$, according as $s < 3$ or $s = 3$,

$$\tfrac{1}{2}\Sigma_i C_{is} \partial F(C_{13}, C_{23}, C_{33}) / \partial C_{i3} = \tfrac{1}{2}\Sigma_i C_{is} \partial F / \partial C_i \, ,$$

where F is $F (C_1, C_2, C_3)$. For $s = 1$ or 2, this is S or R in (66). For $s = 3$, it is C by (6). It remains to find the Greek letters in

$$G = a y_1^2 + \beta y_2^2 + C y_3^2 + 2R y_2 y_3 + 2S y_1 y_3 + 2\tau y_1 y_2.$$

Its matrix is

$$\begin{pmatrix} a & \tau & S \\ \tau & \beta & R \\ S & R & C \end{pmatrix}.$$

By (29), the adjoint of G is Δg. Hence

$$\beta C - R^2 = \Delta a \, , \qquad RS - \tau C = \Delta t \, , \qquad aC - S^2 = \Delta b \, .$$

Comparison with (70) gives $\beta = B$, $\tau = T$, $a = A$. Hence G is (69).

20. Tests for equivalence of ternary forms.

THEOREM 33. *Let f and f_1 be primitive ternary forms having the same invariants Ω and Δ. Let ϕ have the determinant $-\Omega C \neq 0$, where C is not divisible by 4. To proper representations of ϕ by f and f_1 let correspond the respective roots R, S, and R_1, S_1, of (67) such that either*

$$(71) \qquad R \equiv R_1 \, , \quad S \equiv S_1; \quad or \; R \equiv -R_1 \, , \quad S \equiv -S_1 \qquad (mod \; C) \, .$$

Then f and f_1 are equivalent.

I. In the first case in (71), we choose R and S as representative of the root in question both for f and f_1. By Theorem 32 we can find two transformations T_1 and T_2 of determinant unity one of which transforms f into g and the other transforms f_1 into g_1, such that the reciprocals of both g and g_1 are (69). The reciprocals of the reciprocals are g and g_1, which are therefore identical. Then $T_1 T_2^{-1}$ replaces f by f_1.

II. In the second case in (71), we choose R, S and $-R$, $-S$ as representatives of the roots in question for f and f_1, respectively. Since (70) are unaltered by the mere change in sign of both R and S, they determine the same A, B, T as before. Hence f_1 is equivalent to a form g_1 whose reciprocal is

$$A Y_1^2 + B Y_2^2 + C Y_3^2 - 2R Y_2 Y_3 - 2S Y_1 Y_3 + 2T Y_1 Y_2 .$$

This becomes (69) under the transformation $Y_1 = -y_1$, $Y_2 = -y_2$, $Y_3 = y_3$ of determinant unity. Hence the reciprocals of g and g_1 are equivalent. Then g and g_1 themselves are equivalent by § 4.

THEOREM 34. *If* $|C|$ *is a prime or double an odd prime, two primitive ternary forms having the same invariants* Ω *and* Δ *are equivalent if they properly represent the same binary form of determinant* $-\Omega C$.

By (67), $R^2 \equiv R_1^2$, $RS \equiv R_1 S_1$, $S^2 \equiv S_1^2$ (mod C). Let p be an odd prime factor of C. Then $R \equiv \pm R_1$ (mod p). If $R \not\equiv 0$, $RS \equiv \pm RS_1$ implies $S \equiv \pm S_1$, and we have (71) modulo p. The latter is true also if $R \equiv 0$. If 2 is a factor of C, $R \equiv R_1$, $S \equiv S_1$ (mod 2). This proves (71). Hence Theorem 33 implies Theorem 34.

THEOREM 35. *Let* f *be a ternary form having the invariants* Ω *and* Δ. *Let* ϕ *be a binary form of determinant* $-\Omega C$. *If* ϕ *is represented properly by* f *and* f *is a positive form, then* ϕ *is a positive form and* $C > 0$. *But if* f *is indefinite and of positive determinant, then* ϕ *is indefinite or negative, according as* $C > 0$ *or* $C < 0$.

By the convention in § 8, $\Omega > 0$ or $\Omega < 0$, according as f is positive or indefinite. By Theorem 27, the determinant D of ϕ is $-\Omega C$.

If f is positive, evidently ϕ is positive, whence $D < 0$, $C > 0$. But if f is indefinite, D and C have the same sign. If $C > 0$, ϕ is therefore indefinite. If $C < 0$, ϕ is definite. Since f represents ϕ, there exists a transformation (59) which replaces f by f_1, where $f_1(y_1, y_2, 0) = \phi$. By the proof of Theorem 13, C is the third coefficient of the reciprocal F_1 of f_1. The first coefficient a of ϕ is also that of f_1. By Theorem 12, a and C are represented simultaneously and properly by f_1 and F_1. The case $a > 0$, $C < 0$ is excluded by Theorem 14. Hence ϕ is a negative form.

21. Sufficient conditions for representation.

THEOREM 36. *Let* $\phi = (a, t, b)$ *be a primitive form of determinant* $-\Omega C \neq 0$ *such that* ϕ *is positive if* $\Omega > 0$, *but is negative or indefinite if* $\Omega < 0$. *Let* $\Delta > 0$ *and assume that congruences* (67) *are solvable. If C and Δ are either relatively prime or are the doubles of relatively prime odd integers, then φ is represented properly by a primitive ternary form f having the invariants* Ω *and* Δ.

This f is positive if $\Omega > 0$, *indefinite if* $\Omega < 0$. *If* Δ *is odd, f is properly primitive. If* Δ *is even, f is properly or improperly primitive, according as φ is properly or improperly primitive. The reciprocal F of f is properly primitive in each of the four cases:* Ω *odd;* Ω *and* Δ *both even;* Ω *even and* ΔC *odd;* Ω *and C even,* Δ *odd, and*[1]

$$(72) \qquad \phi \equiv \Delta \ (mod \ 4) \ when \ \phi \ is \ odd \ .$$

But if Δ *is a multiple of* 4 *and if C is double an odd integer prime to* Δ, *then φ is represented properly only by primitive ternary forms having the invariants* 2Ω *and* $\frac{1}{4}\Delta$.

By (67) there exist integers A, B, T satisfying (70). Since a, t, b have no common factor > 1,

$$(73) \qquad \text{any common divisor of } A, B, C, R, S, T \text{ divides } \Delta \ .$$

There exist rational solutions r and s of

$$(74) \qquad tr - bs = \Omega S \ , \qquad ar - ts = -\Omega R \ ,$$

since the determinant of their coefficients is

$$(75) \qquad ab - t^2 = \Omega C \ .$$

Solution by determinants yields r and s as quotients of linear functions of R and S by C. Determine c by

$$(76) \qquad sS + rR + cC = \Omega \Delta \ .$$

Multiply this by Ω and apply (74) and (75). Hence the determinant of the matrix

$$M = \begin{pmatrix} a & t & s \\ t & b & r \\ s & r & c \end{pmatrix}$$

is $\Omega^2 \Delta$. The adjoint of M is the matrix M whose element in the ith row and jth column is the cofactor of the element in the jth row and ith column of

---

[1] If (72) holds for one odd number represented by ϕ, it holds for all by § 30. If C is double an odd integer, Ω is even, Δ is odd, and $\phi \equiv \Delta + 2 \pmod{4}$ when ϕ is odd, it can be proved that F is improperly primitive.

M. In view of (74) and (75), we know the elements of the last row and last column of

$$M = \begin{pmatrix} \Omega u & \Omega v & \Omega S \\ \Omega v & \Omega w & \Omega R \\ \Omega S & \Omega R & \Omega C \end{pmatrix}.$$

By (10), the adjoint of M is dM, viz., a matrix obtained by multiplying each element of M by d. Hence

$$wC - R^2 = \Delta a , \qquad RS - vC = \Delta t , \qquad uC - S^2 = \Delta b .$$

Comparing these equations with (70), we see that $w = B$, $v = T$, $u = A$. By considering further elements of the adjoint of M, we now get

$$(77) \qquad ST - AR = \Delta r , \qquad RT - BS = \Delta s , \qquad AB - T^2 = \Delta c .$$

Hence the denominators of r, s, c are divisors of Δ.

I. Let C and Δ be relatively prime. Since the denominators of r and s are divisors of both C and Δ, r and s are integers. The same proof now applies to c by (76). Hence the literal coefficients $a, \ldots , t$ of

$$(78) \qquad f(x, y, z) = ax^2 + by^2 + cz^2 + 2ryz + 2sxz + 2txy$$

are all integers. It is a primitive form since ϕ is primitive. If the determinant $\Omega^2\Delta$ of the matrix M of f is odd, a, b, c are not all even; if ϕ is properly primitive, a and b are not both even; in either case, f is properly primitive. But if $\Omega\Delta$ is even and ϕ is improperly primitive, then a and b are even and t is odd, whence ΩC is odd by (75), and Δ is even. By (74), $r \equiv S$, $s \equiv R$ (mod 2), whence $sS + rR$ is even, and c is even by (76). Hence f is improperly primitive.

Since $f(x, y, 0) = \phi$, ϕ is represented properly by f. By (73), the g.c.d. of $A, \ldots , T$ is 1. Hence the g.c.d. of the elements of matrix M is Ω. The determinant of f was seen to be $\Omega^2\Delta > 0$. If $\Omega > 0$, ϕ is positive by hypothesis, and f is positive by Theorem 8 since a and (75) are positive, whence the invariants of f are Ω and Δ. Next, let $\Omega < 0$. Then ϕ is negative or indefinite by hypothesis. We shall prove that f is indefinite and hence conclude that its invariants are again Ω and Δ. If ϕ is indefinite, f is indefinite since it represents ϕ. Finally, let ϕ be negative. Then f is not positive since it represents ϕ. If f were negative, $-f$ would be a positive form of negative determinant $-\Omega^2\Delta$, contrary to Theorem 8.

If $\Omega\Delta$ is odd, F is properly primitive since it is primitive and has the odd determinant $\Delta^2\Omega$. If F is improperly primitive when Δ is even then A, B, C are even and at least one of R, S, T is odd, contrary to (70_1) (70_3), and (77_3). Hence F is properly primitive when Δ is even. Next, let Δ be odd and Ω be even. If C is odd, F is evidently properly primitive. Let C be even. If a and b are even, t is even by (75), whereas ϕ is primitive. If b is odd, (72) gives $b \equiv \Delta \pmod 4$. Then (70_3) shows that S is odd and that $AC \equiv 1 + \Delta b \equiv 2 \pmod 4$, whence A is odd and F is properly primitive. If a is odd, (72) gives $a \equiv \Delta \pmod 4$ and (70_1) gives $BC \equiv 2 \pmod 4$, B odd.

This proves the theorem when C and Δ are relatively prime.

II. Let C and Δ have the g.c.d. 2 and let $\frac{1}{2}C$ be odd. By (70), R and S are even. By the remark below (75), r and s are fractions whose denominators divide $\frac{1}{2}C$. But they divide Δ which is prime to $\frac{1}{2}C$. Hence r and s are integers. The same proof now applies to c by (76). By (73), the g.c.d. of A, . . . , T is 1 or 2.

II$_1$. Assume also that $\frac{1}{2}\Delta$ is odd. If A, . . . , T were all even, a, t, b would be all even by (70), whereas ϕ is primitive. Hence the g.c.d. of A, . . . , T is 1. Proceed as in case I.

II$_2$. Now let $\frac{1}{2}\Delta$ be even. By (70), BC and AC are multiples of 4, whence B and A are even. Then T is even by (77_3). Hence the g.c.d. of A, . . . , T is 2. The invariants of f are now 2Ω and $\frac{1}{4}\Delta$.

22. Condition that a represented binary form be primitive.

THEOREM 37. *If* $\phi = (a, t, b)$ *has the determinant* $-\Omega C$ *and is represented properly by a primitive ternary form* f *having the invariants* Ω *and* Δ, *and if* C *is prime to* $\Omega\Delta$, *then* ϕ *is primitive.*

As in the proof of Theorem 29, we may take $f(x, y, 0) \equiv \phi$. Let ΩA, . . . , ΩT denote the cofactors of a, . . . , t in the determinant of f, with the notation (78). Then (70) and (77) hold. The reciprocal of f is (69), whose determinant is $\Omega\Delta^2$. By (70) and (77_3), we get

$$(79) \qquad \Delta(Aa + 2Tt + Bb) = \Omega\Delta^2 + C\Delta c .$$

Elimination of C from this by (75) gives

$$\Omega(Aa + 2Tt + Bb) = \Omega^2\Delta + c(ab - t^2) .$$

Hence the g.c.d. g of a, t, b divides $\Omega^2\Delta$, and divides ΩC by (75). Thus g divides Ω and hence is prime to C. We remove the factor Δ from (79) and conclude that g divides c.

If we multiply the elements of the first or second column of the determinant of f by the cofactors of the elements of the third column and add, we get

$$aS+tR+sC=0 \ . \qquad tS+bR+rC=0 \ .$$

Hence g divides sC and rC and hence divides s and r. Since g divides the six literal coefficients $a, \ldots, t$ of the primitive form f, $g=1$.

23. All representations of numbers found from those of binary by ternary forms. The following simple discussion is not used later in this book, but rounds out the theory presented in this chapter.

In Theorem 27 we saw that to every proper representation of a binary ϕ of determinant $-\Omega C$ by a ternary f corresponds a proper representation $C=F(C_1, C_2, C_3)$ of C by the form F reciprocal to f. The converse is

THEOREM 38. *To every proper representation of C by F corresponds a proper representation by f of some binary form ϕ of determinant $-\Omega C$.*

Given $C=F(Z_1, Z_2, Z_3)$, where the g.c.d. of the Z_i is 1, we can find, by Theorem 9 and Remark 1 following it, integers a_i and b_i such that

$$(80) \qquad a_2b_3-a_3b_2=Z_1 \ , \qquad a_3b_1-a_1b_3=Z_2 \ , \qquad a_1b_2-a_2b_1=Z_3 \ .$$

The proof of Theorem 13 yields the desired form ϕ.

By the upper signs in Theorem 28, to (proper) representations of equivalent binary forms of determinant $-\Omega C$ by f corresponds the same (proper) representation of C by F. This is supplemented by

THEOREM 39. *To proper representations of non-equivalent binary forms ϕ and ψ of determinant $-\Omega C$ by f correspond different proper representations of C by F.*

Let (60) and (63_1) be representations of ϕ and ψ by f, for both of which $C=F(Z_1, Z_2, Z_3)$. Hence we have (80), as well as $g_2h_3-g_3h_2=Z_1$, etc. By Remark 2 in § 9,

$$g_i=a_i\alpha+b_i\gamma \ , \qquad h_i=a_i\beta+b_i\delta \ , \qquad \alpha\delta-\beta\gamma=1 \ .$$

But these are the conditions (63) that transformation (62) has determinant unity and replaces ϕ by ψ, contrary to the hypothesis that ϕ and ψ are not equivalent.

THEOREM 40. *The problem to find all proper representations of a given integer C by a given primitive ternary form F reduces to the problem to find all proper representations of a given binary form by a given primitive ternary form f.*

The reciprocal of the given F is a form f with permuted invariants Ω

and Δ; hence F is the reciprocal of a certain f. By Theorem 38 and the remark before it, we obtain all proper representations of C by F from the proper representations by f of all binary forms of determinant $D = -\Omega C$. By the remark before Theorem 39, we need only employ a set of forms $\phi_1, \phi_2, \ldots$ of determinant D no two of which are equivalent. By Theorem 39, the representations of C by F derived from different ones of these ϕ_i are different.

But if ϕ has exactly τ automorphs (integral transformations of determinant unity which leave ϕ unaltered), we see, by identifying ψ with ϕ in Theorem 28 and taking the upper signs, that exactly τ different proper representations of ϕ by f correspond to a single proper representation of C by F. Here τ is finite if $D < 0$, but infinite if $D > 0$.

CHAPTER IV

EQUIVALENCE OF INDEFINITE, TERNARY, QUADRATIC FORMS

Let the invariants Ω and Δ of two such primitive forms have no common odd factor >1 and let neither be divisible by 4. Let their corresponding characters be equal. We shall prove that they are equivalent if both are improperly primitive; also if both are properly primitive and if their reciprocals are both properly primitive or both improperly primitive.

For the case in which $\Omega\Delta$ is odd, A. Meyer[1] gave an incomplete proof in 1871. Later[2] he "corrected the proof and extended it to even invariants." Bachmann[3] reproduced the former proof with the same errors and obscurities. In his revised proof, Meyer uses results on Pellian equations quite different from those in the paper[4] he cites. Not being able to deduce the former from the latter results, the author developed the new proof in §§ 24–29 and recognized the necessity of extending Meyer's theorem from his case in which p and q are primes to the case in which they are composite, even though we desire only the special case. Also in the remainder of the chapter, serious revisions of the literature were necessary to put the theory on a clear and sound basis.

24. Problem on Pellian equations. Let $E = 2^e G^2 H$, where 2^e is the highest power of 2 dividing E, and G^2 is the largest odd square dividing E, whence H is a product of distinct odd primes. We seek positive integers a prime to $2E$ for which the least positive integral solutions T and U of

$$(81) \qquad t^2 - aEu^2 = 1$$

are such that neither $T+1$ nor $T-1$ is divisible by a.

THEOREM 41. *If $e \leq 4$, aHG is odd,*

$$(82) \qquad (T \mp 1)(T \pm 1) = 2^e a H G^2 U^2 \ ,$$

[1] *Zur Theorie der unbestimmten ternären quad. Formen*, Zürich, 1871.

[2] *Jour. für Math.*, CVIII (1891), 125–39. Here he made the error noted in § 33, footnote.

[3] *Arith. quad. Formen*, I (1898), 233–51.

[4] Meyer, *Vierteljahrsschrift Naturf. Gesell. Zürich*, XXXII (1887), 363–82.

and if $T \mp 1$ is divisible by a, there exist integral solutions of at least one of the following equations having $\delta d = H$:

(83) $$\delta x^2 - ady^2 = \pm 1 \ or \ \pm 2 \quad if \ e = 0 \ ,$$

(84) $$\delta x^2 - ady^2 = \pm 1 \qquad\qquad if \ e = 2 \ or \ 4 \ ,$$

(85) $$\delta x^2 - 2ady^2 = \pm 1 \ or \ \pm 2 \ if \ e = 1 \ or \ 3 \ .$$

The details of the proof are needed also in § 26.

First, let $e = 0$, T odd. Then $T = 2a\lambda \pm 1$ and $T^2 - 1$ is divisible by 8, whence $U = 4u$ and

$$\lambda(a\lambda \pm 1) = 4G^2u^2H \ .$$

Since the factors on the left are relatively prime, the g.c.d. of λ and $4G^2u^2$ is a square y^2, whence $\lambda = dy^2$, $2Gu = xy$, where d is prime to x. Thus H/d is an integer δ, whence $a\lambda \pm 1 = \delta x^2$, or (83$_1$).

Second, let $e = 0$, T even. Then $T = a\lambda \pm 1$, where λ is odd, and $\lambda(a\lambda \pm 2) = HG^2U^2$. As in the first case,

$$\lambda = dy^2 \ , \qquad GU = xy \ , \qquad H = \delta d \ , \qquad a\lambda \pm 2 = \delta x^2 \ ,$$

which gives (83$_2$).

Henceforth let $e > 0$. Then T is odd,

$$T = 2a\lambda \pm 1 \ , \qquad 4\lambda(a\lambda \pm 1) = 2^e HG^2U^2 \ .$$

Third, let $e = 1$. Then $U = 2u$. The g.c.d. of λ and G^2u^2 is a square y^2. We may write $\lambda = 2dy^2$ or dy^2, where d is odd in the latter case. Then $Gu = yz$, where z is prime to $2d$ or d. Hence $H = \delta d$, $a\lambda \pm 1 = \delta z^2$ or $2\delta z^2$, respectively. Taking $x = z$ or $x = 2z$, we get (85$_1$) or (85$_2$).

Fourth, let $e = 2$. Then $U = 2u$. The g.c.d. of λ and G^2u^2 is a square μ^2. Then $\lambda = 4d\mu^2$ or $d\mu^2$, where d is odd in the latter case. Then $Gu = \mu z$, where z is prime to $4d$ or d. Hence $H = \delta d$, $a\lambda \pm 1 = \delta z^2$ or $4\delta z^2$, respectively, whence

$$\delta z^2 - ad(2\mu)^2 = \pm 1 \qquad or \qquad \delta(2z)^2 - ad\mu^2 = \pm 1 \ ,$$

both of type (84).

Finally, let $e \gtreqless 3$. The g.c.d. of λ and G^2U^2 is a square μ^2, and $\lambda = 2^{e-2}d\mu^2$ or $d\mu^2$, according as λ is even or odd. Hence $GU = \mu\nu$, $H = \delta d$, $a\lambda \pm 1 = \delta\nu^2$ or $2^{e-2}\delta\nu^2$, respectively, whence

$$\delta\nu^2 - 2^{e-2}ad\mu^2 = \pm 1 \qquad or \qquad 2^{e-2}\delta\nu^2 - ad\mu^2 = \pm 1 \ .$$

If e is even, both of these equations are of type (84). If e is odd, we take $x = \nu$, $y = 2^{\frac{1}{2}(e-3)}\mu$ in the first equation and get (85₁), but take $x = 2^{\frac{1}{2}(e-1)}\nu$, $y = \mu$ in the second and get (85₂).

This completes the proof of Theorem 41 also when $e > 4$.

25. The binary forms f(δ) and their characters.

When e is fixed and $\delta d = H$, we write $f(\delta)$ for $\delta x^2 - ady^2$, where $a = a$ if e is even, but $a = 2a$ if e is odd. Then the left member of each equation (83) − (85) is $f(\delta)$.

Let H be the product of the distinct odd primes $p_1, \ldots, p_n$. Thus there are exactly 2^n positive divisors δ of H. The set S of the 2^n forms $f(\delta)$ has the property that the product of any two of its forms is another one of the set. For, let also $\delta_1 d_1 = H$, and let ϵ be the g.c.d. of δ and δ_1. Then $\delta\delta_1/\epsilon$ is a divisor of H. The product of $f(\delta)$ by $f(\delta_1) = \delta_1 x_1^2 - ad_1 y_1^2$ is

$$\frac{\delta\delta_1}{\epsilon^2}\left(\epsilon x x_1 + \frac{\epsilon a H}{\delta\delta_1}\,yy_1\right)^2 - \frac{\epsilon^2 a H}{\delta\delta_1}\left(\frac{\delta_1}{\epsilon}\,x_1 y + \frac{\delta}{\epsilon}\,xy_1\right)^2,$$

in which all indicated fractions are equal to integers. Hence

(86) $$f(\delta) \cdot f(\delta_1) = f(\delta\delta_1/\epsilon^2) .$$

In case $\delta_1 = \delta$, then $\delta\delta_1/\epsilon^2 = 1$. Let m and m' be both represented by $f(\delta)$ and let neither be divisible by p_i. Then (86) gives

$$mm' = f(1) = X^2 - aHY^2 \equiv X^2 \pmod{p_i} , \qquad (mm' | p_i) = 1 ,$$

since X is not divisible by p_i. Hence $(m | p_i) = (m' | p_i)$. Thus $(m | p_i)$ has the same value ± 1 for all numbers m which are represented by $f(\delta)$ and are not divisible by p_i. Without danger of confusion, we here replace m by $f(\delta)$ and call $(f(\delta) | p_i)$ the *character of the form $f(\delta)$ modulo p_i*. In this symbol we are free to take as $f(\delta)$ any integer m represented by the form $f(\delta)$ which is not divisible by p_i. The last condition need not be stated since the symbol $(m | p_i)$ is used only when m is not divisible by the prime p_i. For a particular m, $(m | p_i)$ is the quadratic character of the integer m modulo p_i.

THEOREM 42. *We can choose the quadratic characters of a moduli $p_1, \ldots, p_n$ so that the set S contains one and only one form having prescribed characters moduli $p_1, \ldots, p_n$.*

To give a proof by induction from $n - 1$ to n, consider the set S' of 2^{n-1} forms

$$F(\Delta) = \Delta x^2 - ADy^2 , \qquad \Delta D = H' = p_1 \ldots p_{n-1} ,$$

where $A = a'$ or $2a'$, according as e is even or odd. Assume that the quadratic characters of a' moduli $p_1, \ldots, p_{n-1}$ have been chosen so that S' contains one and only one form having prescribed characters moduli $p_1, \ldots, p_{n-1}$. In particular, these are $+1$ for $F(1) = x^2 - AH'y^2$ and for no other form in S'.

To each of the 2^{n-1} forms $F(\Delta)$ correspond two forms f obtained by multiplying the coefficient of y^2 or x^2 by p_n and replacing a' by a and hence A by a. On the one hand, we obtain

$$f(\Delta) = \Delta x^2 - a D p_n y^2 , \qquad \Delta(D p_n) = H' p_n = H .$$

We choose the quadratic characters of a so that

$$(87) \qquad (a p_n | p_i) = (a' | p_i) \qquad (i = 1, \ldots, n-1) .$$

We shall prove that

$$(88) \qquad (f(\Delta) | p_i) = (F(\Delta) | p_i) \qquad (i = 1, \ldots, n-1) .$$

If p_i divides D and hence not Δ, we take $x = 1$ and see that each member of (88) is equal to $(\Delta | p_i)$. But if p_i divides Δ and hence not D, we take $y = 1$ and see that the symbols (88) are the products of the respective symbols (87) by $(-Dt | p_i)$, where $t = a/a = A/a'$.

If the left members of (88) are all $+1$, the right members and the hypothesis show that $\Delta = 1$. Hence $f(1)$ is the only one of the 2^{n-1} forms $f(\Delta)$ whose characters moduli $p_1, \ldots, p_{n-1}$ are all $+1$.

On the other hand, we obtain

$$f(\Delta p_n) = \Delta p_n x^2 - a D y^2 , \qquad \Delta p_n D = H .$$

If p_i divides D and hence not Δ, we take $x = 1$ and see that

$$(89) \qquad (f(\Delta p_n) | p_i) = (F(\Delta) | p_i) \cdot (p_n | p_i) \quad (i = 1, \ldots, n-1) .$$

The same is true by (87) also when p_i divides Δ.

Let every left member of (89) be $+1$. From the right members and the hypothesis, we conclude that $F(\Delta)$ is a uniquely determined form of the set S'. Then Δ and D are uniquely determined. We can choose the quadratic characters of a so that not only (87) hold, but also

$$(90) \qquad (-a D | p_n) = -1 .$$

Taking $y = 1$, we have $(f(\Delta p_n) | p_n) = -1$. Hence none of our present 2^{n-1} forms f have all characters $+1$ moduli $p_1, \ldots, p_n$.

Our two results show that $f(1)$ is the only form in the set S whose characters moduli $p_1, \ldots, p_n$ are all $+1$.

Suppose that $f(\delta)$ and $f(\delta_1)$ are distinct forms in S having the same characters moduli $p_1, \ldots, p_n$. If ϵ is the g.c.d. of δ and δ_1, then $\delta\delta_1 \neq \epsilon^2$. By (86), $f(\delta\delta_1/\epsilon^2)$ and $f(1)$ are distinct forms in S whose characters moduli $p_1, \ldots, p_n$ are all $+1$. This contradiction completes the induction.

When $n=1$, H is a prime and S is composed of the two forms x^2-aHy^2 and Hx^2-ay^2, which represent 1 and $-a$, respectively. Hence Theorem 42 holds if $(-a|H)=-1$, to which (90) reduces when $n=1$.

This completes the proof of Theorem 42.

26. Equations $f(\delta)=1$. By Theorem 42, $\delta=1$. Then

$$(91) \qquad x^2-aHy^2=1 \ (e \text{ even}), \qquad x^2-2aHy^2=1 \ (e \text{ odd}) .$$

In the first case of the proof of Theorem 41 with $\delta=1$ and the upper signs, we have $GU=2xy$, $x^2=a\lambda+1$, $T=2x^2-1$. Similarly, if we inspect the remaining cases which there led to an equation of type (91), we find always that

$$T=2x^2-1, \ 2^{\frac{1}{2}e}GU=2xy \qquad \text{if } e \text{ is even} ,$$
$$T=2x^2-1, \ 2^{\frac{1}{2}(e-1)}GU=2xy \qquad \text{if } e \text{ is odd} .$$

When $e=0$, let y be divisible by G. Then y/G is an integer Y and (91_1) becomes $x^2-aEY^2=1$, whence $T=2x^2-1$ and $U=2xY$ are not the least positive solution of (81).

Similarly, when $e=1$ or 3, let $y=GY$. By (91_2), equation (81) has the solution $t=x$, $u=Y$ or $\frac{1}{2}Y$, respectively. Thus $T=2x^2-1$, $U=2xY$ or xY do not give the least positive solution of (81).

When $e=2$ or 4, we shall assume that

$$(92) \qquad a \equiv H \qquad (\text{mod } 4) .$$

Then (91_1) requires that x be odd and y a multiple of 4. If also y is divisible by G, then $y=4GY$. By (91_1), equation (81) has the solution $t=x$, $u=2Y$ or Y. Thus $T=2x^2-1$, $U=4xY$ or $2xY$ do not give the least positive solution of (81).

Finally, let y be not divisible by G. Since xy is divisible by G, x is divisible by a prime s which divides G but not aHy if one of equations (91) holds. Hence $(-aH|s)=1$ or $(-2aH|s)=1$. This proves

THEOREM 43. *Let $e \leq 4$ and let $s_1, \ldots, s_m$ be the primes which divide G, but not H. Then no $f(\delta)=1$ arises in § 24 if we choose the quadratic characters of a so that*

$$(93) \qquad (a|s_k)=-(-2^eH|s_k) \qquad (k=1, \ldots, m) ,$$

and so that $a \equiv H$ (mod 4) in case $e=2$ or 4.

We now introduce certain two positive odd integers p and q. We shall choose the quadratic characters of p so that there shall exist no solutions x, y of any equation $f(\delta) = -1$ or ± 2, and then choose the quadratic characters of q so that those of pq coincide with those of a as fixed in Theorems 42 and 43. Thus pq is a permissible value of a.

27. Cases e = 2, 4. Here $f(\delta) = \delta x^2 - ady^2$, $\delta d = H$. By (84) and §26, it remains only to require that each $f(\delta) = -1$ be impossible.

I. Let every prime factor p_i of H be $\equiv 1 \pmod 4$. Then $(-1\,|\,p_i) = +1$, and Theorem 42 shows that $f(\delta) = -1$ implies $\delta = 1$. Then $x^2 - aHy^2 = -1$. This has no integral solutions if $(-1\,|\,p) = -1$, whence $x^2 \not\equiv -1 \pmod p$.

II. Let H have a prime factor $\equiv 3 \pmod 4$. By Theorem 42, there is a unique $f(\delta)$ whose characters moduli $p_1, \ldots, p_n$ are the same as those of -1. For this δ, $f(\delta) = -1$ will be impossible if $(-\delta\,|\,p) = -1$, whence $(\delta\,|\,p) = -(-1\,|\,p)$, $\delta x^2 \not\equiv -1 \pmod p$. Here $\delta > 1$ since $(f(\delta)\,|\,p_i) = (-1\,|\,p_i)$ is not 1 for every p_i because there is a $p_i \equiv 3 \pmod 4$.

Write $\delta_r = 1$ and $\delta_r = \delta$ in the respective cases I and II. Then all equations $f = -1$ are impossible if $(-\delta_r\,|\,p) = -1$.

28. Cases e = 0, 1, 3. In view of (83), (85) and §26, it remains to require that no one of -1, ± 2 be represented by any $f(\delta)$.

I. Let $H = 1$ or let every prime factor p_i of H be $\equiv 1 \pmod 8$. Then $(-1\,|\,p_i) = (\pm 2\,|\,p_i) = +1$. By Theorem 42, either of $f(\delta) = -1$, ± 2 implies that $\delta = 1$. Let π be p or q. Evidently $f(1) \equiv x^2 \equiv -1 \pmod \pi$ is impossible if $\pi \equiv 3$ or 7 $\pmod 8$. Similarly, $f(1) \neq 2$ if $\pi \equiv 3$ or 5 $\pmod 8$, $f(1) \neq -2$ if $\pi \equiv 5$ or 7 $\pmod 8$. Hence no one of -1, ± 2 is represented by any $f(\delta)$ if p and q are incongruent positive integers chosen from those $\equiv 3$, 5, or 7 $\pmod 8$.

Then $pq \equiv r \pmod 8$, where $r = 3$, 5, or 7. If $r = 3$ and $(-2\,|\,p) = -1$, then $(p, q) \equiv (5, 7)$ or $(7, 5) \pmod 8$. If $r = 5$ and $(-1\,|\,p) = -1$, then $(p, q) \equiv (3, 7)$ or $(7, 3)$. If $r = 7$ and $(2\,|\,p) = -1$, then $(p, q) \equiv (3, 5)$ or $(5, 3)$.

The following synthesis of these results is in accord with those in II and III. Write $\delta_r = 1$ and restrict p to positive integers prime to $2E$ which satisfy

$$(94) \qquad (-1\,|\,p)^{\frac{1}{8}(r^2-1)} \ (2\,|\,p)^{\frac{1}{2}(r-1)} \ (\delta_r\,|\,p) = -1$$

for the various values 3, 5, 7 of r. To each p let correspond all positive integers q such that $pq \equiv r \pmod 8$ and such that $a = pq$ satisfies the conditions in Theorems 42 and 43.

II. Let H contain prime factors P of at least two of the forms $8k+3$, $8k+5$, $8k+7$. They occur among $p_1, \ldots, p_n$. Since

	$P=8k+3$	$8k+5$	$8k+7$
$(-1\,|\,P)$	-1	$+1$	-1
$(2\,|\,P)$	-1	-1	$+1$
$(-2\,|\,P)$	$+1$	-1	-1

no two of -1, 2, -2 have the same quadratic character for all the moduli $p_1, \ldots, p_n$. Hence Theorem 42 shows the existence of unique distinct divisors δ_5, δ_7, δ_3, each >1, of H such that $f(\delta_5), f(\delta_7)$, and $f(\delta_3)$ have the same characters moduli $p_1, \ldots, p_n$ as -1, 2, -2 respectively. It remains only to require that each of

$$(95) \qquad f(\delta_5) = -1 \,, \qquad f(\delta_7) = 2 \,, \qquad f(\delta_3) = -2$$

be impossible. If $\pi = p$ or q is such that $(\delta_5\,|\,\pi) = -(-1\,|\,\pi)$, then $f(\delta_5) \equiv \delta_5 x^2 \equiv -1 \pmod{\pi}$ is impossible, whence (95_1) is impossible, and we denote this case by $I_5(\pi)$. A similar exclusion of (95_2) or (95_3) is denoted by $I_7(\pi)$ or $I_3(\pi)$, respectively. By (86), with δ, δ_1 replaced by δ_5, δ_7, we conclude that $\delta_3 = \delta_5 \delta_7 / \epsilon^2$, whence $(\delta_3\,|\,\pi) = (\delta_5\,|\,\pi)(\delta_7\,|\,\pi)$, which is used below in case $I_3(\pi)$.

Each δ_k is a divisor of H and hence is a product of certain p_i. By the quadratic reciprocity law, we get $(p_i\,|\,a)$ from the known $(a\,|\,p_i)$; by multiplication, we get the value of $(\delta_k\,|\,a)$. Hence the latter determine N in

$$(96) \qquad N = (\delta_5\,|\,a)[3 - 2(\delta_7\,|\,a)] \,, \qquad a \equiv rN \pmod{8} \,,$$

where the congruence determines a modulo 8 when r is any chosen one of 3, 5, 7.

(i) Let $(\delta_5\,|\,a) = -(-1\,|\,a)$, $(\delta_7\,|\,a) = (2\,|\,a)$. In each of the possible cases $a \equiv 1, 3, 5, 7 \pmod 8$, we readily see that $r = 7$. Then (94) becomes $(\delta_7\,|\,p) = -(2\,|\,p)$. Write $(\delta_5\,|\,p) = \pm(-1\,|\,p)$, whence $(\delta_5\,|\,q) = \mp(-1\,|\,q)$, $(\delta_7\,|\,q) = -(2\,|\,q)$. For the upper signs, we have $I_5(q)$, $I_7(p)$, $I_3(p)$. For the lower signs, $I_5(p)$, $I_7(p)$, $I_3(q)$.

(ii) Let $(\delta_5\,|\,a) = (-1\,|\,a)$, $(\delta_7\,|\,a) = -(2\,|\,a)$. Then $r = 5$ and (94) becomes $(\delta_5\,|\,p) = -(-1\,|\,p)$. Let π be that one of p, q for which $(\delta_7\,|\,\pi) = -(2\,|\,\pi)$. Then if σ is the remaining one of p, q, $(\delta_7\,|\,\sigma) = (2\,|\,\sigma)$. Hence $I_5(p)$, $I_5(q)$, $I_7(\pi)$, $I_3(\sigma)$.

(iii) Let $(\delta_5\,|\,a) = -(-1\,|\,a)$, $(\delta_7\,|\,a) = -(2\,|\,a)$. Then $r = 3$ and (94) becomes $(\delta_3\,|\,p) = -(-2\,|\,p)$. Thus $(\delta_3\,|\,a) = (-2\,|\,a)$, $(\delta_3\,|\,q) = -(-2\,|\,q)$. Let π

be that one of p, q for which $(\delta_5 \,|\, \pi) = -(-1 \,|\, \pi)$. If σ is the other one, then $(\delta_5 \,|\, \sigma) = (-1 \,|\, \sigma)$, and

$$(\delta_7 \,|\, \sigma) = (\delta_3 \,|\, \sigma)(\delta_5 \,|\, \sigma) = -(-2 \,|\, \sigma)(-1 \,|\, \sigma) = -(2 \,|\, \sigma) .$$

Hence $I_3(p)$, $I_3(q)$, $I_5(\pi)$, $I_7(\sigma)$.

(iv) Let $(\delta_5 \,|\, a) = (-1 \,|\, a)$, $(\delta_7 \,|\, a) = (2 \,|\, a)$. Then $r = 1$, contrary to $r = 3$, 5 or 7.

Cases (i)–(iv) are exhaustive.

III. When l is a fixed one of 3, 5, 7, let one or more of the prime factors p_i of H be $\equiv l \pmod 8$ and all the remaining p_i be $\equiv 1 \pmod 8$. In the cases

$$l = 3,\ q \equiv 5 \text{ or } 7;\ l = 5,\ q \equiv 3 \text{ or } 7;\ l = 7,\ q \equiv 3 \text{ or } 5 \pmod 8 ,$$

at least one of l and q is $\equiv 3 \pmod 4$, whence $f(1) \neq -1$; one is $\equiv 3$ or 5 $\pmod 8$, whence $f(1) \neq 2$; one is $\equiv 5$ or 7 $\pmod 8$, whence $f(1) \neq -2$. Likewise when q is replaced by p. Hence $f(1) = -1$ or ± 2 are all impossible except when

(97) $$p \equiv 1 \text{ or } l \text{ and } q \equiv 1 \text{ or } l \pmod 8 .$$

Take $s = 2$ if $l = 5$, $s = -1$ if $l = 3$ or 7. Take $t = -1$, 2, or -2, according as $l = 5$, 7, or 3, respectively. Then $(t \,|\, p_i) = +1$ for every p_i, and Theorem 42 shows that $f(\delta) = t$ implies that $\delta = 1$, a case just discussed. By the same theorem there is a unique δ for which

$$(f(\delta) \,|\, p_i) = (s \,|\, p_i) = (st \,|\, p_i) \qquad (i = 1, \ldots, n) ,$$

and this $\delta \neq 1$. If π_1 denotes p or q, $f(\delta) = s$ is impossible if $\delta x^2 \equiv s \pmod{\pi_1}$ is not solvable and hence if (98_1) holds. Similarly for $f(\delta) = st$ and (98_2):

(98) $$(\delta \,|\, \pi_1) = -(s \,|\, \pi_1), \ (\delta \,|\, \pi_2) = -(st \,|\, \pi_2), \text{ each } \pi_i \text{ one of } p, q .$$

If r is any one of 3, 5, 7, we take

(99) $$a \equiv r \pmod 8 \text{ if } (\delta \,|\, a) = 1, \ a \equiv rl \pmod 8 \text{ if } (\delta \,|\, a) = -1 ,$$

(100) $$\delta_r = 1 \text{ or } \delta \text{ according as } r \equiv l \pmod 8 \text{ or not} .$$

For every positive integer p prime to $2E$ and satisfying (94) and for every positive integer q such that $a = pq$ satisfies (99), we shall prove that (98) holds and (97) fails, whence no one of -1, ± 2 is represented by any of the 2^n forms f.

(i) Let $(\delta \mid a) = -(s \mid a)$. Then (98_1) holds for a single one of p, q.

If $a \equiv 1 \pmod 8$, then $(s \mid a) = (st \mid a)$, $(\delta \mid a) = -(st \mid a)$, and (98_2) holds for a single one of p, q. Also, $(s \mid a) = 1$, $(\delta \mid a) = -1$, $a \equiv rl$, $r \equiv l \pmod 8$, $\delta_r = 1$.

If $a \equiv l \pmod 8$, then $(s \mid a) = (st \mid a)$, and as before (98_2) holds for a single one of p, q. Also, $(s \mid a) = -1$, $(\delta \mid a) = 1$, $a \equiv r$, $r \equiv l \pmod 8$, $\delta_r = 1$, and, by case I, neither p nor q is $\equiv 1$ or $l \pmod 8$. The latter is true also if $a \equiv 1 \pmod 8$.

Finally, let $a \not\equiv 1$, $a \not\equiv l \pmod 8$. Then (97) evidently fails. The proof that (98_2) holds falls into three cases. First, let $l = 3$. Then $a \equiv 5$ or $7 \pmod 8$, $s = -1$, $st = 2$. If $a \equiv 5$, $(s \mid a) = 1$, $(\delta \mid a) = -1$, $a \equiv rl$, $r \equiv 7$, $r \not\equiv l \pmod 8$, $\delta_r = \delta$. If $a \equiv 7$, $(s \mid a) = -1$, $(\delta \mid a) = 1$, $a \equiv r$, $r \equiv 7$, $r \not\equiv l \pmod 8$, $\delta_r = \delta$. In both cases, (94) becomes $(2 \mid p) = -(\delta \mid p)$, which is (98_2) with $\pi_2 = p$. Second, let $l = 5$. Then $a \equiv 3$ or $7 \pmod 8$, $s = 2$, $st = -2$. If $a \equiv 3$, $(s \mid a) = -1$, $(\delta \mid a) = 1$, $a \equiv r$, $r \equiv 3$, $r \not\equiv l \pmod 8$, $\delta_r = \delta$. If $a \equiv 7$, $(s \mid a) = 1$, $(\delta \mid a) = -1$, $a \equiv rl$, $r \equiv 3$, $r \not\equiv l \pmod 8$, $\delta_r = \delta$. In both cases, (94) becomes $(-2 \mid p) = -(\delta \mid p)$, which is (98_2) with $\pi_2 = p$. Third, let $l = 7$. Then $a \equiv 3$ or $5 \pmod 8$, $s = -1$, $st = -2$. If $a \equiv 3$, $(s \mid a) = -1$, $(\delta \mid a) = +1$, $a \equiv r$, $r \equiv 3$, $r \not\equiv l \pmod 8$, $\delta_r = \delta$. If $a \equiv 5$, $(s \mid a) = 1$, $(\delta \mid a) = -1$, $a \equiv rl$, $r \equiv 3$, $r \not\equiv l \pmod 8$, $\delta_r = \delta$. In both cases, (94) becomes $(-2 \mid p) = -(\delta \mid p)$, which is (98_2) with $\pi_2 = p$.

(ii) Let $(\delta \mid a) = (s \mid a)$. First, let $l = 5$, whence $s = 2$, $st = -2$. If $a \equiv 3$ or $5 \pmod 8$, then $(s \mid a) = -1$, $(\delta \mid a) = -1$, $a \equiv 5r$, $r \not\equiv 1$, $a \not\equiv 5$, $a \equiv 3 \pmod 8$. But if $a \equiv 1$ or 7, $(s \mid a) = 1$, $(\delta \mid a) = 1$, $a \equiv r \not\equiv 1$, $a \equiv 7 \pmod 8$. In either case, $r \equiv 7$, $\delta_r = \delta$, and (94) gives $(\delta \mid p) = -(2 \mid p)$, which is (98_1) with $\pi_1 = p$. Since $(s \mid a) = -(st \mid a)$ if $a \not\equiv 1$ or $l \pmod 8$, then $(\delta \mid a) = -(st \mid a)$ for $a \equiv 3$ or 7, whence (98_2) holds. Also, (97) contradicts $a = pq \equiv 3$ or $7 \pmod 8$.

Second, let $l = 3$ or 7, whence $s = -1$. If $a \equiv 1$ or $5 \pmod 8$, then $(s \mid a) = 1$, $(\delta \mid a) = 1$, $a \equiv r \not\equiv 1$, $a \equiv 5$. But if $a \equiv 3$ or $7 \pmod 8$, then $(s \mid a) = -1$, $(\delta \mid a) = -1$, $a \equiv rl$, $r \not\equiv 1$, $a \not\equiv l$, $a \equiv 5l \pmod 8$. In either case, $r \equiv 5$, $\delta_r = \delta$, and (94) gives $(\delta \mid p) = -(-1 \mid p)$, which is (98_1) with $\pi_1 = p$. Since $a \not\equiv 1$ or $l \pmod 8$, $(s \mid a) = -(st \mid a)$, whence $(\delta \mid a) = -(st \mid a)$, and (98_2) holds. Also, (97) fails.

29. Summary of our results on Pellian equations.

Theorem 44. *Let $E = 2^e G^2 H$, where 2^e is the highest power of 2 dividing E, and G^2 is the largest odd square dividing E. Let $e \leq 4$. Determine as in Theorems 42 and 43 the quadratic characters of a with respect to the prime factors of GH.*

When $e = 0$, 1, or 3, let r be any preassigned one of the numbers 3, 5, 7. Distinguish cases I, II, III of § 28 on the basis of the residues modulo 8 of the prime factors of H. In each case we defined a unique divisor δ_r of H. For I, $a \equiv r \pmod 8$; for II or III, a is determined modulo 8 by r in (96) or (99), respectively. Employ all positive integers p prime to $2E$ which satisfy

(94). *To each p let correspond all positive integers q such that $pq \equiv a \pmod 8$ and such that*

(101) $(pq \mid \pi) = (a \mid \pi)$ *for every prime factor π of GH.*

When e = 2 or 4, we have the conditions

(102) $a \equiv H \pmod 4$, $(-\delta_r \mid p) = -1$,

where δ_r is defined in § 27. The conditions on q are (101) and $pq \equiv a \pmod 4$.

For all such positive integers p and q the least positive integral solutions T and U of $t^2 - pqEu^2 = 1$ are such that neither $T+1$ nor $T-1$ is divisible by pq.

If p_1 and q_1 have the required properties, the same is true of all positive integers p and q such that

$$p \equiv p_1, \qquad q \equiv q_1 \pmod{8GH}.$$

This is evident for (101) and is true for (94) since $(\delta \mid p) = (\delta \mid p_1)$ by the reciprocity law. Since p_1 is prime to $8GH$, there are infinitely many primes of the form $p_1 + 8GHx$ by Dirichlet's theorem on primes in arithmetical progressions.

COROLLARY. *Theorem 44 holds for infinitely many primes p and infinitely many primes q.*

30. When all binary forms of a genus are represented by one indefinite ternary form f. If $p_1, \ldots, p_k$ are the distinct odd prime factors of D, then[1] $(m \mid p_i)$ has the same value ± 1 for all integers m which are not divisible by p_i and are represented by a given properly primitive, binary, quadratic form ϕ of determinant D. We call $(\phi \mid p_i)$ the *character* of ϕ modulo p_i.

Each of the following symbols is readily shown (*loc. cit.*) to have the same value for all odd integers n represented by ϕ:

(103) $\begin{cases} \delta = (-1)^{\frac{1}{2}(n-1)} \text{ if } D \equiv 0 \text{ or } 3 \pmod 4, \\ \epsilon = (2 \mid n) \text{ if } D \equiv 0 \text{ or } 2 \pmod 8, \\ \delta\epsilon \text{ if } D \equiv 0 \text{ or } 6 \pmod 8, \end{cases}$

and is called a *character* of ϕ.

Let ϕ and ψ be properly primitive forms of the same determinant D. If each character has the same value for ϕ as for ψ, ϕ and ψ are said to belong to the same *genus*. Since equivalent forms represent the same integers and hence have the same characters, they belong to the same genus.

If an indefinite primitive, ternary, quadratic form f has odd invariants Ω and Δ and represents properly a properly primitive, binary, quadratic

[1] A generalization (*Introd.*, p. 83) of the case in § 25 above.

form Φ whose determinant $-\Omega C$ is prime to 2Δ, then f represents every binary form in the same genus as Φ. We shall prove the following generalization:

Theorem 45. *Let 2^e be the largest power of 2 dividing Δ and let d^2 be the largest square dividing Δ. According as e is even or odd, write $\Delta = Hd^2$ or $\Delta = 2Hd^2$, whence H is odd. Let Q denote the quotient of $-\Omega C$ by the largest square dividing it. Assume that $e \leqq 4$ and that[1] Q is not a divisor of $2H$. If the indefinite, primitive, ternary, quadratic form f with the invariants Ω and Δ represents properly a properly primitive, binary, quadratic form Φ of determinant $-\Omega C$, then f represents properly every form Φ_1 of this determinant in the same genus as Φ, provided there hold the compatibility conditions (111)– (114) in terms of generic characters that $\phi = -\Phi$ may represent an a in Theorem 44 with E replaced[2] by Δ.*

Since Φ is represented by the indefinite form f, Theorem 35 shows that Φ and Φ_1 are both negative or both indefinite, whence $\phi = -\Phi$ and $\phi_1 = -\Phi_1$ are both positive or both indefinite.

Thus ϕ is equivalent to a form $\psi = ax^2 + 2lxy + by^2$ having $a > 0$. By Theorem 6 there exist integers ξ and η such that $\psi(\xi, \eta)$ is prime to any assigned integer n. The same is then true of $\psi(\xi + nk, \eta)$ for every integer k. But

$$a\psi(\xi + nk, \eta) = (a\xi + ank + l\eta)^2 + (ab - l^2)\eta^2 ,$$

which is positive when k is sufficiently large. Thus ψ represents positive integers prime to n.

In view of Theorem 28, our present theorem will follow if proved when Φ is replaced by any equivalent form. Hence we may take $\phi = (a, l, b)$, where a is positive and prime to $2\Omega\Delta C$.

Let (60) be a proper representation of Φ by f. We can choose integers c_i so that the determinant of transformation (59) is unity. This replaces f by a form t such that $t(y_1, y_2, 0) = \Phi$. Since f and t represent the same binary forms by Theorem 29, we may choose t as the f of our theorem. Then

$$f = -ax^2 - by^2 + cz^2 + 2ryz + 2sxz - 2lxy .$$

Denote the reciprocal of f by

$$F = AX^2 + BY^2 + CZ^2 + 2RYZ + 2SXZ + 2LXY .$$

---

[1] The theorem holds also for the rather trivial case $Q = 1$ (whence the determinant $-\Omega C$ is a square). In footnotes due to Mr. Ross, we shall extend the theorem to the cases $Q = -1, \pm 2$, except for the subcase $Q = -1$, $e = 2$ or 4, H a product of primes $\equiv 1 \pmod 4$, in which our method fails. We now have the additional compatibility conditions (M) and (N).

[2] Our d is the former $2^{e/2}G$ or $2^{(e-1)/2}G$, according as e is even or odd.

Let T and U be the least positive integers for which $T^2 - a\Delta U^2 = 1$ and write

$$g = T + RU , \qquad h = -BU , \qquad j = CU , \qquad k = T - RU .$$

Then $gk - hj = 1$ since $\Omega^2(BC - R^2) = -a\Omega^2\Delta$. Thus

(104) $$x = x_1 , \qquad y = gy_1 + hz_1 , \qquad z = jy_1 + kz_1$$

has determinant unity and replaces f by an equivalent form f_1. By Theorem 2, the transformation contragredient to (104) is

(105) $$X = X_1 , \qquad Y = kY_1 - jZ_1 , \qquad Z = -hY_1 + gZ_1 ,$$

which replaces the adjoint of f by the adjoint of f_1 and hence replaces F by the reciprocal F_1 of f_1. Give to f_1 and F_1 notations like those for f and F but with subscripts 1 on the coefficients and variables. Then

$$a_1 = a , \qquad l_1 = lg - sj , \qquad C_1 = Cg^2 - 2Rgj + Bj^2 .$$

Inserting the values of g, h, j, k, we get

(106) $$C_1 = C[T^2 + (BC - R^2)U^2] = C(T^2 - a\Delta U^2) = C ,$$

(107) $$l_1 = lT + (lR - sC)U = lT - aSU ,$$

since the sum of the products of the elements $-a$, $-l$, s of the first column of the matrix of f by the cofactors ΩS, ΩR, ΩC of the elements of the third column is zero.

We shall later find the conditions under which

(i) Both ϕ and ϕ_1 represent properly the product of two distinct primes p and q not dividing $2\Omega\Delta C$;

(ii) Neither $T + 1$ nor $T - 1$ is divisible by pq.

We may then take $a = pq$. Since $\Omega C = ab - l^2$, (i) shows that l is prime to both p and q. By (107), $l_1^2 \equiv l^2T^2 \equiv l^2 \pmod{a}$. Hence $\pm l$ and $\pm l_1$ are roots of

(108) $$w^2 \equiv -\Omega C \pmod{a} .$$

Evidently l and $-l$ are incongruent. Since $T^2 \equiv 1$, $l_1 \equiv -l_1$ and (107) would give $l \equiv 0$. Finally, if $l_1 \equiv \pm l$, then $l(T \mp 1) \equiv 0$, and $T \mp 1 \equiv 0$, contrary to (ii). Since (108) has at most four roots, $\pm l$ and $\pm l_1$ give all its roots.

Let g be any binary form of determinant $-\Omega C$ which represents a properly. Then g is equivalent to a form $h = ax^2 + 2mxy + ny^2$, where $m^2 - an = -\Omega C$. Thus m is a root of (108). If we replace m by $m + ka$, we obtain a form which can be derived from h by replacing x by $x+ky$. Hence every binary form of determinant $-\Omega C$ which represents a properly is equivalent to one of $(a, \pm l, b)$, $(a_1, \pm l_1, b_1)$, where $a_1 = a$.

Since $(a, -l, b)$ is derived from $\phi = (a, l, b)$ by replacing x by x and y by $-y$, it is called improperly equivalent to ϕ. Hence by (i), ϕ_1 is properly or improperly equivalent to one of ϕ and $\tau = (a_1, l_1, b_1)$. If it be ϕ, then Φ_1 is properly or improperly equivalent to Φ, whence, by Theorem 28, Φ_1 as well as Φ is represented properly by f. But if it be τ, then Φ_1 is properly or improperly equivalent to $(-a_1, -l_1, -b_1) = f_1(x_1, y_1, 0)$, whence Φ_1 is represented properly by f_1 and hence by f (Theorem 29).

Hence Theorem 45 will follow when conditions (i) and (ii) are satisfied. For brevity we shall denote a class by any form in it. Since ϕ and ϕ_1 are in the same genus, they have the same characters. Hence the class $\phi\phi_1$ derived from them by composition has all its characters $+1$ and hence is in the principal genus (*Introd.*, pp. 141–2). Hence by Theorem 51, $\phi\phi_1$ arises by duplication of a class of properly primitive forms ψ of determinant $-\Omega C$, so that $\phi\phi_1 = \psi^2$. Since we may replace ψ by $-\psi$, we may assume that ψ is positive or indefinite. Denote the class $\psi\phi_1^{-1}$ by μ. Then

$$(109) \qquad\qquad \phi_1 = \psi\mu^{-1}, \qquad \phi = \psi\mu.$$

Let κ be a properly primitive, positive or indefinite, binary, quadratic form of determinant $-\Omega C$. A positive integer p_1 prime to $2\Omega C$ is called compatible with the characters χ of κ if $\chi(p_1) = \chi(\kappa)$ for every χ. Then the well known product relation (127) between the characters holds with n replaced by p_1, and with $D = -\Omega C$, $Q = \pm P$ or $\pm 2P$. Conversely, if p_1 satisfies (127), Theorem 52 shows the existence of such a form κ whose characters are compatible with p_1.

Since[1] Q is not a divisor of $2H$, Q (and therefore P) has an odd prime

---

[1] Let $Q = -1$ or ± 2. If $\delta_r > 1$, the conclusion in the text holds. Hence let $\delta_r = 1$. In case $e = 0$, 1, or 3, we desire that (94) and (127), with p and n replaced by p_1, shall be satisfied. We employ δ, ϵ, and $\delta\epsilon$ of (103). If $Q = -1$, (127) becomes $\delta = 1$ and we must choose $p_1 \equiv 5 \pmod 8$ and $r = 3$ or 7. If $Q = 2$, (127) becomes $\epsilon = 1$ and we must choose $p_1 \equiv 7 \pmod 8$ and $r = 3$ or 5. If $Q = -2$, (127) becomes $\delta\epsilon = 1$ and we must choose $p_1 \equiv 3 \pmod 8$ and $r = 5$ or 7. In summary,

(J) $\left\{\begin{array}{l}\text{In case } Q = -1 \text{ or } \pm 2, \; \delta_r = 1 \text{ and } e = 0, \text{ 1, or 3, both (94) and (127) hold if and}\\ \text{only if } \lambda(p_1) = 1 \text{ and } \lambda(r) = -1, \text{ where } \lambda \text{ denotes } \delta, \; \epsilon, \text{ or } \delta\epsilon, \text{ according as } Q = -1,\\ 2, \text{ or } -2.\end{array}\right.$

In case $e = 2$ or 4, we desire that (102) and (127) be satisfied. Since $\delta_r = 1$, (102) becomes $\delta = -1$. If $Q = 2$, (127) becomes $\epsilon = 1$, and we must take $p_1 \equiv 7 \pmod 8$. If $Q = -2$, (127) becomes $\delta\epsilon = 1$ and we must take $p_1 \equiv 3 \pmod 8$. But if $Q = -1$, (127) becomes $\delta = 1$ and is incompatible with (102): $\delta = -1$. In this last case, H is a product of primes $\equiv 1 \pmod 4$ by § 27.

factor not dividing H and hence not dividing the divisor δ_r of H. Hence we can find a positive integer p_1 prime to $2\Omega C\Delta$ which satisfies both (127) and $L(p_1) = -1$, where $L(p)$ denotes the left member of (94) or (102_2). We saw that there exists a properly primitive, positive or indefinite, binary, quadratic form of given determinant $-\Omega C$ with assigned characters satisfying (127), and hence such a form κ for which there is a positive integer p_1, prime to $2\Omega C\Delta$, compatible with the characters of κ and satisfying $L(p_1) = -1$. Let K denote the set of all such forms κ. We distinguish two cases according as ψ of (109) is or is not in K.

I. ψ in K. There exists a positive integer p_1 prime to $2\Omega C\Delta$ for which $L(p_1) = -1$ and $\chi(p_1) = \chi(\psi)$ for every character of ψ. As in Theorems 42 and 43 with $E = \Delta$, determine the quadratic character of an integer a with respect to the odd prime factors of Δ. Determine the residue of a modulo 4 or 8 as in Theorem 44 with $p = p_1$, $q = q_1$. Determine a positive integer q_1 prime to $2\Omega C\Delta$ such that (101) holds with q replaced by q_1, and such that $p_1 q_1 \equiv a \pmod{8}$ and $(q_1 | \rho) = (\mu | \rho)$ for every odd prime factor ρ of ΩC which does not divide Δ, where $\mu = \psi \phi_1^{-1}$ as before. Using (101), (111), (112), and the hypothesis that ϕ is in the same genus as ϕ_1 and hence as ϕ_1^{-1}, since the latter class contains the forms opposite to those in class ϕ_1, we get

$$(p_1 q_1 | \pi) = (a | \pi) = (\phi | \pi) = (\phi_1^{-1} | \pi) , \qquad (p_1 | \pi) = (\psi | \pi) ,$$
$$(q_1 | \pi) = (\psi | \pi)(\phi_1^{-1} | \pi) = (\mu | \pi) ,$$

for every odd prime π dividing both ΩC and Δ. Hence q_1 is compatible with the characters of μ for all odd primes. A like result is next proved for such of the characters δ, ϵ, $\delta\epsilon$ in (103) as exist for a given determinant D. Let λ be any one of them. We shall later show that if conditions[1] (113) and (114) hold, we can impose on a not only the earlier character conditions, but also the further condition

(110) $\lambda(a) = \lambda(\phi)$, λ ranging over those of the characters
$$\delta, \; \epsilon, \; \delta\epsilon \text{ that exist .}$$

Hence

$$\lambda(q_1) = \lambda(p_1)\lambda(a) = \lambda(\psi)\lambda(\phi_1^{-1}) = \lambda(\psi\phi_1^{-1}) = \lambda(\mu) .$$

Thus q_1 is compatible with all the characters of μ.

Hence, for every integer y, $q = q_1 + 8\Omega C\Delta y$ is compatible with the characters of μ, and $p = p_1 + 8\Omega C\Delta x$ with the characters of ψ. Since these linear forms are primitive, the form[2] ψ represents infinitely many primes p, and the form μ as well as μ^{-1} represents infinitely many primes q.

[1] And (M) and (N).

[2] By a theorem stated by Dirichlet in 1840 and proved by A. Meyer in *Jour. für Math.*, CIII (1888), 98–117; exposition by Bachmann, *Analytische Zahlentheorie*, 1894,

By (109), both ϕ_1 and ϕ represent the product pq. Evidently p and q satisfy the conditions in Theorem 44. Hence both conditions (i) and (ii) are satisfied. This proves Theorem 45 in our case I.

II. ψ not in K. Let n be a positive integer prime to $2\Omega C\Delta$ which is represented properly by ψ. Since ψ is not in K, $L(n) = +1$. We proved that there exists a class κ_0 in K. Let p_0 be a positive integer prime to $2\Omega C\Delta$ which is compatible with the characters of κ_0 and is such that $L(p_0) = -1$. Then $L(p_0 n) = L(p_0)L(n) = -1$, and the product $p_0 n$ is compatible with the characters of class $\psi \kappa_0^{-1}$. Hence the latter is a class κ_1 in the set K. Consider the class $\phi_0 = \phi^{-1}\kappa_0^2$. Then

$$\phi_1 = \phi^{-1}\psi^2 = \phi^{-1}\kappa_0^2 \kappa_1^2 = \phi_0 \kappa_1^2 , \qquad \phi_0^{-1}\phi_1 = \kappa_1^2 .$$

Hence ϕ_0^{-1} and ϕ_1 have the same characters and are in the same genus. Theorem 45 holds for them by case I with ψ replaced by κ_1. Hence if f represents ϕ_0^{-1} properly, it represents ϕ_1 properly. Also, $\phi_0\phi = \kappa_0^2$. Hence if f represents ϕ properly, it represents ϕ_0 properly. Since the class ϕ_0^{-1} contains the opposite of each form in class ϕ_0, if f represent ϕ_0 properly, it represents ϕ_0^{-1} properly by Theorem 28. Therefore if f represents ϕ properly, it represents ϕ_1 properly. This proves Theorem 45 in the present case II.

Finally we shall derive the compatibility conditions[1] (111)–(114) and prove that they imply (110).

If ϕ represents an integer a prime to its determinant $D = -\Omega C$, then $(\phi | t) = (a | t)$ for every odd prime factor t of D. Theorems 42 and 43 determined the quadratic character of a with respect to each odd prime factor of Δ, but left it arbitrary for further odd primes. Hence we have compatibility for all odd primes if

$$(111) \qquad\qquad (\phi | \pi) = -(-2^e H | \pi)$$

for every odd prime π dividing both ΩC and d, but not H, and

$$(112) \qquad\qquad (\phi | \vartheta) = (a | \vartheta)$$

for every prime ϑ dividing ΩC and H.

---

pp. 272–307. A long, but elementary, proof is due to F. Mertens; *Sitzungsber. Ak. Wiss. Wien (Math.)*, CIV (1895), IIa, 1093–1153, 1158; simplification, *ibid.*, CIX (1900), IIa, 415–80.

[1] And (M) and (N).

A. Let[1] $e = 0$, 1, or 3. In § 28, r and hence a has exactly three distinct odd residues modulo 8.

A$_1$. Let $D \equiv 0 \pmod 8$. Then ϕ of determinant D has all three characters (103). Hence two odd integers represented by ϕ yield the same value of δ and the same value of ϵ and hence are congruent modulo 8. Then representation of any of the three a's by ϕ may fail, and compatibility requires

(113) $\phi \equiv$ some $a \pmod 8$ is solvable if $e = 0$, 1, or 3, $\Omega C \equiv 0 \pmod 8$.

Henceforth, we employ $\phi = (a, l, b)$, $l^2 - ab = D$, a odd. Evidently ϕ represents a, b, $u = a + 2l + b$, $v = a + 4l + 4b$.

A$_2$. Let $D \equiv 1 \pmod 4$. If b is odd, l is even, $ab \equiv -1$, $b \not\equiv a \pmod 4$. Thus ϕ *represents integers having two different odd residues modulo* 8. Hence ϕ represents a number which is congruent modulo 8 to one of the three a's, and there is no compatibility condition. If b is even, l is odd and $b \equiv 0$, $u \equiv a + 2 \not\equiv a \pmod 4$, and the same conclusion holds.

A$_3$. Let $D \equiv 3 \pmod 4$. Then δ is a character and $a \equiv a' \pmod 4$ if a and a' are odd numbers represented by ϕ. First, let b be odd. Then $b \equiv a \pmod 4$ and l is even, $v \equiv 5a \not\equiv a \pmod 8$, and the italicized statement holds. Next, let b be even. Then l is odd, $b \equiv 2 \pmod 4$, $v \equiv a + 4 \not\equiv a \pmod 8$.

A$_4$. Let $D \equiv 4 \pmod 8$. If b is odd, $b \equiv a \pmod 4$ as in A_3. The italicized statement holds unless $b \equiv a \pmod 8$, whence $l^2 \equiv 1 + 4 \pmod 8$,

---

[1] Let also $Q = -1$ or ± 2. In case II of § 28, $\delta_r > 1$ and hence (127) and (94) are compatible. In case I, $\delta_r = 1$, $pq \equiv a \equiv r \pmod 8$, whence, if ϕ represents pq, then (J) imply

(M) $\begin{cases} \lambda(\phi) = -1 \text{ if } e = 0, 1 \text{ or } 3. \ H \text{ is } 1 \text{ or a product of primes} \equiv 1 \pmod 8 \text{ and } \lambda \text{ de-} \\ \text{notes } \delta, \ \epsilon, \text{ or } \delta\epsilon, \text{ according as } Q = -1, 2, \text{ or } -2. \end{cases}$

This implies (110). For III, we shall prove

(N) $\begin{cases} \lambda(\phi) = -1 \text{ if } \lambda(l) = +1, \text{ where } \lambda \text{ is } \delta, \ \epsilon, \text{ or } \delta\epsilon, \text{ according as } Q = -1, 2, \text{ or} -2; \text{ for} \\ e = 0, 1, \text{ or } 3 \text{ and for } l \text{ and } H \text{ as in III of § 28.} \end{cases}$

For, if $\lambda(l) = \lambda(\phi) = 1$, then $\phi \equiv 1$ or $l \pmod 8$. We shall write d for the δ in III of § 28. If $(d | a) = 1$, $r \equiv a$, $a \equiv 3$, 5 or 7 $\pmod 8$. Hence if ϕ represents $pq \equiv a \pmod 8$, then $a \equiv l \pmod 8$, $\delta_r = 1$, and (127) and (94) are incompatible by (J). But if $(d | a) = -1$, $r \equiv al$, and a has any one of the three odd residues $\not\equiv l \pmod 8$. Hence if ϕ represents $pq \equiv a$, then $a \equiv 1 \pmod 8$. Hence $r \equiv l$, $\delta_r = 1$, and (127) and (94) are incompatible by (J). If $\lambda(l) = +1$, (N) implies (110).

Next, let $\lambda(l) = -1$. First, let $(d | a) = 1$; then $r \equiv a$, $a \equiv 3$, 5, or 7 $\pmod 8$. When $a \equiv l$, then $r \equiv l \pmod 8$, whence $\delta_r = 1$. Since $\lambda(r) = \lambda(l) = -1$, (127) and (94) are compatible by (J). But when $a \not\equiv l$, then $\delta_r > 1$ and (127) and (94) are evidently compatible. For, if $\delta_r = 1$, then $l \equiv r \equiv a \pmod 8$. Second, let $(d | a) = -1$; then $a \equiv rl \pmod 8$ and a has any one of the three odd residues $\not\equiv l \pmod 8$. When $a \equiv 1$, then $r \equiv l \pmod 8$, $\delta_r = 1$, $\lambda(r) = \lambda(l) = -1$, and (127) and (94) are compatible. But when $a \not\equiv 1 \pmod 8$, then $\delta_r > 1$ and (127) and (94) are compatible. For, if $\delta_r = 1$, $r \equiv l$, $a \equiv 1 \pmod 8$. Hence when $\lambda(l) = -1$, (127) and (94) are compatible for any of the three permissible odd residues of a modulo 8. The argument in the text under $A_1 - A_6$ applies and shows that (113) is the only compatibility condition modulo 8.

which is impossible. If b is even, then $l=2L$, $b=4B$, $L+B$ is odd and $u\equiv a+4$ (mod 8).

A_5. Let $D\equiv 2$ (mod 8). If b is even, l is even, $b\equiv 2a$, $u\equiv 3a\not\equiv a$ (mod 4) and the italicized statement holds. Here ϵ is a character. Thus if b is odd, $b\equiv \pm a$ (mod 8). For the lower sign, $b\not\equiv a$. For the upper sign, $l^2\equiv 1+2$ (mod 8), which is impossible.

A_6. Let $D\equiv 6$ (mod 8). When b is even, A_5 holds. When b is odd, the character $\delta\epsilon$ shows that $b\equiv a$ or $3a$ (mod 8). For the former, $l^2\equiv 1+6$ (mod 8), which is impossible.

Hence unless $D\equiv 0$ (mod 8), there is no compatibility condition. In cases A_2-A_6 we proved that $\phi\equiv$ some a (mod 8), while in case A_1 we secured this property by (113). Thus (113) implies (110).

B. Let $e=2$ or 4. Then $a\equiv H$ (mod 4) is the only condition on a modulo a power of 2. In cases A_2, A_5, and A_6, we saw that ϕ represents two odd numbers incongruent modulo 4, and then there is no compatibility condition. Since a may be chosen congruent to either H or $H+4$ modulo 8, and since $\lambda(H)=-\lambda(H+4)$ when λ is ϵ or $\delta\epsilon$, we can satisfy (110).

But if $D\equiv 0$ or 3 (mod 4), ϕ has the character δ. If ϕ represents the odd numbers a and a', then $a\equiv a'$ (mod 4), whence compatibility requires

(114) $\phi\equiv a\equiv H$ (mod 4) is solvable if $e=2$ or 4, $-\Omega C\equiv 0$ or 3 (mod 4).

If $D\equiv 4$ (mod 8) or $D\equiv 3$ (mod 4), $\lambda=\delta$ is the only one of the three characters and (114) implies (110). If $D\equiv 0$ (mod 8) and if λ is ϵ or $\delta\epsilon$, we choose a to be congruent modulo 8 to that one of H or $H+4$ for which (110) holds as before.

Conditions (111)–(114) are vacuous if $e=0$ and ΩC is prime to 2Δ. Hence Theorem 45 implies the simple special case mentioned before it.

31. Representation by binary forms. In case A_2 we find that, when b is odd, no two of a, b, $v\equiv a+4$, $b+4l+4a\equiv b+4$ are congruent modulo 8, while if b is even the same is true of a, u, v, $a-2l+b$. This with the results in A_1, A_3-A_6 prove

THEOREM 46. *A properly primitive, binary, quadratic form ϕ properly represents integers congruent to any assigned odd residue ρ modulo 8 which is in accord with those of the characters δ, ϵ, $\delta\epsilon$ which exist for ϕ. For example, if ϵ exists and if n is one odd number represented, then $(2\,|\,\rho)=(2\,|\,n)$.*

32. Characters of a ternary quadratic form. Let the primitive ternary form f have the invariants Ω and Δ. Let p and q be any odd prime factors of Ω and Δ, respectively. Let u_1, u_2, u_3 and v_1, v_2, v_3 be any two sets of integers for which neither $f(u)$ nor $f(v)$ is divisible by p; such sets exist by Theorems 6 and 7. The coefficients of the adjoint ϕ of f are all divisible by Ω and hence by p. The first fundamental identity (32) shows that $f(u) \cdot f(v)$ is congruent to a square modulo p, whence $(f(u)|p) = (f(v)|p)$. Similarly, if F is the reciprocal of f, and if the u_i and v_i are integers for which neither $F(u)$ nor $F(v)$ is divisible by q, the second fundamental identity (33) gives $(F(u)|q) = (F(v)|q)$. Then $(f(u)|p)$ and $(F(u)|q)$ are called *characters* of f for each odd prime factor p of Ω and q of Δ.

For Ω even, let m_1 and m_2 be odd numbers represented by f. Then $s = \frac{1}{2}\Sigma_i u_i \partial f(v)/\partial v_i$ is odd by (32). Hence if Ω is divisible by $k=4$ or 8, then $m_1 m_2 \equiv 1$, $m_1 \equiv m_2$ (mod k).

Similarly, if Δ is divisible by $k=4$ or 8, and if M_1 and M_2 are odd numbers represented by F, (33) shows that $M_1 \equiv M_2$ (mod k).

Hence f has the characters[1]

(115) $(-1)^{\frac{1}{2}(f-1)}$ if $\Omega \equiv 0$ (mod 4), $(-1)^{\frac{1}{8}(f^2-1)}$ if $\Omega \equiv 0$ (mod 8) ,

(116) $(-1)^{\frac{1}{2}(F-1)}$ if $\Delta \equiv 0$ (mod 4), $(-1)^{\frac{1}{8}(F^2-1)}$ if $\Delta \equiv 0$ (mod 8).

Two primitive forms f and f_1 are said to be in the same *genus* if their like characters are all equal.

I. Let f and F be both properly primitive. After a preliminary transformation of f we may assume by the Corollary to Theorem 18 that

(117) $$f = ax^2 + by^2 + cz^2 + 2ryz + 2sxz + 2txy ,$$

and $F = AX^2 + \ldots$, where a and C are positive integers prime to each other and to $2\Omega\Delta$. Then

(118) $$ab - t^2 = \Omega C , \qquad BC - R^2 = \Delta a .$$

Hence

$$(-\Omega|a) = (C|a) , \qquad (-\Delta|C) = (a|C) ,$$

and the quadratic reciprocity law gives

(119) $$(-\Omega|a) \cdot (-\Delta|C) = (-1)^{\frac{1}{4}(a-1)(C-1)} .$$

Write $\beta = 1$ or -1, according as $\Delta = Hd^2$ or $\Delta = 2Hd^2$ in the notations of Theorem 45. Let ω^2 be the largest square dividing Ω and write $\gamma = 1$ or -1, according as $\Omega = h\omega^2$ or $\Omega = 2h\omega^2$. Thus H and h are odd. Then

$$(-\Omega|a) = \gamma^{\frac{1}{2}(a^2-1)}(-1)^{\frac{1}{2}(a-1)}(h|a) , \qquad (h|a) = (-1)^{\frac{1}{4}(a-1)(h-1)}(a|h) ,$$

(120) $$(-\Omega|a) = \gamma^{\frac{1}{2}(a^2-1)}(-1)^{\frac{1}{4}(a-1)(h+1)}(a|h) .$$

---

[1] In *Phil. Trans.*, CLVII (1867), 255–98 (*Coll. Math. Papers*, I, 455–509), H. J. S. Smith found other cases in which one of the functions (115) or their product is a "character"; likewise for (116). For example, (115₁) if Ω is odd, $\Delta \equiv 0$ (mod 4), $F \equiv \Omega$ (mod 4). But we shall use the term character only for the cases in the text.

Similarly,

$$(121) \qquad (-\Delta \mid C) = \beta^{\frac{1}{2}(C^2-1)}(-1)^{\frac{1}{4}(C-1)(H+1)}(C \mid H) \ .$$

Inserting these values into (119) and writing

$$(122) \qquad \Psi = (-1)^{\psi} , \qquad \psi = \tfrac{1}{2}(h+C)\cdot\tfrac{1}{2}(H+a) ,$$

we get the important formula[1]

$$(123) \qquad \gamma^{\frac{1}{2}(a^2-1)}\beta^{\frac{1}{2}(C^2-1)}(a \mid h)(C \mid H) = (-1)^{\frac{1}{4}(h+1)(H+1)}\Psi \ .$$

If we multiply the factors of ψ by the odd numbers h and H, we see from $h^2 \equiv H^2 \equiv 1 \pmod 8$ that

$$(124) \qquad \psi \equiv \tfrac{1}{2}(1+hC)\cdot\tfrac{1}{2}(1+Ha) \qquad \pmod 2 \ .$$

II. Let f be improperly primitive. Thus a, b, c are even. By the proof of Theorem 19, Ω is odd, Δ is even, and F is properly primitive. By the Theorems 13 and 20, we may assume (after a transformation of f) that $k = \frac{1}{2}a$ and C are positive odd integers prime to each other and to $\Omega\Delta$. The following deduction of relation (125) between the characters is not used in this book. By (118), $-\Omega C \equiv t^2 \pmod k$, $-2\Delta k \equiv R^2 \pmod C$. Hence

$$(-\Omega \mid k)(-2\Delta \mid C) = (C \mid k)(k \mid C) = (-1)^{\frac{1}{4}(k-1)(C-1)} \ .$$

Here $\Omega = h\omega^2$ is odd, whence by (120),

$$(-\Omega \mid k) = (-1)^{\frac{1}{4}(k-1)(h+1)}(k \mid h) \ .$$

Whether $\beta = 1$ or -1 as in I, $(-2\Delta \mid C) = (-\beta)^{\frac{1}{2}(C^2-1)}(-H \mid C)$. Replacing $(H \mid C)$ by its value from the reciprocity law, and noting that $(k \mid h) = (2 \mid h)(a \mid h)$, we see that

$$(125) \begin{cases} (-1)^{\frac{1}{4}(h^2-1)}(-\beta)^{\frac{1}{2}(C^2-1)}(a \mid h)(C \mid H) = (-1)^g , \\ g = \tfrac{1}{4}[(k-1)(h+1)+(C-1)(H+1)+(k-1)(C-1)] \\ \qquad\qquad\qquad\qquad\qquad \equiv \tfrac{1}{4}(h+1)(H+1) \pmod 2 \ . \end{cases}$$

It remains to verify the last congruence. Since a and b are even and ΩC is odd, (118_1) shows that t is odd, and hence $\Omega C \equiv -1$, $\Omega \equiv -C \pmod 4$. But $\Omega = h\omega^2 \equiv h \pmod 4$. Hence $\frac{1}{2}(C+h)$ is even. Two of the three parts of g

---

[1] When Ω and Δ are odd, whence $\beta = \gamma = 1$, Smith called Ψ a character. But (123) serves to express it in terms of the characters of $f = a$ and $F = C$ with respect to the odd prime factors of h and H respectively.

are products of $\frac{1}{2}(C-1)$ by an integer. Since $\frac{1}{2}(C-1) \equiv \frac{1}{2}(-h-1)$ (mod 2), g is unaltered modulo 2 when C is replaced by $-h$.

III. If F is improperly primitive, we obtain from (125) another relation between the characters by interchanging a and C, h and H, α and β.

33. Cases in which every genus of ternary forms contains a single class. Our main object is to prove[1]

Theorem 47. *Two properly primitive, indefinite, ternary, quadratic forms with properly primitive reciprocals, or two improperly primitive, indefinite, ternary forms are equivalent if they belong to the same genus and if their invariants have no common odd factor >1 and neither is divisible by 4.*

We shall however establish general tests for equivalence without restrictions on Ω and Δ.

First let f and F be both properly primitive. We may assume the initial properties in I, § 32. By (118),

$$\Phi = ax^2 + 2txy + by^2 , \qquad \psi = BY^2 + 2RYZ + CZ^2$$

are properly primitive. Hence each represents infinitely many primes. After applying an integral transformation on x and y of determinant unity, we may assume that a is a prime not dividing $2\Omega\Delta$; while the determinant of Φ and hence C is unaltered. Next, we apply a transformation of type (104) to f and (105) to F. Without altering a we may therefore replace C by any number represented by ψ. We may therefore take a and C to be distinct primes not dividing $2\Omega\Delta$.

Let also f_1 and its reciprocal F_1 be properly primitive, where f_1 and f are in the same genus with the invariants Ω and Δ. Give to f_1 and F_1 notations like those for f and F with subscripts 1 on all letters. As before we may assume that a_1 and C_1 are distinct primes not dividing $2\Omega\Delta$.

The general case will be reduced in III to one of the special cases I, II.

I. Let $C = C_1$. Then $\Phi = (a, t, b)$ and $\Phi_1 = (a_1, t_1, b_1)$ are properly primitive forms of the same determinant $-\Omega C$. They have the same character with respect to each odd prime factor of Ω, since f and f_1 belong to the same genus, and since every integer represented by Φ is represented by f and likewise for Φ_1 and f_1. Next, (118$_2$) and $B_1C - R_1^2 = \Delta a_1$ imply

$$(\Phi \mid C) = (a \mid C) = (-\Delta \mid C) = (a_1 \mid C) = (\Phi_1 \mid C) .$$

Consider the case $\Omega \equiv 0$ (mod k), $k = 4$ or 8. Employ odd values of f, f_1, Φ, Φ_1. Since $\Omega C = ab - t^2$, $a\Phi \equiv (ax + ty)^2 \equiv 1$, $\Phi \equiv a$ (mod k). Similarly, $\Phi_1 \equiv a_1$. Likewise, by (49), $af \equiv u^2 \equiv 1$, $f \equiv a$ (mod k), and $f_1 \equiv a_1$. Since f

---

[1] By combining cases of Theorems 48 and 50. Here Meyer incorrectly omitted the primitive and imprimitive conditions.

and f_1 are in the same genus, and have the character (115_1) if $k=4$, and both characters (115) if $k=8$, we have $f \equiv f_1 \pmod{k}$. Hence $a \equiv a_1$, $\Phi \equiv \Phi_1$ (mod k). This proves that when $\Omega C \equiv 0 \pmod{k}$, Φ and Φ_1 have the same character δ or same characters δ, ϵ, and $\delta\epsilon$ in (103), according as $k=4$ or $k=8$.

Let β denote a properly primitive, positive or indefinite, binary, quadratic form whose determinant D is not a square. Write $D = \pm 2^c P S^2$, where $c=0$ or 1, and P is a product of distinct odd primes. Let n be any positive integer, prime to $2D$, which is represented properly by β. Then β is equivalent to a form (n, u, v) having $u^2 - nv = D$, whence $u^2 \equiv D \pmod{n}$, $(D \mid n) = 1$. Write

$$(126) \quad r = \tfrac{1}{2}(\pm P - 1) , \quad s = (-1)^r , \quad l = (-1)^c , \quad h = \tfrac{1}{8}(n^2 - 1) , \quad j = \tfrac{1}{2}(n - 1) .$$

By the reciprocity law, $(D \mid n) = 1$ becomes

$$(127) \qquad\qquad s^j l^h (n \mid P) = +1 .$$

The left member is seen to be either a character or a product of characters of β, except when $s = l = P = 1$, $\pm = +$, and then $D = S^2$, a case always excluded. Hence the characters are dependent and satisfy the product relation (127).

In the paragraph preceding the last, we accounted for either all or all but one of the characters of Φ. In the latter case we employ (127). Hence every character of Φ coincides with the like character of Φ_1. In other words, Φ and Φ_1 are in the same genus.

Define Q so that $-\Omega C = D = QS^2$. Since C is a prime not dividing $2\Omega\Delta$, C divides Q, whence Q is not a divisor of 2Δ.

We may therefore apply Theorem 45 with f and f_1 interchanged and Φ and Φ_1 interchanged, and conclude that f_1 (as well as f) represents Φ properly when the compatibility conditions (111)–(114) hold. In them, π and ϑ must now divide Ω since C is prime to Δ and hence to d and H. Since both f and f_1 then properly represent Φ, in whose determinant $-\Omega C$ the factor C is a prime, they are equivalent by Theorem 34.

Let 2^m denote the highest power of 2 dividing Ω. Then the following are sufficient (but not necessary) conditions for the equivalence of f and f_1:

$$(128) \quad \begin{cases} e \leq 4; \ (f \mid \pi) = -(2^e H \mid \pi), \ (f \mid \vartheta) = (-a \mid \vartheta) \\[4pt] \text{for every odd prime } \pi \text{ as in dividing } \Omega \text{ and } d, \text{ but not } H, \text{ and} \\ \text{every common prime factor } \vartheta \text{ of } \Omega \text{ and } H \ ; \\ \text{(i) if } e=0, 1 \text{ or } 3, \ m>2, \text{ then } -f \equiv \text{ some } a \pmod{8} \text{ is solvable }; \\ \text{(ii) if } e=2 \text{ or } 4, \ m>1, \text{ or } m=0 \text{ and } F \equiv \Omega \pmod{4} \text{ is solvable, then} \\ \quad -f \equiv a \pmod{4} \text{ is solvable.} \end{cases}$$

In fact, if an integer is represented by $\Phi = -\phi$, it is represented by f (which properly represents Φ), whence the initial relations (128) imply (111) and (112), but not conversely. If $\Omega C \equiv 0$, then $\Omega \equiv 0 \pmod 8$, characters (115) show that all odd integers represented by f are congruent modulo 8, whence (i) of (128) implies (113). If $-\Omega C \equiv 3$, whence $C \equiv \Omega \pmod 4$, then $F \equiv \Omega \pmod 4$ is solvable since F represents C. Hence the final case $m = 0$, $F \equiv \Omega \pmod 4$ of (128), (ii), implies (114), since f has the character (115$_1$) by the first footnote in § 32. We may avoid that footnote by adding at the end of (ii) in (128) the new assumption that every odd value of f is congruent to at least one a modulo 4.

II. Let $a = a_1$. Then ψ and ψ_1 are properly primitive, binary forms of the same determinant $-\Delta a$. If ω^2 is the largest square dividing Ω, we write $\Omega = -h\omega^2$ or $\Omega = -2h\omega^2$, according as m is even or odd. When we replace E by $-\Omega$ in §§ 24–29, let a become a'. Apply case I to $f' = -F$, $f_1' = -F_1$, whose reciprocals are $F' = -f$ and $F_1' = -f_1$, respectively. The invariants of f' are $\Omega' = -\Delta$ and $\Delta' = -\Omega$. The following are sufficient conditions for the equivalence of F and F_1 and hence of f and f_1:

(129) $\begin{cases} \text{In (128) interchange } e \text{ and } m, h \text{ and } H, \Omega \text{ and } \Delta, d \text{ and } \omega, a \text{ and} \\ \quad a'; \text{ replace } f \text{ by } -F, \text{ and } F \text{ by } f. \end{cases}$

Since conditions (128) are all vacuous for the case in Theorem 47, the same must be true of (129).

III. Let $C \neq C_1$, $a \neq a_1$. Let k be any integer prime to $4\Omega C$ such that $\chi(k) = \chi(a)$ for every character χ of $\phi = (a, t, b)$, where ϕ (the former Φ) is of determinant $D = -\Omega C$ by (118$_1$), and a and C are distinct primes not dividing $2\Omega\Delta$. Let L be any prime $\equiv k \pmod{4\Omega C}$. Since $t^2 \equiv D \pmod a$, $(D \mid a) = 1$. We shall prove

(130) $$(D \mid L) = 1.$$

(i) D odd. First, let $D \equiv 1 \pmod 4$. By the reciprocity law, $(a \mid D) = 1$, and (130) is equivalent to $(L \mid D) = 1$. But $(L \mid D) = (k \mid D) = (a \mid D)$ since $\chi(k) = \chi(a)$. Second, let $D \equiv 3 \pmod 4$. Then ϕ has the character

$$a = (-1)^{\frac{1}{2}(a-1)} = (-1)^{\frac{1}{2}(k-1)} = (-1)^{\frac{1}{2}(L-1)} = \lambda \ .$$

By the reciprocity law, $(a \mid D) = a$, $(L \mid D) = \lambda$.

(ii) D double an odd integer d. Then $(d \mid a) = (2 \mid a)$ and (130) holds if $(d \mid L) = (2 \mid L)$. By hypothesis, $(L \mid d) = (a \mid d)$. In view of the reciprocity law, it remains only to prove

(131) $\quad (-1)^z (2 \mid a) = (-1)^s (2 \mid L) \ , \ z = \tfrac{1}{4}(d-1)(a-1) \ , \ s = \tfrac{1}{4}(d-1)(L-1) \ .$

First, let $D \equiv 2$ (mod 8). Then ϕ has the character

$$(2\,|\,a) = (2\,|\,k) = (2\,|\,L)\;,$$

while $d \equiv 1$ (mod 4). This proves (131).

Second, let $D \equiv 6$ (mod 8). Then ϕ has the character

$$(2\,|\,a)(-1\,|\,a) = (2\,|\,k)(-1\,|\,k) = (2\,|\,L)(-1\,|\,L)\;,$$

while $d \equiv 3$ (mod 4), whence $(-1)^z = (-1\,|\,a)$, $(-1)^s = (-1\,|\,L)$. This proves (131).

(iii) $D = 4d$, d odd. The proof in (i) applies with D replaced by d.

(iv) $D = 2^n d$, $n \geq 3$, d odd. Then ϕ has the characters $(-1)^{\frac{1}{2}(a-1)}$ and $(2\,|\,a)$, which are equal to the like functions of L. By the reciprocity law,

$$(2\,|\,L)^n = (2\,|\,a)^n = (d\,|\,a) = (-1)^{\frac{1}{2}(a-1)\cdot\frac{1}{2}(d-1)}(a\,|\,d)$$
$$= (-1)^{\frac{1}{2}(L-1)\cdot\frac{1}{2}(d-1)}(L\,|\,d) = (d\,|\,L)\;,$$

which proves (130).

By (130) there exist integral solutions g and h of $g^2 - hL = D$, whence L is represented by $(L,\,g,\,h)$ of determinant D. This form was shown to have the same characters as ϕ and hence is in the same genus as ϕ. When (128) hold, we saw that f represents properly every binary form in the same genus as ϕ, and hence represents $L = 4\Omega C x + k$. Likewise, f_1 represents all primes of certain linear forms $L_1 = 4\Omega C_1 y + k_1$ compatible with the characters χ of $\phi_1 = (a_1, t_1, b_1)$, i.e., for which $\chi(k_1) = \chi(a_1)$ and k_1 is prime to $4\Omega C_1$. We shall prove that we can select one of the permissible k and one of the k_1 so that $k \equiv k_1$ (mod 4Ω), whence $k_1 = k + 4\Omega q$. Since C and C_1 are distinct primes, there exist solutions r and s of $Cr - C_1 s = q$. Write $j = 4\Omega C r + k$. Then $j = 4\Omega C_1 s + k_1$. For $x = C_1 z + r$, L becomes $J = 4\Omega C C_1 z + j$. For $y = C z + s$, L_1 becomes the same J. Hence all primes of the form J are represented by both L and L_1 and hence by f and f_1. After suitable transformation of the latter we therefore have $a = a_1$ (case II).

It remains to discuss the conditions for compatibility. Since f and f_1 are in the same genus, $(a\,|\,p) = (a_1\,|\,p)$ for every odd prime factor p of Ω. We next treat characters modulo 4 or 8.

III$_1$. Ω odd. If $-\Omega C \equiv 1$ (mod 4), ϕ has none of the characters (103) modulo 4 or 8, and k is $\equiv +1$ or -1 (mod 4) at our choice. Likewise for k_1 if $-\Omega C_1 \equiv 1$ (mod 4). Hence we may take $k \equiv k_1$ (mod 4) unless perhaps in the case $-\Omega C \equiv -\Omega C_1 \equiv 3$ (mod 4). Then $C \equiv C_1$ (mod 4). Here $\gamma = 1$. In (123), $(a\,|\,h) = (a_1\,|\,h)$, $(C\,|\,H) = (C_1\,|\,H)$ since f and f_1 are in the same genus.

If Δ is odd, then $\beta = 1$, and (123) requires the Ψ be the same for f and f_1. By (124) this gives $a \equiv a_1$ (mod 4), whence $k \equiv k_1$ (mod 4).

If $\Delta \equiv 0 \pmod 8$, (116_2) gives

$$(132) \qquad \tfrac{1}{8}(C^2-1) \equiv \tfrac{1}{8}(C_1^2-1) \pmod 2 ,$$

and the preceding proof holds. It holds also if $\Delta \equiv 4 \pmod 8$, whence $\beta = 1$.

Finally, let $\Delta \equiv 2 \pmod 4$. Then Δa is the double of an odd number $4n \pm 1$, whence $\Delta a \equiv \pm 2 \pmod 8$. By Theorem 46, each of the properly primitive forms $(B, 2R, C)$ of determinant $-\Delta a$ and $(B_1, 2R_1, C_1)$ of determinant $-\Delta a_1$ represents integers $\equiv 1$ and integers congruent to -1 (mod 4). Hence we may assume that C and C_1 are not congruent modulo 4. But this case was treated above.

III$_2$. $\Omega \equiv 2 \pmod 4$. Then $\gamma = -1$. If $\Delta \equiv 0 \pmod 8$, we have (132); then (123) gives

$$(133) \qquad \tfrac{1}{8}(a^2-1)+\tfrac{1}{2}(1+hC)\cdot\tfrac{1}{2}(1+Ha) \equiv \tfrac{1}{8}(a_1^2-1)+\tfrac{1}{2}(1+hC_1)\cdot\tfrac{1}{2}(1+Ha_1) \pmod 2.$$

If $\Delta \equiv 4 \pmod 8$, then $\beta = 1$ and (123) again becomes (133). In both cases, $\Delta \equiv 0 \pmod 4$ and (116_1) gives $F \equiv F_1$, $C \equiv C_1 \pmod 4$. First, let $hC \equiv hC_1 \equiv -1 \pmod 4$; then the products in (133) are even and the forms ϕ and ϕ_1 have the same character $\epsilon = (2|a) = (2|a_1)$. Second, let $hC \equiv hC_1 \equiv 1 \pmod 4$. Since $(H-1)(a-1)$ is a multiple of 4, $\tfrac{1}{2}(1+Ha) \equiv \tfrac{1}{2}(a-1)+\tfrac{1}{2}(H+1)$, (133) gives

$$\tfrac{1}{8}(a^2-1)+\tfrac{1}{2}(a-1) \equiv \tfrac{1}{8}(a_1^2-1)+\tfrac{1}{2}(a_1-1) \pmod 2 ,$$

and ϕ and ϕ_1 have the same character $\delta\epsilon$.

Next, let Δ be odd. Then $\beta = 1$ and (123) becomes (133). If $C \equiv C_1 \pmod 4$, the above proof applies. Hence let $C \equiv -C_1 \pmod 4$. The determinant $-\Omega C$ of ϕ is double an odd integer and hence is $\equiv \pm 2 \pmod 8$. The same is true of ϕ_1. By Theorem 46, ϕ represents integers $\equiv 1$ and integers $\equiv 3$ (mod 4). Likewise for ϕ_1. If ϕ and ϕ_1 represent the same odd residue modulo 8, they have the same character ϵ of $\delta\epsilon$. Let the contrary be true. Then we may take $a_1 \equiv a+4 \pmod 8$. In (133) we may replace C_1 by $-C$ and the final a_1 by a without disturbing the congruence. We get $\tfrac{1}{2}(1+Ha)hC \equiv 1 \pmod 2$, whence $Ha \equiv 1$, $a \equiv H \pmod 4$, whereas ϕ represents integers $\equiv 1$ and integers $\equiv 3 \pmod 4$. Hence this case is excluded.

Finally, let $\Delta \equiv 2 \pmod 4$. As in the final case of III$_1$, we may take $C \equiv -C_1 \pmod 4$. Here $\beta = -1$ and (123) gives a congruence derived from (133) by adding $u = \tfrac{1}{8}(C^2-1)$ to the left member and $v = \tfrac{1}{8}(C_1^2-1)$ to the right. In case $C_1 \equiv -C \pmod 8$, then $u \equiv v \pmod 2$ and the proof for Δ odd applies. Hence let $C_1 \equiv 4-C \pmod 8$, whence $v \equiv u+1 \pmod 2$. As in the case Δ odd we now get $\tfrac{1}{2}(1+Ha)hC \equiv 0 \pmod 2$, $Ha \equiv -1$, $a \equiv -H \pmod 4$, whereas ϕ represents integers $\equiv$ both 1 and 3 (mod 4).

III$_3$. $\Omega \equiv 0$ (mod 4). Since f and f_1 belong to the same genus, (115) gives $a \equiv a_1$ (mod 4 or 8), according as $\Omega \equiv 4$ or 0 (mod 8).

Hence in all cases under III$_2$ and III$_3$, ϕ and ϕ_1 have the same characters modulo $m = 4$ or 8, whence $k \equiv k_1$ (mod m). This completes the proof of

THEOREM 48. *Let f and f_1 be properly primitive, indefinite, ternary, quadratic forms in the same genus with the invariants Ω and Δ, such that the reciprocals of f and f_1 are properly primitive. If conditions (128) and (129) hold, f and f_1 are equivalent.*

34. Improperly primitive, ternary forms f.

THEOREM 49. *Employ the definitions in the first three sentences of Theorem 45. Assume that $e \leq 3$ and that Q is prime to H. If the improperly primitive, indefinite, ternary, quadratic form f with the invariants Ω and Δ represents properly a primitive, binary, quadratic, form Φ of determinant $-\Omega C$, then f represents every form Φ_1 in the same genus as Φ, provided $\phi = -\Phi$ satisfies*

$$(134) \qquad (\phi \,|\, \pi) = -(-2^{e+1}H \,|\, \pi) \,, \qquad (\phi \,|\, \vartheta) = (2a \,|\, \vartheta) \,,$$

for every prime π dividing both ΩC and d, but not H, and for every prime ϑ dividing ΩC and H. Here (134) are the only compatibility conditions that ϕ may represent the double of an $\mathfrak{a}$ in Theorem 44.

Since the proof is analogous to that in § 30, we shall merely indicate the variations. Here a, b, c are even, whence ϕ is improperly primitive and $-\Omega C \equiv 1$ (mod 4). Thus there are no characters of ϕ modulo 4 or 8. Here $a = 2pq$ and we employ $T^2 - 2pq\Delta U^2 = 1$ and Theorem 44 with $E = 2\Delta$. The forms ϕ and ϕ_1 arise by composition of $J = (2, 1, \frac{1}{2}(1+\Omega C))$ with properly primitive forms P and P_1, respectively; while

$$PP_1 = \psi^2 \,, \qquad \psi P_1^{-1} = \mu \,, \qquad \phi = J\psi\mu \,, \qquad \phi_1 = J\psi\mu^{-1} \,.$$

We next obtain the analog of Theorem 48 when f and f_1 are improperly primitive, indefinite forms. We have the facts in II of § 32. In § 33, $\frac{1}{2}\Phi$ and ψ are properly primitive. Hence we may assume that $\frac{1}{2}a$ and C are distinct primes not dividing $2\Omega\Delta$. Similarly for $\frac{1}{2}a_1$ and C_1.

I. If $C = C_1$, Φ and Φ_1 are improperly primitive forms of determinant $-\Omega C$ which are in the same genus. By Theorem 49, also f_1 properly represents Φ and hence is equivalent to f if $e \leq 3$ and

$$(135) \qquad (f \,|\, \pi) = -(2^{e+1}H \,|\, \pi) \,, \qquad (f \,|\, \vartheta) = (2a \,|\, \vartheta)$$

for every prime π dividing Ω and d, but not H, and for every prime ϑ dividing Ω and H.

II. Let $a = a_1$. Since a and b are even, while Ω and C are odd, (118) shows that t is odd and $-1 \equiv \Omega C \equiv \Omega C_1$, $C \equiv C_1$ (mod 4). By (118$_2$), $\psi = (B, R, C)$ and $\psi_1 = (B_1, R_1, C_1)$ are properly primitive and have the same determinant $-\Delta a$, which is a multiple of 4. As in § 33, I, they have the same character with respect to $\frac{1}{2}a$ and each odd prime factor of Δ. Since $C \equiv C_1$ (mod 4), they have the same character δ in (103). They have also the same characters ϵ and $\delta\epsilon$ if the latter exist, by a proof similar to that in I, § 33.

Hence ψ and ψ_1 are in the same genus. We apply Theorem 45 with f replaced by $-F$ and hence with the interchanges in (129), and the interchange of C and a. The new (114) is vacuous since Ω is odd, $m = 0$, whence $m \neq 2$, $m \neq 4$. The new (113) has $\Delta a \equiv 0$ (mod 8), whence $e \geq 2$ since $\frac{1}{2}a$ is odd. Thus also F_1 properly represents ψ and hence is equivalent to F if

$$(136) \quad \left\{ \begin{array}{l} (F \mid \pi) = -(-h \mid \pi) , \qquad (F \mid \vartheta) = (a' \mid \vartheta) , \qquad \Omega = -h\omega^2 , \\ \qquad F \equiv a' \ (\text{mod } 8) \text{ is solvable when } e \geq 2 , \end{array} \right.$$

for every odd prime π dividing both Δ and ω, but not h, and every prime ϑ dividing Δ and h. Then also f and f_1 are equivalent.

III. Let $C \neq C_1$, $a \neq a_1$. Under the conditions at the end of I, f represents properly every binary in the same genus as Φ. We proceed as in § 33, III, with f and ϕ replaced by our $\frac{1}{2}f$ and $\frac{1}{2}\Phi$, and conclude that $\frac{1}{2}f$ and $\frac{1}{2}f_1$ both represent the same prime, whence, after transformation, $a = a_1$ (case II).

THEOREM 50. *Two improperly primitive, indefinite, ternary, quadratic forms in the same genus with the invariants Ω and Δ are equivalent if $e \leq 3$ and (135) and (136) hold.*

These conditions are all vacuous for the case in Theorem 47, the proof of which is now complete.

COROLLARY. *Two primitive, indefinite, ternary, quadratic forms with improperly primitive reciprocals are equivalent if they belong to the same genus and if their invariants have no common odd factor > 1 and neither is divisible by 4.*

For, their reciprocals belong to the same genus (§§ 4, 32) and hence are equivalent by Theorem 47. Then the initial forms are equivalent by § 4. They must be properly primitive by Theorem 19.

CHAPTER V

GENERA AND REPRESENTATION OF NUMBERS

We shall make several important applications of the preceding theory. There exist primitive, binary or ternary, quadratic forms having any assigned characters (Theorems 52, 58). We shall establish Theorems 54–57 on the representation of integers by ternary forms. For the case $\Omega\Delta$ odd, Theorem 56 was given by A. Meyer[1] with the omission of condition (142). Theorems 55 and 57 are new.

35. Gauss's celebrated theorem on duplication.

LEMMA. *Let* $\phi = (a, t, b)$ *be a primitive quadratic form of determinant* $-\Omega C$, *where* C *is odd and prime to* Δ. *If* $(\phi|p) = (-\Delta|p)$ *for every prime factor* p *of* C, *congruences* (67) *are solvable.*

Let p^k be the highest power of p dividing C. If p divides a and b, it divides t by $t^2 - ab = -\Omega C$, whereas ϕ is primitive. Thus one of a and b is not divisible by p.

First, let a be not divisible by p. Then

$$(a|p) = (\phi|p) = (-\Delta|p) \ ,$$

whence $R^2 + \Delta a \equiv 0 \pmod{p^k}$ is solvable for R. Determine an integer S so that $aS + tR \equiv 0 \pmod{p^k}$. Then

$$0 \equiv (aS + tR)R \equiv a(RS - \Delta t) \ , \qquad RS \equiv \Delta t \ ,$$
$$0 \equiv (aS + tR)S \equiv aS^2 + \Delta t^2 \equiv a(S^2 + \Delta b) \qquad (\text{mod } p^k) \ ,$$

whence (67) are solvable. Second, if b is not divisible by p, we interchange a and b, R and S, in the preceding proof.

Let $\psi = (\lambda, \mu, \nu)$ be a properly primitive form of determinant D such that each character of ψ is $+1$ (whence ψ is said to be in the principal genus), and such that ψ is a positive form if $D < 0$. Let $\Omega = -1$, $\Delta = 1$, $\phi = -\psi$. Then ϕ has determinant $D = C$. By hypothesis, $(\psi|p) = 1$ for each odd prime factor p of D. Then $(\phi|p) = (-1|p) = (-\Delta|p)$, whence the lemma shows that congruences (67) are solvable when D is odd.

The last result is true for any D. This is evident if D is double an odd integer, since (67) are solvable modulo 2. If $D \equiv 4 \pmod 8$, ψ has the character $(-1)^{\frac{1}{2}(n-1)} = 1$, whence every odd number n represented by ψ is $\equiv 1$

[1] *Vierteljahrsschrift Naturf. Gesell. Zürich*, XXIX (1884), 209–22.

(mod 4). We may assume that λ is odd. Since $\phi = -\psi$, $a \equiv -1$ (mod 4). Modulo 4, congruences (67) have the solution $R = 1$, $S = t$. If D is divisible by 8, ψ has the three characters (103), which are $+1$ if and only if $n \equiv 1$ (mod 8). Thus $a \equiv -1$ (mod 8). Let 2^k be the highest power of 2 dividing D. Then $R^2 \equiv -a$ (mod 2^k) is solvable. The proof of the lemma shows that (67) are solvable modulo 2^k.

By Theorem 36, ϕ is represented properly by a properly primitive, indefinite, ternary, quadratic form f having the invariants $\Omega = -1$ and $\Delta = 1$, such that the reciprocal of f is properly primitive. Since f has determinant $\Omega^2 \Delta = 1$, f has no characters. Hence all such forms f are in the same genus. They are all equivalent by Chapter X. One such f is $-x^2 + 2yz$. Hence ψ is represented properly by $x^2 - 2yz$, whence there is an identity in ξ, η:

$$(137) \qquad \lambda \xi^2 + 2\mu \xi \eta + \nu \eta^2 \equiv (g\xi + h\eta)^2 - 2(j\xi + k\eta)(l\xi + m\eta) \ ,$$

where $g, \ldots, m$ are integers such that their determinants $q = jm - lk$, $r = lh - gm$, $s = gk - jh$ have no common factor > 1. As in § 17, q, r, s are cofactors, whence

$$gq + jr + ls = 0 \ , \qquad hq + kr + ms = 0 \ .$$

If s and r are both even and hence q odd, then gq and hq are even, whence g and h are even. The identity (137) shows that λ and ν are even, whereas ψ is properly primitive. Since we may interchange the last two factors in (137), we may replace r by $-s$ and s by $-r$. Hence we may assume that s is odd. Since $-\psi$ is represented properly by $f = -x^2 + 2yz$, Theorem 27 shows that $D = F(q, r, s)$, where $F = X^2 - 2YZ$ is the reciprocal of f. Hence $D = q^2 - 2rs$. We have now proved that $(s, -q, 2r)$ is a properly primitive form of determinant D. For the pairs of values

$$\xi = \quad k \ , \qquad m \ , \qquad h \ , \qquad h+k \ , \qquad h+m \ , \qquad k+m$$
$$\eta = -j \ , \qquad -l \ , \qquad -g \ , \qquad -g-j \ , \qquad -g-l \ , \qquad -j-l \ ,$$

the identity (137) gives in turn

$$s^2 = \lambda k^2 - 2\mu kj + \nu j^2 \ , \qquad r^2 = \lambda m^2 - 2\mu ml + \nu l^2 \ ,$$
$$2sr = \lambda h^2 - 2\mu hg + \nu g^2 \ , \qquad -sq = \lambda hk - \mu(gk + jh) + \nu gj \ .$$
$$-qr = \lambda hm - \mu(gm + lh) + \nu gl \ , \qquad q^2 - sr = \lambda km - \mu(jm + lk) + \nu jl \ ,$$

where the last three were obtained by subtracting two of the first three and canceling the common factor 2. Elimination of sr between the third and sixth gives

$$2q^2 = \lambda(h^2 + 2km) - 2\mu(hg + kl + mj) + \nu(g^2 + 2jl) \ .$$

Write

$$X = kxu + hxv + hyu + 2myv ,$$
$$Y = jxu + gxv + gyu + 2lyv .$$

Then our relations give

$$(sx^2 - 2qxy + 2ry^2)(su^2 - 2quv + 2rv^2) = \lambda X^2 - 2\mu XY + \nu Y^2 .$$

Replacing Y by $-Y$, we conclude that the class to which ψ belongs arises by composition of the class to which $(s, -q, 2r)$ belongs with itself. Then the class of ψ is said to arise by *duplication*. But ψ was any form in the principal genus.

THEOREM 51. *Every properly primitive class of the principal genus of any determinant D arises by duplication from a properly primitive class, where the classes are positive if $D < 0$.*

In his *Introd.*, pages 149–50, the author presented the proof by Dedekind which employs a complete knowledge of the properties of the solutions of $ax^2 + by^2 + cz^2 = 0$, and readily deduced from Theorem 51 a result equivalent to

THEOREM 52. *For any given D not a square, there exists a properly primitive, positive or indefinite, binary, quadratic form of determinant D having any assigned values of the characters consistent with the product relation (127).*

36. Representation of certain numbers by ternary forms.

From our lemma and Theorem 36 we have

THEOREM 53. *Let $\phi = (a, t, b)$ be a primitive, negative or indefinite, binary form of determinant $-\Omega C \neq 0$, where $\Omega < 0$. Let ϕ be properly primitive if Δ is even. Let $\Delta > 0$ and let C and Δ be either the doubles of relatively prime odd integers or be relatively prime and C be not divisible by 4. Let $(\phi \,|\, p) = (-\Delta \,|\, p)$ for every odd prime factor p of C. If Ω and C are even and Δ is odd, let $\phi \equiv \Delta \pmod 4$ when ϕ is odd. Then ϕ is represented properly by a properly primitive, indefinite, ternary, quadratic form h with the invariants Ω and Δ and having a properly primitive reciprocal.*

From this and earlier theorems, we shall deduce

THEOREM 54. *Let f be a properly primitive, ternary, indefinite, quadratic form whose invariants $\Omega < 0$ and $\Delta > 0$ have no common odd factor > 1 and neither is divisible by 4, such that the reciprocal F of f is properly primitive. Let m and Ω be either the doubles of relatively prime odd integers or be relatively prime and m not divisible by 4. Then m is represented properly by f if there exists a primitive, positive or indefinite, binary, quadratic form ψ of determinant $-\Delta m$, with ψ properly primitive when Ω is even, such that*

$$(138) \qquad (\psi \,|\, p) = (-\Omega \,|\, p) , \qquad (\psi \,|\, \tau) = (F \,|\, \tau) , \qquad (m \,|\, \omega) = (f \,|\, \omega) ,$$

for every odd prime factor p of m, τ of Δ, and ω of Ω, and, in case Δ and m are even and Ω is odd,

(139) $\psi \equiv \Omega \pmod 4$ *when ψ is odd* .

The properly primitive form $f_1 = -F$ has the invariants $\Omega_1 = -\Delta < 0$ and $\Delta_1 = -\Omega > 0$ and has the properly primitive reciprocal $F_1 = -f$. The form $\phi = -\psi$ is negative or indefinite. By (138_1), $(\phi \mid p) = (-\Delta_1 \mid p)$. Let C denote $-m$. By the last two relations (138),

(140) $(\phi \mid \tau) = (f_1 \mid \tau)$, $(C \mid \omega) = (F_1 \mid \omega)$

for every odd prime factor τ of Ω_1, and ω of Δ_1. The determinant of ϕ is that of ψ and is $-\Delta m = -\Omega_1 C$. If Ω_1 and C are even and Δ_1 is odd, (139) gives $\phi \equiv \Delta_1 \pmod 4$ when ϕ is odd. We see that Theorem 53 applies when Ω and Δ are replaced by Ω_1 and Δ_1, respectively, and yields a form h, which represents ϕ properly, such that h and f_1 have the same invariants Ω_1 and Δ_1. By (140), they have the same characters (§ 32) since every integer represented by ϕ is represented by h and since C is represented by the reciprocal of h (Theorem 27). By definition, h and f_1 therefore belong to the same genus. They are both properly primitive, indefinite, ternary forms having properly primitive reciprocals. Hence they are equivalent by Theorem 47. Thus ϕ is represented properly by f_1 (Theorem 29), and C is represented properly by F_1 (Theorem 27). Hence $m = -C$ is represented properly by $f = -F_1$.

Theorem 55. *Let f be a properly primitive, ternary, indefinite, quadratic form with the invariants Ω and $\Delta > 0$ and properly primitive reciprocal F. Let*

(141) $(m \mid \omega) = (f \mid \omega)$ *for all odd primes ω dividing Ω* ,

(142) $(-\Omega \mid \rho) = (F \mid \rho)$ *for all primes ρ dividing m and Δ* .

Then f represents m properly if $m\Delta$ is double an odd integer and if m, Δ, Ω satisfy the conditions in Theorem 54, whence Ω is not divisible by 4 and either (i) $\Delta = 2\Delta_1$, m and Δ_1 are odd and prime to Ω, or (ii) $m = 2m_1$, m_1 and Δ are odd and prime to Ω.

We seek a properly primitive, binary, quadratic form ψ whose determinant $D = -\Delta m$ is the double of an odd integer and hence is $\equiv 2$ or 6 (mod 8), such that the characters of ψ will have the values to be assigned presently.

In the notations (126) and preceding it, $c = 1$, $l = -1$, $\pm P \equiv 1$ or 3 (mod 4), $s = 1$ or -1, respectively. In the notations (103), ψ has the character $\epsilon = (-1)^h$ or $\delta\epsilon = (-1)^i (-1)^h$, respectively, but no others of ϵ, δ, $\delta\epsilon$. We can choose the value of this character, which is $s^j l^h$ in both cases, so that (127) is satisfied, whatever be the values of the remaining characters found by the first two relations (138). The latter are compatible if (142) holds. Then the desired ψ exists by Theorem 52. Thus Theorem 54 implies Theorem 55.

Theorem 56. *Let f be a properly primitive, ternary, indefinite, quadratic form having a properly primitive reciprocal F and relatively prime invariants Ω and Δ such that Δ is odd and positive and Ω is not divisible by 4. Let m be odd and prime to Ω. Then m is represented properly by f if $\Delta m \equiv 1$ (mod 4) and (141) and (142) hold, or if $\Delta m \equiv 7$ (mod 8), (141), (142), and*

$$(143) \qquad (F \,||\, \Delta_1 \,|/g) = (-\Omega \,||\, m_1 \,|/g)$$

hold, where Δ_1 and m_1 are the quotients of Δ and m by their largest square factors, and g is the g.c.d. of Δ_1 and m_1. Also, m is represented if $\Delta m \equiv 3$ (mod 8), Ω is odd and (141) and (142) hold, or if $\Delta m \equiv 3$ (mod 8), Ω is even, and (141)–(143) hold.

First, let $-\Delta m \equiv 3$ (mod 4). Then the desired ψ has the character $(-1)^j$ but no further character modulo 4 or 8. Since only the remaining characters were prescribed by (138), which are compatible if (142) holds, we can then choose a value of $(-1)^j$ such that (127) is satisfied. Hence a properly primitive ψ exists by Theorem 52.

Second, let Ω be odd and $D = -\Delta m \equiv 1$ (mod 4). Write $D = \pm PS^2$. Since $\pm P \equiv D \equiv 1$ (mod 4), r is even and $s = l = 1$, whence (127) is $(n \,|\, P) = 1$, and properly primitive forms exist for only half of the combinations of characters. But there now exists an improperly primitive form $\phi = (2, 1, \frac{1}{2}(1-D))$ of determinant D. By Theorem 7 and the first part of the proof of Theorem 45, ϕ represents the double of a *positive* integer M prime to any assigned integer, say $2D$. For all such represented integers $2M$, $(2M \,|\, q)$ has the same value, where q is a prime factor of D, whence each $(\phi \,|\, q)$ is a character. Since ϕ is equivalent to a form $(2M, \alpha, \beta)$ with $\alpha^2 - 2M\beta = D$, we have $(D \,|\, M) = 1$. Since D and $M > 0$ are odd and relatively prime, the reciprocity law gives $(M \,|\, D) = 1$, whence $(M \,|\, P) = 1$. Let π range over the prime factors of P. Then

$$\Pi(2M \,|\, \pi) = (2 \,|\, P)(M \,|\, P) = (2 \,|\, P) ,$$

which is $+1$ or -1, according as $\pm P \equiv 1$ or 5 (mod 8).

If $\pm P \equiv 5$ (mod 8), whence $\Delta m \equiv 3$ (mod 8), the permissible combinations of characters of improperly primitive forms, viz., those for which $\Pi(2M \,|\, \pi) = -1$, are precisely those which were excluded for properly primitive forms, and *vice versa*. Hence to every combination of characters corresponds either a properly or improperly primitive form of determinant D. Thus the conditions on ψ in Theorem 54 can always be satisfied if (142) holds.

But if $\pm P \equiv 1$ (mod 8), whence $\Delta m \equiv 7$ (mod 8), the permissible characters for improperly primitive forms coincide with those for properly primitive forms. Hence ψ exists if and only if (142) and $(\psi \mid P) = 1$ hold. Since $\pm P = -\Delta_1 m_1/g^2$, the latter is $(\psi \mid g^{-2} \mid \Delta_1 m_1 \mid) = 1$. By (138),

$$(\psi \mid \mid m_1 \mid /g) = (-\Omega \mid \mid m_1 \mid /g) , \qquad (\psi \mid \mid \Delta_1 \mid /g) = (F \mid \mid \Delta_1 \mid /g) .$$

Hence our condition is equivalent to (143).

Third, let Ω be even and $D = -\Delta m \equiv 1$ (mod 4). Improperly primitive forms are now not admissible. As in the preceding paragraph, properly primitive forms ψ exist if and only if (142) and $(\psi \mid P) = 1$ hold, and the latter is equivalent to (143).

The following Theorems 57 and 58 are not used in this book.

Theorem 57. *Let f be a properly primitive, ternary, indefinite, quadratic form with the invariants Ω and $\Delta > 0$, and properly primitive reciprocal F. Let m and Δ be doubles of odd integers prime to Ω and let Ω be not divisible by 4. Then m is represented properly by f if $-\frac{1}{4}\Delta m \equiv 1$ (mod 4), (141), (142), and*

$$(144) \qquad (F \mid \mid \Delta' \mid /g) = (-\Omega \mid \mid m' \mid /g)$$

hold, where Δ' and m' are the quotients of $\frac{1}{2}\Delta$ and $\frac{1}{2}m$ by their largest square factors, and g is the g.c.d. of Δ' and m'; also when $-\frac{1}{4}\Delta m \equiv 3$ (mod 4) if Ω is odd and (141) and (142) hold, or if Ω is odd and (141) and (142) hold and

$$(145) \qquad (F \mid \mid \Delta' \mid /g) = (-1)^{\frac{1}{2}(\Omega-1)}(-\Omega \mid \mid m' \mid /g) .$$

Employ the notations (126). Since $-\Delta m \equiv 4$ (mod 8), the form ψ desired in Theorem 54 has the character $\delta = (-1)^j$, but not ϵ or $\delta\epsilon$ in (103). Here $c = 0$, $l = 1$, and S is double an odd integer; thus $\frac{1}{4}D = -\frac{1}{4}\Delta m$ is the product of $\pm P$ by an odd square.

If $-\frac{1}{4}\Delta m \equiv 1$ (mod 4), then r is even and (127) is $(n \mid P) = 1$. The determinant of an improperly primitive, binary form is odd and hence $\neq -\Delta m$. Hence ψ exists if and only if (142) and $(\psi \mid P) = 1$ hold. Since $\pm P$ is $-\Delta'm'/g^2$, the latter condition is $(\psi \mid g^{-2} \mid \Delta'm' \mid) = 1$. By (138) this is equivalent to (144).

If $-\frac{1}{4}\Delta m \equiv 3$ (mod 4), then $\pm P \equiv 3$ (mod 4) and r is odd, $s = -1$, $s^j l^h = \delta$. If Ω is even, δ can be chosen so that (127) is satisfied, whatever be the values of the remaining characters found by the first two relations (138), which are compatible by (142). But if Ω is odd, $\delta = (-1)^{\frac{1}{2}(\Omega-1)}$ by (139). Then (127) becomes $\delta(\psi \mid P) = 1$, which is equivalent to (145) by the former argument.

37. Existence of genera of ternary, quadratic forms.

THEOREM 58. *Let* Ω *be odd and* Δ *be positive and either odd or double an odd integer. There exists a primitive, ternary, quadratic form* f *with the invariants* Ω *and* Δ *having any assigned characters.*[1]

The only characters (§ 32) are $(f|r)$ and $(F|s)$, where F is the reciprocal of f, and r (or s) ranges over the distinct prime factors of Ω (or Δ). Let v_r and V_s be the assigned values of $(f|r)$ and $(F|s)$.

We can evidently choose a positive integer C prime to Δ such that $C \equiv \Omega \pmod 4$ and $(C|s) = V_s$ for each s. Let p range over the distinct prime factors of C. By Theorem 52 there exists a properly primitive, positive or indefinite, binary, quadratic form ϕ of determinant $D = -\Omega C$ whose characters have the following values:

$$(146) \qquad (\phi|r) = v_r , \quad (\phi|p) = (-\Delta|p) , \quad \delta = (-1)^{\frac{1}{2}(\phi-1)} = (\phi|\Omega C) .$$

In fact, $D \equiv -\Omega^2 \equiv 3 \pmod 4$, whence δ is the only one of the characters (103) which exists, while the relation (127) between the characters of ϕ is evidently now (146₃).

By (146₂), the conditions in the lemma of § 35 hold, whence congruences (67) are solvable.

Since $C > 0$, Ω and D have opposite signs. Thus if $\Omega < 0$, ϕ is indefinite; while, if $\Omega > 0$, ϕ is definite and hence positive.

Theorem 36 shows that ϕ is represented properly by a primitive ternary form f having the invariants Ω and Δ, such that f is positive if $\Omega > 0$, and indefinite if $\Omega < 0$. By Theorem 27, C is represented properly by F. Hence

$$v_r = (\phi|r) = (f|r) , \quad V_s = (C|s) = (F|s) .$$

---

[1] Smith proved a generalization by means of his formulas (123) and (125).

CHAPTER VI

QUADRATIC DIOPHANTINE EQUATIONS

We shall prove that every indefinite quadratic form q in five or more variables is a zero form (so that $q=0$ has integral solutions not all zero). No complete proof of this remarkable theorem has been published previously. We shall find necessary and sufficient conditions that $ax^2+by^2+cz^2+du^2=0$ shall have integral solutions not all zero, except for the case in which just two of the coefficients are even and $\frac{1}{4}abcd\equiv5$ (mod 8). Details had been given by A. Meyer[1] only when a, b, c, d are odd, but require a correction in the auxiliary Theorem 56.

38. Quadratic Diophantine equations in n variables, $n\geqq5$. We shall first prove

THEOREM 59. *If the integers $a, \ldots, e$ are not zero and not all of like sign, there exist integral solutions not all zero of*

$$(147) \qquad ax^2+by^2+cz^2+du^2+ev^2=0 \ .$$

Assume the theorem for all such equations (147) whose determinant is numerically $<N$. We shall prove it true for (147) when $|abcde|=N$. This follows at once if a, b, c have a common factor $p>1$. Write $a=pA$, $b=pB$, $c=pC$. Then

$$Ax^2+By^2+Cz^2+pdU^2+peV^2=0$$

has the determinant $abcde/p$ and its coefficients are not all of like sign. Hence it has integral solutions $x, \ldots, V$ not all zero. Then x, y, z, $u=pU$, $v=pV$ satisfy (147).

Suppose that $a=A\alpha^2, \ldots, e=E\epsilon^2$, where one of $\alpha, \ldots, \epsilon$ exceeds unity. Then the determinant of

$$AX^2+BY^2+CZ^2+DU^2+EV^2=0$$

is numerically $<N$. Hence it has integral solutions $X, \ldots, V$ not all zero. Multiplication by $\alpha^2 \ldots \epsilon^2$ shows that (147) has the solutions $x=\beta\gamma\delta\epsilon X, \ldots, v=\alpha\beta\gamma\delta V$.

[1] *Vierteljahrsschrift Naturf. Gesell. Zürich*, XXIX (1884), 209–22.

Hence it suffices to prove the theorem when

(148) $\left\{\begin{array}{l}\text{The coefficients are without square factors and no three of them}\\ \quad\text{have a common factor} >1.\end{array}\right.$

If all of the odd coefficients are of like sign, their number is 3 or 4; we take them negative by changing all signs if necessary. If 4, denote the single even one by c. If 3, denote the even ones by c and d. In both cases we may take c positive.

But if there occur two odd coefficients of opposite signs, denote them by a and b. We may take at least one of d and e to be odd. If two of a, b, c are positive, we change all signs.

Hence a and b are odd, at least one of d and e is odd, two of a, b, c are negative and the third is positive. Thus $f = ax^2 + by^2 + cz^2$ is properly primitive and indefinite and has a positive determinant. Let (ab) denote the positive g.c.d. of a and b. Since (ab) is prime to (ac), their product divides a. Hence we may write

$$a = (ab)(ac)\alpha , \qquad b = (ab)(bc)\beta ,$$
$$c = (ac)(bc)\gamma , \qquad d = (de)\delta, \quad e = (de)\epsilon .$$

Hence (ab), (ac), (bc), (de), α, β, γ are relatively prime in pairs. For example, if a prime p divides α and β, it divides a, b, and (ab), and p^2 divides a, contrary to (148).

The adjoint of f has the coefficients bc, ac, ab, whose positive g.c.d. is denoted by $-\Omega$ (§ 8). Hence the reciprocal of f is properly primitive, and $\Omega = -(ab)(ac)(bc)$. But $abc = \Omega^2\Delta$. Hence $\Delta = \alpha\beta\gamma$. We see that Ω, Δ, (de) are relatively prime in pairs. Also, (de) is odd.

We shall prove that integers u and v can be chosen so that $m = -du^2 - ev^2$ is represented by f. Denote $\delta u^2 + \epsilon v^2$ by $\phi(u, v)$.

I. Let c be even. Then α, β, and Ω are odd, while γ and Δ are doubles of odd integers. Let ω_i range over the distinct prime factors of Ω. Neither δ nor ϵ is divisible by ω_i. Hence if g_i is any assigned integer, $\phi \equiv g_i$ (mod ω_i) is known to have solutions u_i, v_i. Since g_i may be chosen as either a quadratic residue or non-residue of ω_i,

(149) $\qquad (\phi \,|\, \omega_i) = +1$ or -1 at pleasure .

By § 5, ϕ represents an integer prime to Δ; let u_0, v_0 be the representing numbers. Determine integers u and v so that

(150) $\quad u \equiv u_i , \quad v \equiv v_i \pmod{\omega_i} , \quad u \equiv u_0 , \quad v \equiv v_0 \pmod{\Delta} ,$

for each i. For these integers u and v we have (149) and $\phi(u, v) = M$, where M is prime to Δ and to each ω_i and hence to $\Delta\Omega$. Then $m = -(de)M = -du^2 - ev^2$ is represented by f. This follows from case (i) of Theorem 55. In fact, m is prime to $\Delta\Omega$, whence (142) is satisfied vacuously. Also, (141) is equivalent to $(\phi \mid \omega) = (-(de)f \mid \omega)$, which can be satisfied in view of (149).

II. Let c be odd. We may take d odd. If ϵ is odd, take $s = 0$ or 2; then $\phi(1, s) = k$, where $k = \delta$ or $\delta + 4\epsilon$. If ϵ is even, take $s = 0$ or 1; then $k = \delta$ or $\delta + \epsilon$. In each case the two values of k are odd and incongruent modulo 8. Employ (150) and $u \equiv 1$, $v \equiv s \pmod{8}$. Now m is odd and prime to $\Delta\Omega$, while $m \not\equiv 7\Delta \pmod{8}$ when k is suitable chosen. As in I, the theorem now follows from Theorem 56.

Theorem 60. *If q is any indefinite quadratic form in $x_1, \ldots, x_n$, where $n \geq 5$, there exist integral solutions not all zero of $q = 0$.*

There exists[1] a linear transformation T with rational coefficients of determinant $\neq 0$ which replaces q by $Q = g_1 X_1^2 + \ldots + g_r X_r^2$, where $r \leq n$, and each g_i is rational and $\neq 0$. If $r < n$, we can choose rational (and then integral) values not all zero of the x_i such that $X_1 = 0, \ldots, X_r = 0$, whence $q = Q = 0$. Hence let $r = n$. Write $g_i = G_i/D$, where the G_i and D are all integers. Since q is indefinite, we may choose the notation so that $G_1, \ldots, G_5$ are not all of like sign. By Theorem 59, there exist integers $X_1, \ldots, X_5$ not all zero such that $G_1 X_1^2 + \ldots + G_5 X_5^2 = 0$. Take $X_i = 0 (i > 5)$. By means of T we obtain rational solutions x_i of $q = 0$, and from them integral solutions.

39. Conditions for integral solutions not all zero of

$$(151) \qquad ax^2 + by^2 + cz^2 + du^2 = 0 \qquad (abcd \neq 0) .$$

If a, b, c have a common factor $p > 1$ we deduce as in § 38 a like equation of smaller determinant $abcd/p^2$ which is solvable[2] if and only if (151) is solvable. Repetitions lead to an equation no three of whose coefficients have a common factor > 1. If $a = Aa^2$, etc., we see as in § 38 that (151) is solvable if and only if $AX^2 + \ldots = 0$ is solvable. Hence we may assume property (148).

Denote the positive g.c.d. of i and j by (ij). Then a is divisible by (ab), (ac), (ad), which are relatively prime in pairs. Hence a is divisible by their product. Thus there are integers $\alpha, \beta, \gamma, \delta$ such that

$$(152) \qquad \begin{cases} a = (ab)(ac)(ad)\alpha , & b = (ab)(bc)(bd)\beta , \\ c = (ac)(bc)(cd)\gamma , & d = g\delta , \quad g = (ad)(bd)(cd) . \end{cases}$$

Then $(ab), \ldots, (cd)$, $\alpha, \beta, \gamma, \delta$ are relatively prime in pairs.

---

[1] Dickson, *Modern Algebraic Theories*, p. 70; *Höhere Algebra*, p. 63.

[2] In integers not all zero. Likewise in all cases.

Consider the case in which a and b have a common prime factor p. Then $cz^2+du^2\equiv0$ (mod p) and neither c nor d is divisible by p. Either $(-cd|p)=1$ or $z=pZ$, $u=pU$, $a=pA$, $b=pB$, and (151) is equivalent to

$$(153) \qquad Ax^2+By^2+cpZ^2+dpU^2=0 ,$$

in which x and y are not both divisible by p, since we may assume that x, y, z, u have no common factor >1. Thus $(-AB|p)=1$, which is equivalent to $(-ha\beta|p)=1$, where

$$(154) \qquad h=(ac)(ad)(bc)(bd) , \quad k=(ab)(ad)(bc)(cd) , \quad l=(ab)(ac)(bd)(cd) .$$

Our two cases are as follows: either $(-cd|p)=1$, which is equivalent to $(-h\gamma\delta|p)=1$, or $(-h\gamma\delta|p)=-1$ and $(-ha\beta|p)=1$. If $(a\beta\gamma\delta|p)=1$, the second case is excluded and the condition for the first is equivalent to $(-ha\beta|p)=1$. But if $(a\beta\gamma\delta|p)=-1$, either $(-h\gamma\delta|p)=1$ or $(-h\gamma\delta|p)=-1$ and the latter implies $(-ha\beta|p)=+1$, whence one of the above two cases must arise whatever be the values of $a, \ldots, d$. We therefore ignore the case $(a\beta\gamma\delta|p)=-1$.

Hence necessary conditions for the solvability of (151) are[1]

$$(155) \qquad \begin{cases} -ha\beta \text{ is a quad. residue of every } p(ab) \text{ and } p(cd) , \\ -ka\gamma \text{ is a quad. residue of every } p(ac) \text{ and } p(bd) , \\ -la\delta \text{ is a quad. residue of every } p(ad) \text{ and } p(bc) , \end{cases}$$

where $p(ab)$ is a common odd prime factor of a and b such that $a\beta\gamma\delta$ is a quadratic residue of $p(ab)$.

An equation (151) with property (148) will be called *normal* with respect to π in the following case:

$$(156) \qquad \begin{cases} \text{If } \pi \text{ is a prime factor of any two coefficients, the negative of the} \\ \text{product of the remaining two coefficients is a quadratic residue} \\ \text{of } \pi . \end{cases}$$

We next show that any equation (151) having properties (148) and (155) is equivalent to an equation having properties (148) and (156). If a and b are divisible by the prime p, we saw that (151) implies that either $(-cd|p)=1$, whence (151) is normal with respect to p, or (153) with $(-AB|p)=1$, whence (153) is normal with respect to p.

---

[1] For example, let $a=1$, $b=3$, $c=-2$, $d=-6$. Then $a=\beta=1$, $\gamma=\delta=-1$, $k=2$, and $-ka\gamma=2$ is a non-residue of $p(bd)=3$. Hence $x^2+3y^2-2z^2-6u^2=0$ has no solutions in integers not all zero.

Of the six products of two coefficients of (153), four are equal to the products of the corresponding coefficients of (151), while $p^2AB = ab$, $cp \cdot dp = p^2cd$. Hence for both equations, each of the six products has the same quadratic character with respect to any odd prime $\neq p$. Moreover, the product of the coefficients of (153) is the product of those of (151). After a finite number of repetitions of this process, we reach an equation having the property (156).

Theorem 61. *Necessary conditions that an equation* (151) *having properties* (148) *be solvable* (*in integers not all zero*) *are* (155) *and that* a, b, c, d *be not all of like signs. Let these conditions be satisfied. If* $abcd \equiv 2, 3, 5, 6,$ *or* 7 *mod* 8), *it is solvable. If* $abcd \equiv 1$ (*mod* 8), *it is solvable if and only if*

$$(157) \qquad\qquad a+b+c+d \equiv 0 \qquad (mod\ 8) \ .$$

Finally, let a *and* b *be even. If* $\frac{1}{4}abcd \equiv 3$ (*mod* 4), *it is solvable. Next let* $\frac{1}{4}abcd \equiv r$ (*mod* 8), *where* $r = 1$ *or* 5. *If* (151) *is solvable, one of*

$$(158) \qquad \begin{cases} \frac{1}{2}ra + \frac{1}{2}b + c + d \equiv \frac{1}{2}(c^2d^2 - 1) & (mod\ 8)\ , \\ \frac{1}{2}ra + \frac{1}{2}b + c + d \equiv \frac{1}{2}(c^2d^2 - 1) + r - 1 & (mod\ 8) \end{cases}$$

holds. If (158_1) *holds,* (151) *is solvable. If*[1] $r = 1$, *congruences* (158) *are equivalent and hence either is a necessary and sufficient condition that* (151) *be solvable.*

Let the symbol nRm denote that n is a quadratic residue of m. We saw that (148) and (155) imply (148) and (156) for an equivalent equation. Hence we assume the latter. But (156) are equivalent to

$$(159) \qquad \begin{cases} -h\gamma\delta R(ab)\ , & -k\beta\delta R(ac)\ , & -l\beta\gamma R(ad)\ , \\ -h\alpha\beta R(cd)\ , & -k\alpha\gamma R(bd)\ , & -l\alpha\delta R(bc)\ . \end{cases}$$

We may assume that a and b are both even or both odd, that d is odd, and that just two of a, b, c are negative. For, if a and b are even, whence c and d are odd, we may permute c and d if necessary and have a, b, c not all of like sign, and then take two of them negative by changing all signs if necessary. Next, if c alone is even, we may permute a, b, d and have a, b, c not all of like sign. Thus $f = ax^2 + by^2 + cz^2$ is a properly primitive, indefinite

---

[1] The theory is not capable of showing that (151) is solvable if $r = 5$ and (158_2) holds. For then (158_1) fails, whence (170) and (143) fail and we cannot apply Theorem 56 to $f = ax^2 + by^2 + cz^2$. If we take $f = ax^2 + cz^2 + du^2$ and apply Theorem 57, we find again that the sufficient condition that (151) be solvable is precisely (158_1). Evidently no choice of f makes Theorem 55 applicable. Meyer stated incorrectly that (158_1) is a necessary condition.

form of positive determinant. Its invariants are $\Omega=-D$ and $\Delta=ga\beta\gamma$, where $D=(ab)(ac)(bc)$. Its reciprocal form is

(160) $\qquad F=-A\beta\gamma X^2-Ba\gamma Y^2-Ca\beta Z^2\,,\qquad A=(bc)(bd)(cd)\,,$

$\qquad\qquad B=(ac)(ad)(cd)\,,\qquad C=(ab)(ad)(bd)\,,$

and F is properly primitive.

We take $u=1$ and inquire when $m=-d$ can be represented by f. Now m and Δ are prime to Ω, while g is the g.c.d. of m and Δ. In (142), ρ divides g. For example, let ρ divide (ad). Since F represents its first coefficient, which is prime to (ad), $(F\,|\,\rho)=(-A\beta\gamma\,|\,\rho)$, and (142) is equivalent to $(-(ab)(ac)(bd)(cd)\beta\gamma\,|\,\rho)=1$, which is true by (159). To verify (141), let, for example, ω be an odd prime factor of (ab). Then $(f\,|\,\omega)=(c\,|\,\omega)$ and (141) is equivalent to $1=(-cd\,|\,\omega)$, which is true by (156).

In case abd is odd and c is even, Ω is odd and Δ is double an odd integer, Theorem 61 follows from case (i) of Theorem 55.

Theorem 56 shows that (151) is solvable if $abcd$ is odd and $-\Delta d\equiv 1,3$, or 5 (mod 8), and also if a and b are even and $-\Delta d\equiv 1$ (mod 4). Since g is odd, $\Delta d\equiv g^2 a\beta\gamma\delta\equiv a\beta\gamma\delta$ (mod 8). Also,

$$abcd=(ab)^2(ac)^2(ad)^2(bc)^2(bd)^2(cd)^2 a\beta\gamma\delta\,,$$

(161) $\qquad abcd\equiv a\beta\gamma\delta$ (mod 8) if $abcd$ is odd ,

(162) $\qquad \tfrac{1}{4}abcd\equiv a\beta\gamma\delta$ (mod 8) if a and b are even .

Hence $\Delta d\equiv abcd$ or $\tfrac{1}{4}abcd$ (mod 8) in the respective case. This proves Theorem 61 except when $abcd\equiv 1$ (mod 8) or $\tfrac{1}{4}abcd\equiv 1$ (mod 4).

In the latter cases it remains to satisfy condition (143). Since Δ and m have no square factors, $\Delta_1=\Delta$, $m_1=m$, and (143) becomes $(F\,|\,a\beta\gamma)=(-\Omega\,|\,\delta)$. Since F represents its three coefficients, which are prime to a, β, γ, respectively, the condition is equivalent to

(163) $\qquad (-A\beta\gamma\,|\,a)(-Ba\gamma\,|\,\beta)(-Ca\beta\,|\,\gamma)(D\,|\,\delta)=1\,.$

For the moment, write p for the positive one of a, β, γ, and write $-v$ and $-w$ for the remaining two, which are negative. Then

$$(-\beta\gamma\,|\,a)(-a\gamma\,|\,\beta)(-a\beta\,|\,\gamma)=(wp\,|\,v)(vp\,|\,w)(-vw\,|\,p)$$
$$=(w\,|\,v)(v\,|\,w)\cdot(p\,|\,vw)(vw\,|\,p)\cdot(-1)^{\frac{1}{2}(p-1)}=(-1)^n\,,$$

where, by the reciprocity law,

$$n = \tfrac{1}{4}(v-1)(w-1) + \tfrac{1}{4}(vw-1)(p-1) + \tfrac{1}{2}(p-1)$$
$$= \tfrac{1}{4}(v-1)(w-1) + \tfrac{1}{4}(vw+1)(p-1)$$
$$= \tfrac{1}{4}(pvw+p-v-w) = \tfrac{1}{4}(\alpha\beta\gamma+\alpha+\beta+\gamma) \ .$$

In our cases, $\alpha\beta\gamma\delta \equiv r \pmod 8$, where $r=1$ or 5. We write $s = \alpha+\beta+\gamma+r\delta$. Then $4n \equiv s \pmod 8$ and (163) becomes

(164) $$(A\,|\,a)(B\,|\,\beta)(C\,|\,\gamma)(D\,|\,\delta) = (-1)^{\frac{1}{8}s} \ .$$

Write $t=1$ if $abcd$ is odd, $t=2$ if a and b are even and cd is odd. Then $a=ta'$, $b=tb'$, $c=c'$, $d=d'$, where a', $\ldots$, d' are odd integers. Let A', $\ldots$, D', denote the same functions of the latter that A, $\ldots$, D are of a, $\ldots$, d. Hence $A=A'$, $B=B'$, $C=tC'$, $D=tD'$. Then (164) becomes

(165) $$(A'\,|\,a)(B'\,|\,\beta)(C'\,|\,\gamma)(D'\,|\,\delta) = (-1)^{\frac{1}{8}s}(t\,|\,\gamma\delta) \ .$$

By the reciprocity law, this becomes

(166) $$(\alpha\beta\,|\,(c'd'))(\alpha\gamma\,|\,(b'd'))(\alpha\delta\,|\,(b'c'))(\beta\gamma\,|\,(a'd'))$$
$$\cdot (\beta\delta\,|\,(a'c'))(\gamma\delta\,|\,(a'b')) = (-1)^{\frac{1}{8}\lambda}(t\,|\,\gamma\delta) \ ,$$
$$\lambda = s + (A'-1)(a-1) + (B'-1)(\beta-1) + (C'-1)(\gamma-1) + (D'-1)(\delta-1) \ .$$

But $s \equiv 0$, $\alpha\beta\gamma\delta \equiv 1 \pmod 4$, whence

$$a \equiv \beta\gamma\delta = (1+\beta-1) \ldots (1+\delta-1) \equiv 1+\beta+\gamma+\delta-3 \pmod 4 \ ,$$

and similarly $\delta \equiv 1+a+\beta+\gamma-3$, etc. Since $A'-1$ is even, we do not alter λ modulo 8 if we replace $a-1$ by $\beta+\gamma+\delta-3$, and similarly $\beta-1$ by $a+\gamma+\delta-3$, etc. Hence

$$\lambda \equiv \epsilon - 3(A'+B'+C'+D') + a(B'+C'+D') + \beta(A'+C'+D')$$
$$+ \gamma(A'+B'+D') + \delta(A'+B'+C') \pmod 8 \ ,$$

where $\epsilon = s - 3(a+\beta+\gamma+\delta) + 12$. But $a+\beta+\gamma+\delta-s = (1-r)\delta \equiv r-1 \pmod 8$, since δ is odd. Hence $\epsilon \equiv r+3 \pmod 8$.

Since $B' \equiv (a'b')^2 B'$, $C' \equiv (a'c')^2 C'$, $D' \equiv (a'd')^2 D' \pmod 8$,

$$a(B'+C'+D') \equiv a(a'b')(a'c')(a'd')G = a'G \pmod 8 \ ,$$

(167) $$G = (a'b')(c'd') + (a'c')(b'd') + (a'd')(b'c') \ .$$

When a', b', c', d' are permuted cyclically, also A', B', C', D' are permuted cyclically, while (167) is unaltered. Hence the sum of the last four parts of λ is $\equiv (a'+b'+c'+d')G \pmod 8$. We may drop the odd factor G since $a'+ \ldots +d' \equiv 0 \pmod 4$. In fact,

$$1 \equiv a'b'c'd' = (1+a'-1) \ldots \equiv 1+a'+b'+c'+d' \pmod 4 \ .$$

The product of $(a'b')-1$, $(a'c')-1$, $(b'c')-1$, is divisible by 8, whence

$$D' \equiv (a'b')(a'c')+(a'b')(b'c')+(a'c')(b'c')-(a'b')-(a'c')$$
$$-(b'c')+1 \pmod 8 \ .$$

Permuting cyclically and adding, we get

$$A'+B'+C'+D' \equiv \nu-2\mu+4 \pmod 8 \ ,$$

where μ is the sum of the six numbers $(a'b'), \ldots$, while ν is the sum of those twelve products of them by twos in which the two symbols in any product have a common letter. Hence

$$\begin{aligned}(168) \qquad \lambda &\equiv r-1+a'+b'+c'+d'-3\nu+6\mu \pmod 8 \\ &\equiv ra'+b'+c'+d'-3\nu+6\mu \pmod 8 \ ,\end{aligned}$$

since a' is odd. From (159), we have

$$(\gamma\delta \,|\, (a'b')) = (-(a'c')(a'd')(b'c')(b'd') \,|\, (a'b')) \ ,$$
$$(t\beta\delta \,|\, (a'c')) = (-(a'b')(a'd')(c'b')(c'd') \,|\, (a'c')) \ ,$$

and four similar equations. The product of their left members is the product of the left member of (166) by

$$(169) \qquad (t \,|\, (a'c')(a'd')(b'c')(b'd')) \ .$$

The product of their six right members is $(-1)^{\frac{1}{2}(\mu-6)}P$, where P is the product of all twelve terms like $((a'c') \,|\, (a'b'))((a'b') \,|\, (a'c'))$, where each of the two factors has the common letter a'. By the reciprocity law we get $P=(-1)^{\frac{1}{2}j}$, where $j=\nu-4\mu+12$. The product of (169) by $(t \,|\, \gamma\delta)$ in (166) is $(t \,|\, cd)$. Hence

$$(170) \qquad (t \,|\, cd)(-1)^{\frac{1}{2}\lambda} = (-1)^{\frac{1}{2}(\mu-6)}(-1)^{\frac{1}{2}j} \ .$$

If $abcd$ is odd, $t=1$ and (170) gives $a+b+c+d \equiv 4\nu \pmod 8$. But ν is a sum of 12 odd integers. We get (157).

If $\frac{1}{4}abcd \equiv r \pmod 8$, $t = 2$ and (170) gives (158$_1$).

When $abcd \equiv 1 \pmod 8$, (157) is a necessary condition that (151) be solvable. For, the latter implies $x + y + z + u \equiv 0 \pmod 2$. Since $x, \ldots, u$ are not all even by hypothesis, they are either all odd or two of them are odd and two even. We have $ax^2 + by^2 + cz^2 + du^2 \equiv 0 \pmod 8$. In the first case, we get (157). In the second case, let x and y be odd, z and u be even. Then $a + b \equiv 0 \pmod 4$. According as $a + b \equiv 0$ or $4 \pmod 8$, we have $ab \equiv -1$ or $3 \pmod 8$. Then $abcd \equiv 1$ gives $cd \equiv -1$ or $3 \pmod 8$, whence $c + d \equiv 0$ or $4 \pmod 8$. We again get (157).

When $a = 2a'$, $b = 2b'$, $a'b'cd \equiv r \pmod 8$, and (151) is solvable, we shall prove that one of the conditions (158) holds. Now $z + u$ is even. First, let z and u be odd. Then $2a'x^2 + 2b'y^2 + c + d \equiv 0 \pmod 8$.

I. Let x and y be even. Then $c + d$ is divisible by 8 and $c - d$ by 2, whence $c^2 \equiv d^2$, $c^4 \equiv 1$, $c^2d^2 \equiv 1 \pmod{16}$, whence the second member of (158$_1$) is divisible by 8. The same is true of the first member since $-1 \equiv cd \equiv ra'b'$, $ra' \equiv -b' \pmod 8$.

II. Let x and y be odd. Then $c + d \equiv -2(a' + b') \pmod 8$, whence $c + d \equiv 0$, $-1 \equiv cd \equiv a'b'$, $a' + b' \equiv 0 \pmod 4$. Thus $c + d \equiv 0 \pmod 8$. Proceed as in I.

III. Let x be even, y odd. Squaring $-2b' \equiv c + d \pmod 8$, we see that $cd \equiv 1$, $c \equiv d \pmod 4$, $c = d + 4k$, $cd \equiv 1 + 4k \pmod 8$, $c^2d^2 \equiv 1 + 8k \pmod{16}$, $-b' \equiv d + 2k \pmod 4$. Write $b' = 4e - d - 2k$. Then $ra' \equiv b'cd \equiv 4e - d + 2k \pmod 8$. Hence each member of (158$_1$) is $\equiv 4k \pmod 8$.

Second, let $z = 2Z$, $u = 2U$. Then x and y are both odd. We cancel 2 from (151) and are led to the first case with a' and c interchanged and likewise b' and d. These interchanges replace (158$_1$) by

$$rc + d + a' + b' \equiv \tfrac{1}{2}(a'^2 b'^2 - 1) \pmod 8 .$$

But $c(r-1) \equiv a'(r-1)$, $a'b' \equiv rcd \pmod 8$. Since $r^2 - 1$ and $c^2d^2 - 1$ are divisible by 8,

$$a'^2 b'^2 \equiv (1 + r^2 - 1)(1 + c^2d^2 - 1) \equiv 1 + r^2 - 1 + c^2d^2 - 1 \pmod{16} \quad ,$$

$$\tfrac{1}{2}(a'^2 b'^2 - 1) \equiv \tfrac{1}{2}(c^2d^2 - 1) + r - 1 \pmod 8 ,$$

and we obtain (158$_2$).

PART II

MINIMA OF INDEFINITE QUADRATIC FORMS

40. Summary, definitions. Let f be a real indefinite quadratic form in n variables of determinant Δ having a minimum m. Then $m \leqq m_1$, where $m_1^2 = \frac{4}{5}\Delta$ if $n = 2$, $m_1^3 = \frac{2}{3}|\Delta|$ if $n = 3$. All forms of minimum m_1 are equivalent to a unique form f_1. If f is not equivalent to f_1, then $m \leqq m_2$, where m_2 is much smaller than m_1. All forms of minimum m_2 are equivalent to a unique form f_2. Similarly for m_3, f_3, etc. When $n = 4$ there is a subdivision into cases depending on the signature (or index) of f.

The ratios of the coefficients of each f_i are all rational. When $n \geqq 5$ such an f_i has the minimum zero by Theorem 56 and in this sense our problem is trivial if $n > 4$.

Representation by $f(x, y, \ldots)$ will always be understood to be by use of *integers* $x, y, \ldots$ not all zero. For example, $x^2 + xy - y^2$ represents 1, but not zero or a proper fraction.

The lower bound of the absolute values of the numbers represented by f is denoted by $L(f)$. In case f attains (or represents) either L or $-L$, we call L the minimum of f. Our investigation is extended to the case in which neither L nor $-L$ is attained for $n \leqq 4$.

CHAPTER VII

MINIMA OF INDEFINITE, BINARY, QUADRATIC FORMS

41. Literature. The theory is due to A. Markoff[1] who gave a mere sketch of his proof. Once the main Theorem 80 was known, it was possible for R. Remak[2] to give a new proof, using inductions, but avoiding continued fractions. His proof presupposes results obtained by G. Frobenius.[3] Although Remak's proof provides a desirable check, it furnishes no clue to the origin of the theorem and is not really shorter than the present elaboration[4] of Markoff's proof. Moreover, certain auxiliary material on continued fractions is required in the following chapters on 3 and 4 variables.

The exposition by Bachmann[5] lacks many essential details and ignores the important final parts of Theorems 75 and 80.

42. Theorem 62. *Let f be any real, indefinite, binary, quadratic form of discriminant d. Then always* $L(f) \leqq \sqrt{d/5}$, *while evidently* $L(f_0) = \sqrt{d/5}$ *for*

$$(1) \qquad f_0 = \sqrt{d/5} \ (x^2 + xy - y^2) \ .$$

For any f not equivalent to f_0, $L(f) \leqq \sqrt{d/8} = L(f_1)$, *where*

$$(2) \qquad f_1 = \sqrt{d/8} \ (x^2 + 2xy - y^2) \ .$$

For any f which is equivalent to neither f_0 *nor* f_1, *then* $L(f) \leqq 5\sqrt{d/221} = L(f_2)$, *where*[6]

$$(3) \qquad f_2 = \sqrt{d/221} \ (5x^2 + 11xy - 5y^2) \ .$$

For any f which is equivalent to no one of f_0, f_1, f_2, *then* $L(f) \leqq 13\sqrt{d/1517} = L(f_3)$, *where*

$$(4) \qquad f_3 = \sqrt{d/1517} \ (13x^2 + 29xy - 13y^2) \ .$$

---

[1] *Math. Annalen*, XV (1879), 381–406; XVII (1880), 379–99.

[2] *Ibid.*, XCI (1924), 155–82.

[3] *Berlin. Sitzungsberichte*, 1913, 458–87.

[4] With material aid from G. Pall and A. Oppenheim.

[5] *Arith. quad. Formen*, II, 1923, 106–29.

[6] A short, elementary proof of the theorem to this point was found by the author and published in *Introd.*, chap. xi.

The set $f_0, f_1, f_2, f_3, \ldots$ continues indefinitely; each f_i has discriminant d and $L(f_i) > \frac{1}{3}D$, where $D = \sqrt{d} > 0$. Each is proportional to an integral form. Also $L(f_i) \geqq L(f_i)$ if $i \leqq j$. Moreover, if f has discriminant d and if $L(f) > \frac{1}{3}D$, then f is properly or improperly equivalent to one of the f_i.

The investigation will lead to a formula for the f_i, but gives no information concerning forms f having $L(f) < \frac{1}{3}D$.

We require a few standard notations (*Introd.*, § 65). Let

$$(5) \qquad \Phi_i(x, y) = (-1)^i A_i x^2 + B_i xy - (-1)^i A_{i+1} y^2$$

have the positive discriminant D^2. Then $\Phi_i (X, 1) = 0$ has the roots[1]

$$(6) \qquad f_i = \frac{D - B_i}{2(-1)^i A_i}, \qquad s_i = \frac{-D - B_i}{2(-1)^i A_i},$$

which are called the first and second roots of Φ_i. The form Φ_i is called reduced if $|f_i| < 1$, $|s_i| > 1$, $f_i s_i < 0$. Every real indefinite form is equivalent to a reduced form. Equivalent reduced forms constitute a chain. Let $\ldots \Phi_{-1}, \Phi_0, \Phi_1, \Phi_2, \ldots$ constitute a chain; we may give to Φ_i the notation (5), where A_j and B_j are positive for every j. There is a unique integer δ_i such that $x = Y$, $y = -X + \delta_i Y$ replaces Φ_i by Φ_{i+1}; then $1/f_i = \delta_i - f_{i+1}$ and similarly with s instead of f. Write

$$(7) \qquad F_i = \frac{(-1)^i}{f_i} = \frac{D + B_i}{2A_{i+1}}, \qquad S_i = \frac{(-1)^{i+1}}{s_i} = \frac{D - B_i}{2A_{i+1}}.$$

Write $g_i = (-1)^i \delta_i$. Then $g_i > 0$, $F_i > 1$, $0 < S_i < 1$,

$$(8) \qquad F_i = g_i + 1/F_{i+1}, \qquad 1/S_i = g_{i-1} + S_{i-1}.$$

Hence F_1 may be developed into a continued fraction

$$g_1 + \cfrac{1}{g_2 + \cfrac{1}{g_3 + \cdots}} = (g_1, g_2, g_3, \ldots).$$

Similarly,

$$(9) \qquad F_i = (g_i, g_{i+1}, g_{i+2}, \ldots), \qquad S_i = (0, g_{i-1}, g_{i-2}, \ldots),$$

where the g_j are all positive integers. By (7),

$$(10) \qquad F_i + S_i = D/A_{i+1}, \qquad F_i - S_i = B_i/A_{i+1}, \qquad F_i S_i = A_i/A_{i+1}.$$

---

[1] If $A_i = 0$ the theorem is trivial for Φ_i which then represents zero.

Write K_i for $F_i + S_i$. If $K_i > 3$ for a certain i, then $A_{i+1} < \frac{1}{3}D$ and the lower bound of the A's, which is $L(f)$ by a theorem of Lagrange (*Introd.*, page 111), is $< \frac{1}{3}D$. Since such a case is ignored in our theorem, we desire that

$$(11) \qquad K_j \leqq 3 \text{ for every integer } j .$$

Let $(g_i) = (\ldots, g_{-1}, g_0, g_1, \ldots)$ be a set of positive integers for which (11) holds. Then each g_j is 1 or 2 since $g_i \geqq 3$ implies $K_i > F_i > 3$.

The set (G_i) defined by $G_i = g_{-i}$ has the same terms as the set (g_i) but taken in reverse order. Evidently

$$(G_i, G_{i+1}, \ldots) = g_{-i} + S_{-i} , \qquad (0, G_{i-1}, G_{i-2}, \ldots) = -g_{-i} + F_{-i} ,$$

whose sum is K_{-i}. Hence (11) holds for the *reverse set* (G_i) if and only if it holds for (g_i).

If every $g_j = 1$, then

$$F_j = (1, F_j) , \qquad F_j^2 = F_j + 1 , \qquad F_j = \tfrac{1}{2}(\sqrt{5} + 1) ,$$

$$S_j = 1/F_j = \tfrac{1}{2}(\sqrt{5} - 1) , \qquad F_j - S_j = 1 , \qquad F_j S_j = 1 , \qquad K_j = \sqrt{5} .$$

By (10), $B_j = A_{j+1} = A_j = D/\sqrt{5}$ and Φ_0 is f_0 in (1).

If every $g_j = 2$, then

$$F_j = (2, F_j) , \qquad F_j^2 = 2F_j + 1 , \qquad F_j = \sqrt{2} + 1 ,$$

$$S_j = 1/F_j = \sqrt{2} - 1 , \qquad B_j = 2A_{j+1} , \qquad A_j = A_{j+1} = D/\sqrt{8} , \qquad \Phi_0 = f_1 .$$

We exclude henceforth these two cases. Then both 1 and 2 occur in the set (g_j). The case in which three consecutive g's are 1, 2, 1 contradicts (11), since $g_{i-1} = 1$, $g_i = 2$, $g_{i+1} = 1$ imply[1]

$$K_i = (2, 1, \ldots) + (0, 1, \ldots) > 2\tfrac{1}{2} + \tfrac{1}{2} .$$

Nor can a sequence 2, 1, 2 occur. For, if $g_i = 2$, $g_{i+1} = 1$, $g_{i+2} = 2$, then $g_{i-1} = 2$ by the preceding case, and

$$K_i = (2, 1, 2, \ldots) + (0, 2, \ldots) > (2, 1, 2) + (0, 2, 1) = 2\tfrac{2}{3} + \tfrac{1}{3} = 3 .$$

We write 2_j for a succession of j terms each 2.

[1] If in $p = (q_1, q_2, \ldots)$ we decrease q_k, then p is decreased when k is odd, but is increased when k is even. If we increase q_k, then p is increased when k is odd, but decreased when k is even (*Introd.*, p. 107). Also, $p >$ odd convergent, $p <$ even convergent.

If no 2 precedes a 1, the set is $1_\infty 2_\infty$. This is excluded either by the direct computation

$$K_i = (2_\infty) + (0, 1_\infty) = \sqrt{2} + 1 + \tfrac{1}{2}(\sqrt{5} - 1) > 3 ,$$

or by the fact that the reverse set $2_\infty 1_\infty$ is excluded in the next footnote. These three results show that there is an i for which

$$(12) \qquad\qquad g_{i-1} = g_i = 2 , \qquad g_{i+1} = g_{i+2} = 1 .$$

We shall often use the identity

$$(13) \qquad\qquad (0, 2, x) + (0, 1, 1, x) = 1 \qquad \text{if } x > 0 .$$

Then if $z > 0$,

$$(14) \qquad\qquad (2, z) + (0, 2, x) \leqq 3 \text{ if and only if } z \geqq (1, 1, x) .$$

By (12), $K_i = (2, 1, 1, F_{i+3}) + (0, 2, 1/S_{i-1})$. In (14) take $z = (1, 1, F_{i+3})$, $x = 1/S_{i-1}$; hence

$$(15) \qquad\qquad K_i \leqq 3 \text{ if and only if } F_{i+3} \geqq 1/S_{i-1} \text{ for (12),}$$

where equality on the right (left) implies equality on the left (right), and similarly in (17) and (21). To (14) we add $-2 + 2$ and take $z = 1/y$; we get

$$(16) \qquad\qquad y + (2, 2, x) \leqq 3 \text{ if and only if } 1/y \geqq (1, 1, x) .$$

Take $y = S_{i-1}$, $x = (1, 1, F_{i+3})$; then $K_{i-1} = (2, 2, x) + y$. Hence

$$(17) \qquad\qquad K_{i-1} \leqq 3 \text{ if and only if } 1/S_{i-1} \geqq (1_4, F_{i+3}) \text{ for (12) .}$$

We are now assuming that every $K_i \leqq 3$. Hence we have the final inequalities in (15) and (17). They imply

$$(18) \qquad\qquad F_{i+3} \geqq 1/S_{i-1} \geqq (1_4, F_{i+3}) \geqq (1_4, 1/S_{i-1}) \text{ for (12) .}$$

Hence[1] if either F_{i+3} or $1/S_{i-1}$ is (1_∞), the other is (1_∞). In either case the four g's in (12) are followed and preceded by (1_∞), and the entire set of g's is

$$(19) \qquad\qquad\qquad 1_\infty, 2, 2, 1_\infty .$$

---

[1] This excludes the set $2_\infty 1_\infty$.

Conversely, every $K_j \leqq 3$ for (19). First, we have

(20)   if $g_i = 1$, then $K_j < 2 + 1$.

Hence it remains only to evaluate K_j when g_i is one of the two 2's, viz., K_i and K_{i-1} for the notation (12). We saw that F_{i+3} and $1/S_{i-1}$ are then (1_∞), whence we have equality in both (15) and (17).

By (13), $y + (0, 1, 1, x) \leqq 3$ if and only if $y \leqq (2, 2, x)$. Take $y = F_{i+3}$, $x = (2, 2, 1/S_{i-1})$; hence

(21) $K_{i+3} \leqq 3$ if and only if $F_{i+3} \leqq (2_4, 1/S_{i-1})$ for (12) .

Combining the final inequality with (15), we get

(22) $1/S_{i-1} \leqq F_{i+3} \leqq (2_4, 1/S_{i-1}) \leqq (2_4, F_{i+3})$ for (12) .

Hence either of $F_{i+3} = (2_\infty)$, $1/S_{i-1} = (2_\infty)$ implies the other, and then the set of g's is

(23) $2_\infty, 1, 1, 2_\infty$.

Conversely, every $K_j \leqq 3$ for (23). We note that

(24)   if 2, $g_i = 2$, 2 occur, then $K_j < (2, 2) + (0, 2) = 3$.

It remains to evaluate K_j when g_i is a 2 adjacent to 1, 1, viz., K_i and K_{i+3} for the notation (12); the value of each is 3, since we have equality in both (15) and (21).

Excluding the set (19), we have

(25) $\ldots, 2, 1_n, 2, g_i = 2, 1_m, 2, \ldots$,

where $m \geqq 2$, $n \geqq 0$. If m is odd,

$$F_{i+3} = (1_{m-2}, 2, \ldots) < (1_{m-2}, 1_\infty) = (1_\infty) ,$$

since $(2, \ldots) > 2 > \frac{1}{2}(\sqrt{5} + 1) = (1_\infty)$. But by (18), $F_{i+3} \geqq (1_4, F_{i+3}) \geqq (1_8, F_{i+3}) \geqq \ldots \geqq (1_\infty)$. This contradiction shows that m is even. If n is odd,

$$1/S_{i-1} = (1_n, 2, \ldots) < (1_n, 1_\infty) = (1_\infty) ,$$

whereas the second and fourth parts of (18) give $1/S_{i-1} \geqq (1_\infty)$. Hence n is even. By (18),

$$(1_{m-2}, 2, \ldots) \geqq (1_n, 2, \ldots) \geqq (1_{m+2}, 2, \ldots) .$$

Hence $m-2 \leqq n \leqq m+2$. Write $m = 2m'$, $n = 2n'$. Thus

$$(26) \qquad\qquad m' - n' = -1, 0, \text{ or } 1 ,$$

where $m' \geqq 1$, $n' \geqq 0$.

To prove (26) also when $m' = 0$, we must show that then $n' = 0$ or 1 and hence exclude the case $n \geqq 4$. It suffices to show that $\ldots 1111222 \ldots$ cannot occur. Denote the first of these terms 2 by g_j. Then

$$K_j > (2, 2, 2) + (0, 1, 1, 1, 1) = \tfrac{12}{5} + \tfrac{3}{5} = 3 .$$

Another proof uses the reverse set $\ldots 2221111 \ldots$, for which $n' = 0$, $m' \geqq 2$, contrary to (26).

Except for set (23), we saw that there is only a finite number k of terms 2 just preceding g_{i-1}. Let k be odd. Then $1/S_{i-1} = (2_k, 1, \ldots) > (2_k, 2_\infty) = (2_\infty)$. But by (22), $1/S \leqq (2_4, 1/S) \leqq (2_8, 1/S) \leqq \ldots \leqq (2_\infty)$. This contradiction shows that k is even. Thus the number of consecutive terms 2 is always even. It is convenient to write 2, 2, 1_0, 2, 2 for 2, 2, 2, 2. We have now proved

THEOREM 63. *For the sets* (1_∞), (2_∞), (19) *and* (23), *every* $K_j \leqq 3$. *Any further set* (g_i) *having every* $K_j \leqq 3$ *must be of the form*

$$(27) \qquad\qquad \ldots , 1_{2r_{-1}} , 2, 2, 1_{2r_0} , 2, 2, 1_{2r_1} , \ldots ,$$

where the r_i *are finite integers* $\geqq 0$, *at least two of them not zero, which satisfy the relations*

$$(28) \qquad\qquad r_{k+1} - r_k = -1, 0, \text{ or } 1 \qquad \text{for every } k ,$$

and are such that (18) *and* (22) *hold.*

We next prove the converse: *If* (18), (22), *and* (28) *hold, then every* $K_j \leqq 3$ *for any set* (27). The only cases in addition to (20) and (24) are (I) $g_j = 2$, 1 and (II) 1, $g_j = 2$. For (I), we have 2, $g_j = 2$, 1, 1. Writing i for j, we have (12) and, by (18_1) and (15), we get $K_i \leqq 3$. For (II), we have 1, 1, $g_j = 2$, 2 and we may take $r_0 \geqq 1$ in (27). If $r_1 > 0$, we have $\ldots , 1, 1, g_j = 2, 2, 1, 1, \ldots$; taking $i = j+1$, we have (12) and see that (18_2) and (17) imply that $K_{i-1} = K_j \leqq 3$. But if $r_1 = 0$, (28) with $k = 0$ gives $r_0 = 1$, whence $\ldots , 2, 2, 1, 1, g_j = 2, 2, \ldots$ We take $i = j-3$ and have (12) and see that (22_2) and (21) imply that $K_{i+3} = K_j \leqq 3$.

43. Simpler conditions. Conditions (18) and (22) which involve continued fractions may be replaced by simpler conditions as follows:

THEOREM 64. *Necessary and sufficient conditions that every* $K_j \leq 3$ *for the set* (27) *are* (28) *and*

(29) $\left\{ \begin{array}{l} \textit{If } r_k - r_{k+1} = 1 \textit{ (or } -1), \textit{ then the first of the differences } r_{k+h+1} - r_{k-h} \\ (h = 1, 2, \ldots) \textit{ which is not zero is positive (or negative).} \end{array} \right.$

We first prove that (28) and (29) imply (18) and (22). For any $r_{k+1} > 0$, the term 2 just preceding $1_{2r_{k+1}}$ in (27) is a value of g_i such that (27) contains the terms (12). Then

$$F_{i+3} = (1_{2r_{k+1}-2}, 2, 2, 1_{2r_{k+2}}, \ldots), \qquad 1/S_{i-1} = (1_{2r_k}, 2, 2, 1_{2r_{k-1}}, \ldots).$$

For brevity we omit the subscripts on F and S. By (28), $r_k \geq r_{k+1} - 1$. While $F \geq 1/S$ is automatically true when $r_k > r_{k+1} - 1$, it holds when $r_k = r_{k+1} - 1$ if and only if $(1_{2r_{k+2}}, 2, \ldots) \geq (1_{2r_{k-1}}, 2, \ldots)$. The latter implies $r_{k+2} \leq r_{k-1}$, and when those r's are equal it implies $r_{k+3} \leq r_{k-2}$, etc. Hence it holds if and only if the first difference

(30) $$r_{k+h+1} - r_{k-h} \qquad (h = 1, 2, \ldots)$$

which is not zero is negative. This is the second case of (29).

By (28), $r_k \leq r_{k+1} + 1$. While $(1_4, F) \leq 1/S$ is automatically true when $r_k < r_{k+1} + 1$, it holds when $r_k = r_{k+1} + 1$ if and only if the first difference (30) which is not zero is positive. This is the first case of (29).

Finally, $F \leq (2_4, 1/S)$ is automatically true unless $r_{k+1} = 1$, $r_{k+2} = 0$, and then it is equivalent to

$$(1_{2r_{k+3}}, 2, 2, 1_{2r_{k+4}}, 2, \ldots) \leq (1_{2r_k}, 2, 2, 1_{2r_{k-1}}, 2, \ldots).$$

This holds if and only if the first difference

$$r_{k+h+2} - r_{k+1-h} \qquad (h = 1, 2, \ldots)$$

which is not zero is positive. This is the first case of (29) with k changed to $k+1$.

Conversely, (18), (22), and (28) imply (29). When $r_{k+1} > 0$, we just proved that $F \geq 1/S$ or $(1_4, F) \leq 1/S$ implies (29) if $r_k - r_{k+1} = -1$ or $+1$, respectively. But when $r_{k+1} = 0$, the only admissible hypothesis in (29) is $r_k - r_{k+1} = +1$, and then the conclusion in (29) follows from the preceding paragraph by replacing k by $k-1$.

44. Theorem 65. *Any two r_i differ by at most unity.*

Suppose that two of the r_i are $r \geq 2$ and $r' \leq r-2$.

First, let r' occur to the right of r. If, in proceeding from r to r' through successive r_i, we ascend from r, it is evident from (28) that we must ultimately descend to a term r before reaching r'. Hence it suffices to start with a term r such that no term between r and r' is $\geq r$. Then r is followed by exactly s terms $r-1$, where $s \geq 1$. The last such term $r-1$ is followed by $r-2$, since not by $r-1$ or r. Hence the set of r_i contains

$$r_k = r , \qquad (r-1)_s , \qquad r-2 .$$

Then $r_{k+1} = r-1$, $r_{k+2} \leq r-1$. Since $r_k - r_{k+1} = +1$, (29) with $h=1$ gives $r_{k+2} - r_{k-1} \geq 0$. Thus $r_{k-1} \leq r_{k+2} \leq r_k - 1$, whence $r_k - r_{k-1} = 1$ by (28). Hence r_k is preceded by $r_{k-1} = r-1$ and hence by $(r-1)_t$ for $t \geq 1$.

If $t \geq s$, then $r_{k+h+1} - r_{k-h}$ is evidently zero for $1 \leq h < s$ and is $r-2-(r-1) = -1$ for $h = s$. This contradicts the first case of (29).

Hence $t < s$ and the set of r_i contains

$$R = r_{k-t-1} , \qquad (r-1)_t , \qquad r_k = r , \qquad (r-1)_s , \qquad r-2 ,$$

where R is either r or $r-2$. Since

$$r_k - r_{k+1} = 1 , \qquad r_{k+h+1} - r_{k-h} = 0 \qquad (h = 1, \ldots, t) ,$$

(29) gives $r_{k+t+2} - R \geq 0$. Since $t+2 \leq s+1$, r_{k+t+2} is $\leq r-1$. Hence $R \leq r-1$, whence $R = r-2$. Thus $r_{k+h} - r_{k-1-h}$ is zero for $1 \leq h \leq t-1$ and is $r-1-R=1$ for $h=t$. Since $r_{k-1} - r_k = -1$, this contradicts (29) with k replaced by $k-1$.

Second, let r' occur to the left of r. The reverse set falls under the first case.

45. The four types of sets (r_i). By Theorem 65, the r_i are either all equal or some of them are r and the others are all $r-1$. There are just four possibilities for the set (r_i):

$$R_0: \qquad (r_\infty)$$

$$R_{01}: \qquad (r-1)_\infty , r, (r-1)_\infty$$

$$R_{10}: \qquad r_\infty , r-1, r_\infty$$

$$R: \qquad \ldots , r, (r-1)_{s_i} , r, (r-1)_{s_{i+1}} , r, \ldots ,$$

where the s_i are finite integers ≥ 0, at least two of which are not zero. For, if a set (r_i) is not of one of the types R_0, R_{01}, R_{10}, there occur at least two terms r and at least two terms $r-1$. Suppose that a term $r_k = r-1$ is followed by r_∞ and that $r_j = r-1$ is the term $r-1$ nearest to r_k and at its left. Then $r_k - r_{k+1} = -1$, while the difference in (29) is zero for $h < k-j$, but is $+1$ for $h = k-j$, which contradicts (29). A like statement holds if we interchange r and $r-1$ and the values -1 and $+1$. Similarly or by using the reverse series, we conclude that $r-1$ is not preceded by r_∞, nor r by $(r-1)_\infty$. Hence neither r_∞ nor $(r-1)_\infty$ occurs, whence the series is of type R.

Condition (29) is satisfied vacuously (i.e., the differences are all zero) for sets R_0, R_{01}, R_{10}, as seen by inspection from

(31) $\begin{cases} \text{The two } r\text{'s in any difference in (29) lie at equal distances from} \\ \text{the central pair } r_k,\ r_{k+1}\,. \end{cases}$

It remains to study the set (s_i) of subscripts in R.

THEOREM 66. *If the set* (r_i) *satisfies* (28) *and* (29), *then the set* (s_i) *satisfies*[1] (28) *and* (29), *and conversely.*

I. Let (28) and (29) hold for (r_i). Write r_k for the r just following $(r-1)_{s_i}$. If $s_i > s_{i+1}+1$, then $r_{k-1} - r_k = -1$, and $r_{k+h} - r_{k-h-1}$ is zero for $h = 1, \ldots, s_{i+1}$ (a vacuous statement if $s_{i+1} = 0$), but is $r - (r-1) = +1$ for $h = s_{i+1}+1$. This contradicts (29) with k replaced by $k-1$. Hence $s_i \leqq s_{i+1}+1$. Similarly (or by the reverse series), $s_{i+1} \leqq s_i+1$. Hence (28) holds for (s_i).

Let $s_i - s_{i+1} = -1$ (if $+1$ we use the reverse series). Then $s_{i+1} > 0$ and $r_k - r_{k+1} = r - (r-1) = 1$. By (29) the first non-zero difference $r_{k+h+1} - r_{k-h}$ is positive and hence is $r - (r-1)$. In other words, after pairing off the equal terms equidistant from the central pair r_k, r_{k+1} as in (31), we come to a term r at the right and the equidistant term $r-1$ at the left. Thus the latter term is one of a block of consecutive terms $r-1$ which is longer than the corresponding block of terms $r-1$ at the right. Hence the first non-zero difference $s_{i+1+h} - s_{i-h}$ is negative. This proves (29) for the set (s_i).

II. Let (28) and (29) hold for (s_i). Since r and $r-1$ are the only values of the r_i in set R, (28) is evidently true. Let $s_i - s_{i+1} = -1$, whence $s_{i+1} > 0$, $r_k - r_{k+1} = r - (r-1) = 1$, and the first non-zero difference $s_{i+1+h} - s_{i-h}$ is negative by hypothesis. As at the end of I, this implies that, after pairing off in (r_i) the equal terms equidistant from the pair r_k, r_{k+1}, we come to a term r at the right and the equidistant term $r-1$ at the left. In other words, the first non-zero difference $r_{k+h+1} - r_{k-h}$ is $r - (r-1) = +1$, which proves the first case of (29). To obtain the second case, we start with the reverse set.

---

[1] With of course r's replaced by s's.

46. The derived sets. As in § 45, the set (s_i) is of one of the types

$$S_0: \qquad (s_\infty)$$
$$S_{01}: \qquad (s-1)_\infty, \ s, \ (s-1)_\infty$$
$$S_{10}: \qquad s_\infty, \ s-1, \ s_\infty$$
$$S: \qquad \ldots, \ s, \ (s-1)_{t_i}, \ s, \ (s-1)_{t_{i+1}}, \ s, \ldots,$$

where the t_i are finite integers $\geqq 0$, at least two of which are not zero. Similarly, the set (t_i) is of one of four types T_0, T_{01}, T_{10}, T, and the subscripts in T are denoted by u_i. We shall later prove that, except for sets (35), after a finite number of such steps we reach a set of equal subscripts, so that only the first of the four types then exists.

If any of the sets, say (u_i), satisfies (28) and (29), the same is true of the earlier sets (t_i), (s_i), (r_i) by Theorem 66, and we obtain a set (27) of terms g_i for which every $K_j \leqq 3$. Instead of using the complex conditions (28) and (29), we may therefore investigate all sets (g_i) for which every $K_j \leqq 3$ by means of the *derived sets* (r_i), (s_i), $\ldots$, terminating with a set (c_∞).

For example, consider the set having every $t_i = 1$, and let $s = 1$ and $r = 3$ be the greater value of the s_i and of the r_i, respectively. Then the s_i in S are alternately 0 and 1, and the set $(r_i) = R$ is $\ldots, 2, 3_2, 2, 3_2, 2, \ldots$. Finally, (g_i) in (27) is

$$(32) \qquad \qquad \ldots, \ 2_2, \ 1_4, \ 2_2, \ 1_6, \ 2_2, \ 1_6, \ldots,$$

with the indicated terms repeated periodically in each direction.

Starting with a derived set, say (t_i), and choosing arbitrary integers $\geqq 1$ as the values of s and r, we can determine the earlier derived sets (s_i) and (r_i).

In case (t_i) is of type $T_0 = (t_\infty)$, each of S, R, and (g_i) in (27) is periodic, as in the last example.

Next, let (t_i) be either T_{01} or T_{10} and hence of the form

$$(33) \qquad \qquad \ldots, \ t'', \ t', \ t, \ \tau, \ t', \ t'', \ldots \qquad (\tau = t \pm 1),$$

having equal terms at equal distances from the central pair t, τ. Assign any integral value $\geqq 1$ to s. Then set S is

$$(34) \quad \ldots, \ s, \ (s-1)_{t''}, \ s, \ (s-1) \ _{t'}, \ s, \ (s-1)_t, \ s^*, \ (s-1)_\tau, \ s, \ (s-1)_{t'}, \ldots$$

If $\tau = t + 1$, write σ for the term $s - 1$ just following the s marked by an asterisk; then (34) is of type (33) with the central pair s, σ. If[1] $\tau = t - 1$,

---

[1] The reverse set falls under case $\tau = t + 1$. The sets in (35) are reverse.

write σ for the term $s-1$ just preceding s^*; then (34) is of type (33) with the central pair σ, s. The same proof shows that also R is of type (33). Hence (27) is

$$\ldots, 2, 2, 1_{2t'}, 2, 2, 1_{2t}, 2, 2, 1_{2\tau}, 2, 2, 1_{2t'}, 2, 2, \ldots.$$

If $\tau = t+1$, replace $1_{2\tau}$ by $1, 1, 1_{2t}$. If $\tau = t-1$, replace 1_{2t} by $1_{2\tau}, 1, 1$. Thus (g_i) is of one of the two types

(35) $$\ldots, g', g', g, g, 2, 2, 1, 1, g, g, g', g', \ldots,$$
$$\ldots, g', g', g, g, 1, 1, 2, 2, g, g, g', g', \ldots.$$

Write x for $(g, g, g', g', \ldots)$. Take g_i as the second term 2 in the first set and as the first term 2 in the second set. Then, by (13),

$$K_i = (2, 1, 1, x) + (0, 2, x) = 3 , \qquad K_i = (2, 2, x) + (0, 1, 1, x) = 3 ,$$

in the respective cases (35). Since T_{01} and T_{10} satisfy conditions (28) and (29), the same was proved true for $R = (r_i)$, and Theorem 64 shows that every $K_j \leq 3$ for sets (35). In other words, 3 is the upper bound of the K_j for sets (35). For these sets the upper bound is attained.

47. Lower bound L(f) of numbers represented by f. By (9), a set (g_i) of positive integers determines F_i and S_i and hence by (7) determines the first and second roots (6) of an indefinite binary form Φ_i in (5). These roots determine Φ_i (or its opposite form) up to a constant factor which is determined except for sign when the discriminant D^2 is assigned. Thus a set of g's for which every $K_j \leq 3$ determines a chain of equivalent reduced forms Φ_i for which $L(\Phi_i) \geq \frac{1}{3}D$ and its opposite chain.

Since t, s, and r are arbitrary integers ≥ 1, our preceding result leads to

THEOREM 67. *There are infinitely many classes of real indefinite binary forms f of discriminant $D^2 \neq 0$ for which $L(f) = \frac{1}{3}D$.*

Starting with derived sets (t_∞), we obtained before (33) infinitely many periodic sets (27) for which every $K_j \leq 3$. We now prove that $K_j \neq 3$ in a periodic set (27). The number of terms in a minimum period is evidently even, say $2p$. By (20) and (24), it remains to prove that $K_i \neq 3$ when g_i is 2 and is either followed or preceded by a term 1.

In the first case, the set contains 2, $g_i = 2, 1, 1$. Then $F_i = (2, 1, 1, G)$, $S_i = (0, 2, H)$, where

(36) $$G = (g_{i+3}, g_{i+4}, \ldots) , \qquad H = (g_{i-2}, g_{i-3}, \ldots) .$$

By (13), $K_i = 3$ if and only if $G = H$. Then $g = g_{i+3+2p-4}$ is equal to $h = g_{i-2-(2p-4)}$. By the periodicity, $g = g_{i-1} = 2$, $h = g_{i+2} = 1$. Hence $G \neq H$, $K_i \neq 3$.

In the second case,[1] the set contains 1, 1, $g_i = 2$, 2. Then $F_i = (2, 2, y)$, $S_i = (0, 1, 1, x)$, where

$$(37) \qquad y = (g_{i+2}, g_{i+3}, \ldots), \qquad x = (g_{i-3}, g_{i-4}, \ldots).$$

By (13), $K_i = 3$ if and only if $y = x$. Then $u = g_{i+2+2p-4}$ is equal to $v = g_{i-3-(2p-4)}$. By the periodicity, $u = g_{i-2} = 1$, $v = g_{i+1} = 2$. Hence $K_i \neq 3$. This proves that every $K_j < 3$ and yields

THEOREM 68. *There are infinitely many classes of real indefinite binary forms f of discriminant $D^2 \neq 0$ for which $L(f) > \frac{1}{3}D$.*

We next prove

THEOREM 69. *There is only a finite number of classes of real indefinite binary quadratic forms f of a given discriminant D^2 $(D > 0)$ such that $L(f) \geq \beta$, where β is any assigned number $> \frac{1}{3}D$. Every such f corresponds to a periodic set (g_i).*

It suffices to prove that, if a is any assigned positive number < 3, there is at most a finite number of sets (27) having $K_j \leq a$ for every integer j. All such sets (27) will be shown to be periodic.

Let the quadruple 2, $g_i = 2$, 1, 1, denoted by Q, occur in (27). By (13) and (36), we have

$$(38) \qquad 3 - K_i = (0, 2, G) - (0, 2, H).$$

Let exactly the first $2q$ terms of G be equal to the corresponding terms of H, where $2q$ is an even integer by (27). The larger the value of q, the smaller will be (38). For all sufficiently large q, $3 - K_i$ is arbitrarily small. Hence when $K_i \leq a < 3$, there exists an integer l depending on a such that $q \leq l$.

A like argument applies to the quadruple 1, 1, $g_i = 2$, 2, denoted by Q', and $3 - K_i = (0, 2, x) - (0, 2, y)$ for x and y in (37). Let exactly the first $2q'$ terms of x be equal to the corresponding terms of y. We may choose l so that also $q' \leq l$.

Let $2r_j$ denote the number of terms 1 which immediately precede the pair of terms 2 in Q or Q'. This fixes an origin for the set (r_k).

First, let all the r_k be equal to r. Then (27) has the period 2, 2, 1_{2r}. Then $2q = 2q' = 2r - 2 \leq 2l$. Hence there is only a finite number of values r and therefore of sets (27).

Second, let distinct r_k exist. Take $r_j \neq r_{j+1}$. Let r denote the maximum of the r_k. Let

$$(39) \qquad r_{j+h+1} = r_{j-h} \qquad (h = 1, 2, \ldots, \rho).$$

---

[1] It follows from the first case by reversion. Likewise for Q' below (38).

If $r_j > r_{j+1}$, we may write g_i and g_{i+1} for the two terms 2 between 1_{2r_j} and $1_{2r_{j+1}}$ and see that quadruple Q' occurs. But if $r_j < r_{j+1}$, we may write g_{i-1} and g_i for these terms 2 and see that quadruple Q occurs.

If $r_j > r_{j+1}$, then $r_j - 1 = r_{j+1}$ by (28), and the initial terms

$$1_{2r_{j+1}}, 2, 2, 1_{2r_{j+2}}, \ldots, 1_{2r_{j+\rho+1}}, 2, 2, 1_{2r-2}$$

of y are also the initial terms $1_{2r_{j-2}}, 2, 2, 1_{2r_{j-1}}, \ldots$ of x. Since each $r_k \geq r-1$, the number of these common terms is $\geq 2(\rho+2)(r-1) + 2(\rho+1)$. Hence

$$2l + 2 \geq 2q' + 2 \geq 2(\rho+2)r .$$

But $r \geq 1$. Hence $\rho \leq l-1$. Similarly, for the reverse set containing Q. Thus both ρ and r are finite.

Since ρ is finite, the set (r_k) is neither R_{01} nor R_{10}, and hence is of type R. Consider the set (s_k) of its subscripts.

If the s_k are all equal to s, then $s > 0$ and the set (r_k) is $\ldots, r, (r-1)_s, r, (r-1)_s, r, \ldots$. Taking r_j, r_{j+1} to be either $r, r-1$ or $r-1, r$, we see that the $s-1$ terms to the right or left of that pair are all $r-1$, whence (39) holds with ρ replaced by $s-1$. Since ρ is finite, s is finite, and there is only a finite number of sets (27).

Next, let distinct s_k exist. Take $s_j \neq s_{j+1}$ and let s denote the maximum of the s_k. Let

$$s_{j+h+1} = s_{j-h} \qquad (h = 1, 2, \ldots, \sigma) .$$

Let r' denote the term r between $(r-1)_{s_j}$ and $(r-1)_{s_{j+1}}$. According as $s_j > s_{j+1}$ or $s_j < s_{j+1}$, let r'' denote the term $r-1$ preceding or following r'. In the first case, $s_j - 1 = s_{j+1}$ by (28) and the terms $(r-1)_{s_{j+1}}, r, \ldots, (r-1)_{s_{j+\sigma+1}}$, $r, (r-1)_{s-1}$ which follow r'', r are equal to the corresponding terms which precede them. Since each $s_k \geq s-1$, the number of listed terms is $\geq (\sigma+2)(s-1) + \sigma + 1$. This number cannot exceed the maximum value of ρ, whence $(\sigma+2)s \leq 1 + $ max. ρ. Hence σ and s are limited. Since σ is finite, the set (s_k) is neither S_{01} nor S_{10} and hence is of type S. In the second case, the reverse set falls under the first case.

Either the subscripts t_k in S are all equal and we get a finite number of sets (27) or we have $(\tau+2)t \leq 1 + $ max. σ, and see that (t_k) is of type T.

Either the subscripts u_k in T are all equal and we get a finite number of sets (27) or we have $(v+2)u \leq 1 + $ max. τ, and see that (u_k) is of type U.

The numbers $\rho, \sigma, \tau, v, \ldots$ form a series of decreasing, positive integers and hence terminate. Hence we reach a set, say U, whose subscripts are all equal. Hence there is only a finite number of our sets (27) and all are periodic, as in the special case (32).

We saw that a certain K_i is 3 for sets (19) and (23). Except for (1_∞) and (2_∞), the present sets (27) are the only ones for which every $K_j < 3$. This completes the proof of Theorem 69.

We saw that the sets (1_∞) and (2_∞) determine the forms (1) and (2). This illustrates the following

THEOREM 70. *A set (g_i) of positive integers determines[1] a chain of equivalent reduced forms Φ_i and its opposite chain. If the set is periodic, each corresponding form is the product of an integral form by a constant.*

Since the Φ_i are equivalent, it suffices to prove the theorem for Φ_0. If there are $m+1$ terms in the period, (7) and (9) give

$$1/f_0 = (g_0, g_1, \ldots, g_m, 1/f_0) , \qquad -s_0 = (g_m, g_{m-1}, \ldots, g_0, -s_0) .$$

Let n/d denote the $(m+1)$th and n'/d' the mth convergent to $(g_0, \ldots, g_m)$. It is a simple fact (*Introd.*, page 108) that n/n' is the $(m+1)$th and d/d' is the mth convergent to $(g_m, \ldots, g_0)$. Hence

$$\frac{1}{f_0} = \frac{n/f_0 + n'}{d/f_0 + d'} , \qquad -s_0 = \frac{-ns_0 + d}{-n's_0 + d'} .$$

Thus both f_0 and s_0 satisfy $n'X^2 + (n-d')X - d = 0$, with rational coefficients. We saw below (5) that this equation is $\Phi_0(X, 1) = 0$. Hence the coefficients of $\Phi_0(x, y)$ are proportional to integers.

All numbers represented by such a form Φ_i (for integral values of x, y) are products of a constant by integers. Hence they have a minimum, and Φ_i therefore represents one of the values $\pm L(\phi_i)$.

THEOREM 71. *If the coefficients of a real quadratic form $f(x, y)$ of discriminant $D^2 > 0$ are not proportional to integers, the difference $|f| - \frac{1}{3}D$, if never negative, can be made arbitrarily small for integral values of x and y.*

For, if not, $|f| - \frac{1}{3}D$ always exceeds a positive number p. Take $\beta = p + \frac{1}{3}D$. Then $L(f) \geqq \beta > \frac{1}{3}D$. By Theorem 69, f corresponds to a periodic set (g_i). Then Theorem 70 contradicts our hypothesis. Theorem 71 is equivalent to

THEOREM 72. *Any real binary quadratic form of discriminant $D^2 > 0$ whose coefficients are not proportional to integers has its lower bound $\leqq \frac{1}{3}D$.*

48. Notations, periods π_1 and π_2. We now study in detail the relations between the derived sets $R, S, \ldots, U$, where U is assumed to have all its elements equal to a_0. We denote U by (a_0). The set preceding U is denoted

---

[1] See § 47. For integral forms, the chain of reduced forms is periodic (*Introd.*, p. 104), whence (g_i) is periodic.

by $(a_0; a_1)$, where a_1 is the larger of the two values of its elements. The set before that is denoted by $(a_0; a_1; a_2)$, where a_2 is the larger of the two values of its elements. If n is the number of sets $R, \ldots, U$, we write $R = (a_0; a_1; \ldots; a_{n-1})$.

Thus $(a_0; a_1)$ is the set with the period $a_1, (a_1-1)_{a_0}$. Hence $a_0 > 0$. If $(a_0; \ldots; a_k)$ is (a_i), then $(a_0; \ldots; a_{k+1})$ is

$$\ldots, a_{k+1}, (a_{k+1}-1)_{a_i}, a_{k+1}, (a_{k+1}-1)_{a_{i+1}}, a_{k+1}, \ldots$$

When each term of the latter is written twice consecutively, we obtain a set denoted by $(a_0; \ldots; a_k : a_{k+1})$, with a final colon instead of a semicolon.

For example, $(1; 1; 3)$ has the period $2, 3, 3$, as found before (32). Then $(1; 1; 3; 2)$ has the period $2, 1_2, 2, 1_3, 2, 1_3$. Writing each term of the latter twice, we get the period $2_2, 1_4, 2_2, 1_6, 2_2, 1_6$ of $(1; 1; 3 : 2)$. By (32), the latter is the set (g_i) in (27) when $R = (1; 1; 3)$, with the period $2, 3, 3$.

All of the preceding sets are periodic. By period we shall mean least period. The period a_0 of (a_0) is denoted by both $[a_0]$ and $\{a_0\}$. For our further sets we give notations for two important periods. Write

(40) $[a_0, a_1]$ for $a_1, (a_1-1)_{a_0}$;

(41) $\{a_0, a_1\}$ for $(a_1-1)_{a_0}, a_1$.

Hence of all $a_0 + 1$ periods of $(a_0; a_1)$, we write $[a_0, a_1]$ for the period which begins with a_1, but $\{a_0, a_1\}$ for the period which ends with a_1.

We shall use induction from k to $k+1$ to define the desired two periods in general. For some $k \geq 0$, suppose we know that $a_1, \ldots, a_m$ is the period $[a_0, \ldots, a_k]$ of the set $(a_0; \ldots; a_k)$, and that $a_h, a_{h+1}, \ldots, a_{h+m-1}$ (necessarily a cyclic permutation of $a_1, \ldots, a_m$) is its period $\{a_0, \ldots, a_k\}$. We define $[a_0, \ldots, a_{k+1}]$ to be the period

(42) $a_{k+1}, (a_{k+1}-1)_{a_h}, a_{k+1}, (a_{k+1}-1)_{a_{h+1}}, \ldots, a_{k+1}, (a_{k+1}-1)_{a_{h+m-1}}$

of the set $(a_0; \ldots; a_{k+1})$, and define $\{a_0, \ldots, a_{k+1}\}$ to be its period

(43) $(a_{k+1}-1)_{a_1}, a_{k+1}, \ldots, (a_{k+1}-1)_{a_m}, a_{k+1}$.

The periods $\pi_1(k) = [a_0, \ldots, a_k]$ and $\pi_2(k) = \{a_0, \ldots, a_k\}$ of $(a_0; \ldots; a_k)$ are thus uniquely defined for every $k \geq 0$, since they were defined to be a_0 for $k = 0$. Note that (42) and (43) become (40) and (41) when $k = 0$, whence $m = h = 1$, $a_1 = a_0$.

Lemma 1. *The periods π_1 and π_2 form reverse sets.*

This is true by (40) and (41) when $k=1$. Assume it true for k, so that

$$(44) \qquad\qquad a_h = a_m, \ a_{h+1} = a_{m-1}, \ \ldots, \ a_{h+m-1} = a_1 \ .$$

Then (42) and (43) are reverse sets, and Lemma 1 holds for $k+1$.

Hence the reverse of every period is a period.

Lemma 2. *Except for the end terms, terms in π_1 or π_2 equidistant from the ends are equal.*

Assume this for k, whence

$$a_2 = a_{m-1}, \ a_3 = a_{m-2}, \ \ldots \ ; \qquad a_{h+1} = a_{h+m-2}, \ a_{h+2} = a_{h+m-3}, \ \ldots .$$

Since $\pi_1(k)$ begins with a_k and ends with $a_k - 1$, we have $a_m = a_1 - 1$. Since $\pi_2(k)$ begins with $a_k - 1$ and ends with a_k, we have $a_h = a_{h+m-1} - 1$. Lemma 2 is therefore true for $k+1$ by (42) and (43).

If $a_1, \ldots, a_m$ is the period $\pi_1(k)$ of $(a_0; \ldots ; a_k)$, then any period is of the form $a_j, a_{j+1}, \ldots, a_{j+m-1}$.

Lemma 3. *Then the first of the differences*

$$(45) \qquad\qquad a_1 - a_j, \ a_2 - a_{j+1}, \ \ldots, \ a_m - a_{j+m-1}$$

which is not zero is $+1$, and the last one not zero is -1. Also, the first of the differences

$$(46) \qquad\qquad a_m - a_j, \ a_{m-1} - a_{j-1}, \ \ldots, \ a_1 - a_{j+1-m}$$

which is not zero is -1, and the last one not zero is $+1$.

Assume this double statement for k. Then $\pi_1(k+1)$ is (42), which by (44) may be written as

$$(47) \qquad\quad a, \ (a-1)_{a_m}, \ a, \ (a-1)_{a_{m-1}}, \ \ldots, \ a, \ (a-1)_{a_1} \ ,$$

where the subscript $k+1$ has been omitted from a. To prove (45) for $k+1$, we consider the differences obtained by subtracting from (47) the successive terms of any permutation P of (47). If P begins with $a-1$, the first difference is $a - (a-1) = +1$, as desired. Next, let P be $a, (a-1)_{a_j}, \ldots$. If $a_m \neq a_j$, then $a_m = a_j - 1$ by (46), and the first $1 + a_m$ differences are zero, while the next one is $a - (a-1) = 1$. Let $a_m = a_j$, $a_{m-1} \neq a_{j-1}$, whence $a_{m-1} = a_{j-1} - 1$ by (46); then the first $1 + a_m + 1 + a_{m-1}$ differences are zero, while the next one is $a - (a-1) = 1$. In this manner we prove the first statement concerning (45) for $k+1$.

For the second part, we subtract end terms of P from those of (47). If P ends with a, the last difference is $a - 1 - a = -1$. Next, let $P = \ldots ,$

$(a-1)_{a_{j+1}}, a, (a-1)_{a_j}$. If $a_j \neq a_1$, then $a_1 = a_j + 1$ by (45), and the last a_j differences are zero, while the (a_j+1)th difference, counted from the end, is $a-1-a = -1$. Next, let $a_j = a_1$, $a_{j+1} \neq a_2$, whence $a_2 = a_{j+1} + 1$ by (45). Then the last $a_j + 1 + a_{j+1}$ differences are zero, while the preceding one is $a - 1 - a$.

The second part of Lemma 3 for $k+1$ follows from the first part just proved by using the reverse set.

In our present notations, the set (27) is $(a_0; a_1; \ldots ; a_{n-1}:2)$. This final 2 is denoted by a_n. For $1 \leq k \leq n$, let $a_1, \ldots, a_m$ be as before the period $\pi_1(k)$ of the set $(a_0; \ldots ; a_k)$; then the set $(a_0; \ldots ; a_{k-1}:a_k)$ has the period $a_1, a_1, \ldots, a_m, a_m$. Write

$$x_j = (a_j, a_j, a_{j+1}, a_{j+1}, \ldots a_{j+m-1}, a_{j+m-1}, x_j) ,$$

$$y_j = (a_{j-1}, a_{j-1}, a_{j-2}, a_{j-2}, \ldots, a_{j-m}, a_{j-m}, y_j) ,$$

in which subscripts are to be reduced to $1, \ldots, m$ by adding or subtracting m. Thus $y_1 = (a_m, a_m, a_{m-1}, a_{m-1}, \ldots, a_1, a_1, y_1)$. Denote $x_j + 1/y_j$ by M_j. We shall prove that $M_1 > M_j$ if the set $a_j, a_{j+1}, \ldots, a_{j+m-1}$ is distinct from the set $a_1, \ldots, a_m$. Then one of the differences (45) is not zero, and the first one $\neq 0$ is $+1$. Thus the partial quotients a in the continued fractions x_1 and x_j differ first in an odd place, and the larger a then occurs in x_1, whence $x_1 > x_j$.

The last difference $\neq 0$ in (45) is -1. Read those differences in reverse order. Hence the continued fractions y_1 and y_j differ first in an odd place and the larger a occurs in y_j. Thus $y_j > y_1$. Hence $M_1 > M_j$.

We next employ $N_j = \xi_j + 1/\eta_j$, $N = \xi + 1/\eta$, where

$$\xi_j = (a_j, a_{j+1}, a_{j+1}, a_{j+2}, a_{j+2}, \ldots, a_{j+m-1}, a_{j+m-1}, a_j, \xi_j) ,$$

$$\eta_j = (a_j, a_{j-1}, a_{j-1}, \ldots, a_{j-m+1}, a_{j-m+1}, a_j, \eta_j) ,$$

$$\xi = (a_1, a_m, a_m, a_{m-1}, a_{m-1}, \ldots, a_2, a_2, a_1, \xi) .$$

$$\eta = (a_1, a_2, a_2, \ldots, a_m, a_m, a_1, \eta) .$$

Then

$$x_1 = a_1 + 1/\eta , \qquad 1/y_1 = -a_1 + \xi , \qquad M_1 = N .$$

Assume that one of the differences

$$(48) \qquad a_m - a_{j+1}, a_{m-1} - a_{j+2}, \ldots, a_2 - a_{j+m-1}, a_1 - a_{j+m}$$

is not zero. The set of a's which are here subtracted is the reverse of the set subtracted in (46) and hence also forms a period. Hence the first difference $\neq 0$ in (48) is -1, and the last one $\neq 0$ is $+1$.

First, let $a_1 = a_j$. Then the a's in the continued fractions ξ and ξ_j differ first in an even place, and the larger a then occurs in ξ_j. Hence $\xi > \xi_j$. Next, η and η_j differ first in an even place and the larger a then occurs in η [as seen by reading (48) reversed]. Hence $\eta < \eta_j$, and $N > N_j$.

Second, let $a_1 \neq a_j$, whence $a_1 - 1 = a_j$. We compare $\xi - 1$ with ξ_j. The differences are zero and (48), each taken twice. Hence the continued fractions for $\xi - 1$ and ξ_j differ first in an even place and then the larger a occurs in ξ_j. Hence $\xi - 1 > \xi_j$. Evidently $1 + 1/\eta$ exceeds the proper fraction $1/\eta_j$. Hence $N > N_j$.

THEOREM 73. $M_1 = N$, and M_1 exceeds every M_j and N_j distinct from M_1.

N is a K_j since $a_m a_m \ldots a_1 a_1$ also generates the set (a_i).

In any chosen period (of length $2m$) of the set of g's there are two terms, say g_i and g_j, which give the initial terms of x_1 in M_1 and ξ in N, respectively. Thus $|i - j| < 2m$ and $i - j$ is odd. By the last theorem, K_i and K_j are equal and their common value is the maximum of all K_r. By (5) and (10), $(-1)^{i+1} A_{i+1}$ and $(-1)^{i+1} A_{j+1}$ are of opposite signs but numerically equal, and their common absolute value is the least of all $|A_r|$ for coefficients A_r in the chain of the Φ_i. This proves

Theorem 74. *To each class of real indefinite forms f of discriminant $d = D^2$, $D > 0$, such that $L(f) > \frac{1}{3} D$, corresponds a periodic set* (27) *whose period is of the type*

$$(49) \qquad 2, 2, a, a, \beta, \beta, \ldots, \beta, \beta, a, a, 1, 1 ,$$

where each a, β, $\ldots$ is 1 or 2. Every form of the class is proportional to a form with integral coefficients, whence the minimum a is a value of $|f|$. In fact, both a and $-a$ occur as first coefficients of forms Φ_i of the chain of reduced forms and are uniquely determined in a period.

For cases (1) and (2), (49) becomes 1, 1 and 2, 2, respectively.

49. Determination of the form whose first coefficient is its minimum. We are interested only in sets (g_i) of type (27). For them, $a_n = 2$, $k = n$, as noted before. We may choose the index i so that K_i is M_1. We may assume that i is even by choice between the two corresponding chains in Theorem 70. By Theorem 73, K_i is the maximum of all K_j. But $K_i = D/A_{i+1}$ by (10_1). Hence A_{i+1} is the minimum of all A_j. By definition, $M_1 = x_1 + 1/y_1$. Hence $F_i = x_1$, viz.,

$$F_i = (a_1, a_1, a_2, a_2, \ldots, a_m, a_m, F_i) ,$$

with a period of $2m$ terms. Let

$$(50) \quad P/Q = (a_1, a_1, \ldots, a_m, a_m) , \qquad P'/Q' = (a_1, a_1, \ldots, a_{m-1}, a_{m-1}, a_m)$$

denote the 2mth and $(2m-1)$th convergents (in lowest terms) to F_i. Hence

$$F_i = \frac{PF_i + P'}{QF_i + Q'}, \qquad QF_i^2 + (Q'-P)F_i - P' = 0 .$$

Thus $x + F_i y$ is a factor of the form

(51) $$Qx^2 + (P-Q')xy - P'y^2 .$$

In the maximum K_i, $a_1 = 2$. By (7), $F_{i+1} = (-1)^{i+1}/f_{i+1}$. Hence

$$F_i = (2, F_{i+1}) = 2 + (-1)^{i+1}f_{i+1}, \qquad f_{i+1} = 2 - F_i ,$$

since i is even. Hence we obtain a form G with integral coefficients having the factor $\xi - f_{i+1}\eta$ by applying to (51) the transformation

(52) $$x = \xi - 2\eta , \qquad y = \eta .$$

In view of $L(\Phi) > \frac{1}{3}D$, Φ_{i+1} is proportional to a form having integral coefficients and has the factor $\xi - f_{i+1}\eta$. Thus it is equivalent to G. Hence (52) replaces (51) by a form proportional to Φ_{i+1}. But (52) leaves the coefficient of x^2 unaltered. Hence $Q = A_{i+1}$ is the minimum of Φ_{i+1} of discriminant $(P-Q')^2 + 4P'Q$.

We saw below (6), where now $\delta_i = g_i = 2$, that $x = Y$, $y = -X + 2Y$ replaces Φ_i by Φ_{i+1}. The inverse transformation is $\xi = 2X - Y$, $\eta = X$. Hence the product of (52) by the latter replaces (51) by a form proportional to Φ_i. This product is $x = -Y$, $y = X$.

Relations between P, Q, P', Q' follow from properties of continued fractions. Let P_r/Q_r denote the rth convergent in lowest terms of $(q_1, q_2, \ldots)$, where $q_2, q_3, \ldots$ are positive integers and $q_1 \geqq 0$. Denote the polynomial P_r by $P(q_1, \ldots, q_r)$. Then

   I. $P_r = q_r P_{r-1} + P_{r-2}$, $Q_r = q_r Q_{r-1} + Q_{r-2}$ if $r \geqq 3$.
   II. $P(q_1, q_2, \ldots, q_r) = P(q_r, \ldots, q_2, q_1)$.
   III. $P(q_1, \ldots, q_r) = q_1 P(q_2, \ldots, q_r) + P(q_3, \ldots, q_r)$ if $r \geqq 3$.
   IV. $Q_r = P(q_2, \ldots, q_r)$ if $r \geqq 2$.
   V. $P_r Q_{r-1} - Q_r P_{r-1} = (-1)^r$ if $r \geqq 1$.
   VI. P_r and Q_r are relatively prime.
   VII. $P(\ldots, 1, 1) = P(\ldots, 2)$.
   VIII. If the a_i and b_j are positive integers, and $r \geqq 2$, $s \geqq 2$, then

$$P(a_r, \ldots, a_1, b_1, \ldots, b_s) = P(a_r, \ldots, a_1)P(b_1, \ldots, b_s)$$
$$+ P(a_r, \ldots, a_2)P(b_2, \ldots, b_s) .$$

Properties I–VI follow from *Introd.*,[1] pages 106–8.

To prove VIII by induction on r, assume it true for $r = 1, \ldots, k-1$, where $k \geq 3$. Then, by III and two applications of VIII,

$$
\begin{aligned}
P(a_k, \ldots, a_1, b_1, \ldots, b_s) &= a_k P(a_{k-1}, \ldots, b_s) + P(a_{k-2}, \ldots, b_s) \\
&= [a_k P(a_{k-1}, \ldots, a_1) + P(a_{k-2}, \ldots, a_1)] P(b_1, \ldots, b_s) \\
&\quad + [a_k P(a_{k-1}, \ldots, a_2) + P(a_{k-2}, \ldots, a_2)] P(b_2, \ldots, b_s) \\
&= P(a_k, \ldots, a_1) P(b_1, \ldots, b_s) + P(a_k, \ldots, a_2) P(b_2, \ldots, b_s) ,
\end{aligned}
$$

by two applications of III. Hence VIII holds for $r = k$. For $r = 2$, VIII follows by two applications of III and $P(a_1, a_2) = 1 + a_1 a_2$, $P(a) = a$.

In (50), let $a_1, a_1, \ldots, a_m, a_m$, be the period (49). Then

$$
P = P(2, 2, a, a, \ldots, a, a, 1, 1) , \quad Q = P(2, a, a, \ldots, a, a, 1, 1) ,
$$
$$
Q' = P(2, a, a, \ldots, a, a, 1) ,
$$

by IV, since Q and Q' are Q_r and Q_{r-1}. By III and VII,

$$
P = 2Q + S , \quad S = P(a, a, \ldots, a, a, 1, 1) = P(a, a, \ldots, a, a, 2) .
$$

By II, III, and II,

$$
Q = P(1, 1, a, \ldots, a, 2) = P(1, a, \ldots, a, 2) + S = Q' + S .
$$

Hence

$$
\text{(53)} \qquad\qquad P + Q' = 3Q .
$$

In our present notations, V becomes

$$
\text{(54)} \qquad\qquad PQ' - QP' = +1 .
$$

Elimination of Q' between (53) and (54) gives

$$
\text{(55)} \qquad\qquad P' = 3P - R , \qquad R = (P^2 + 1)/Q ,
$$

where R is an integer. Since (53) gives $P - Q' = 2P - 3Q$, (51) becomes

$$
\text{(56)} \qquad\qquad Qx^2 + (2P - 3Q)xy + (R - 3P)y^2 ,
$$

---

[1] By Theorem 83, $P_r = n_r$ is the numerator of both $(q_1, \ldots, q_r)$ and $(q_r, \ldots, q_1)$, and $Q_r = d_r$ is the denominator of $(q_1, \ldots, q_r)$ and the numerator of $(q_r, \ldots, q_2)$. This proves II and then IV. By I, $P(q_r, \ldots, q_1) = q_1 P(q_r, \ldots, q_2) + P(q_r, \ldots, q_3)$, which with II yields III.

whose discriminant is $d = 9Q^2 - 4$. The maximum K_i is

(57)
$$\frac{D}{A_{i+1}} = \frac{\sqrt{d}}{Q} = \sqrt{9 - \frac{4}{Q^2}} < 3.$$

Theorem 75. *For the set (27) whose period is (49), let*

(58)
$$P/Q = (2, 2, a, a, \beta, \beta, \ldots, \beta, \beta, a, a, 1, 1),$$

where each $a, \beta, \ldots$ is 1 or 2, be the convergent in its lowest terms corresponding to the period. If $d = 9Q^2 - 4$ is the discriminant of the class of corresponding quadratic forms, then the minimum is Q and each form is properly or improperly equivalent to (56), where $R = (P^2 + 1)/Q$ is an integer. Each form (56) is properly equivalent to its negative.

It remains only to prove the final statement.[1] To do this, consider the chain of forms corresponding to N (instead of M_1 as heretofore). Write F_j for ξ in $N = \xi + 1/\eta$. Then j is odd since i was even in $K_i = M_1$. Write

(59)
$$p/q = (a_1, a_m, a_m, a_{m-1}, a_{m-1}, \ldots, a_2, a_2, a_1).$$

When the final a_1 is suppressed, write p'/q' for $(a_1, \ldots, a_2)$. Then

$$F_j = \frac{pF_j + p'}{qF_j + q'}, \qquad qF_j^2 + (q' - p)F_j - p' = 0.$$

Thus $x - F_j y$ is a factor of

(60)
$$f = -qx^2 + (p - q')xy + p'y^2.$$

By (7), $F_{j+1} = 1/f_{j+1}$. In the maximum K_j, $a_1 = 2$. Hence

$$F_j = (2, F_{j+1}) = 2 + f_{j+1},$$

and we obtain a form g with integral coefficients having the factor $X - f_{j+1}Y$ by applying to f the transformation

$$x = X + 2Y, \qquad y = Y.$$

Thus g and therefore f is equivalent to a form proportional to Φ_{j+1}.

---

[1] Shorter proof. By Lemma 1, the infinite set (a_i) is its own reverse. Hence $(a_0; a_1; \ldots : a_n)$ has the form $\ldots g''g'ggg'g'' \ldots$.

Let $a_1, a_1, \ldots, a_m$ be the period (49). From its reverse, we get

$$p = P(2, 1, 1, a, a, \ldots, a, a, 2), \quad q = P(1, 1, a, \ldots, a, 2),$$

$$q' = P(1, 1, a, a, \ldots, a, a) .$$

By II, $q = Q$. By III and two applications of II,

$$p = 2P(1, 1, a, \ldots, a, 2) + P(1, a, \ldots, a, 2) = 2Q + Q' .$$

By II, VII, and the result preceding (53),

$$q' = P(a, a, \ldots, a, a, 2) = S = Q - Q' .$$

Hence $p + q' = 3Q = 3q$, $p - q' = Q + 2Q' = 7Q - 2P$, by (53). By V, $pq' - qp' = +1$. Hence the discriminant of (60) is

$$(p - q')^2 + 4(pq' - 1) = (p + q')^2 - 4 = 9Q^2 - 4 .$$

Thus (60) becomes

$$-Qx^2 + (7Q - 2P)xy + Ty^2 .$$

whose discriminant determines T. The transformation $x = X + 2Y$, $y = Y$ replaces this form by $-QX^2 + (3Q - 2P)XY + \tau Y^2$, whose discriminant is $9Q^2 - 4$ and determines τ. We obtain the negative of (56). This completes the proof of Theorem 75.

50. Markoff numbers. The numbers Q which give the minima of the forms (56), together with 1 and 2, are called *Markoff numbers*. There is one corresponding to every class of forms f of discriminant $D^2 > 0$ for which $L(f) > \frac{1}{3}D$, since every such f is equivalent (by Theorem 75) to a form proportional to (56).

Any set (27) satisfying conditions (28) and (29) has every $K_j \leqq 3$ and therefore yields a value of Q. By means of its derived sets, we saw that to any such set (27) corresponds a unique set of ordered, positive, integers $a_0, \ldots, a_{n-1}$.

Conversely, to every set of n ordered, positive integers $a_0, \ldots, a_{n-1}$ corresponds a set (27) and hence a Markoff number denoted by $Q(a_0, \ldots, a_{n-1}, 2)$. To calculate it, construct as in § 48 the set (27), of terms 1 and 2, denoted by $(a_0; \ldots; a_{n-1}:2)$. Let its period π_1 be (49). Then Q is the denominator of (58). For example, [1, 2] is 2, 1, whence [1:2] is 2, 2, 1, 1, in the notation before (66), and $Q(1, 2)$ is $P(2, 1, 1) = 5$.

We shall prove that every Markoff number is one of a triple of positive, integral solutions of

(61) $$x^2+y^2+z^2=3xyz ,$$

while conversely each number of such a triple of solutions of (61) is a Markoff number.

We extend the definition of our symbols to the new case $a_0=0$ to mean the like symbols with a_0 suppressed. For example, $[0, a_1]$ shall mean $[a_1]$. Also we write

(62) $$Q(1)=1 , \qquad Q(2)=Q(0, 2)=2 .$$

These correspond to sets (1_∞) and (2_∞) and hence to forms (1) and (2).

THEOREM 76. *If* n, a_0+1, a_1, ..., a_n *are positive integers and*

(63) $$Q_1=Q(a_0, \ldots, a_n) , \qquad Q_2=Q(a_1-1, a_2, \ldots, a_n) ,$$
$$Q_3=Q(a_0+1, a_1, \ldots, a_n) ,$$

where Q_2 *shall mean* $Q(a_1-1)$ *if* $n=1$, *then for* $a_n=2$,

(64) $$Q_1^2+Q_2^2+Q_3^2=3Q_1Q_2Q_3 .$$

Consider the sets

$$S_1=(a_0; \ldots ; a_n) , \quad S_2=(a_1-1; a_2; \ldots ; a_n) , \quad S_3=(a_0+1; a_1; \ldots ; a_n) ,$$

where for $n=1$, S_2 shall mean (a_1-1). We shall prove that their periods $\pi=[a_0, \ldots, a_n]$, $\rho=[a_1-1, a_2, \ldots, a_n]$, and $\sigma=[a_0+1, a_1, \ldots, a_n]$ are such that σ is obtained by juxtaposing π and ρ. More exactly, if $\pi+\rho$ denotes the result of writing the terms of ρ after those of π, then

(65) $$\sigma=\pi+\rho \text{ (for } n \text{ odd)}, \quad \sigma=\rho+\pi \text{ (for } n \text{ even) .}$$

We shall prove (65) by induction on n. If $n=1$, then $\sigma=[a_0+1, a_1]$ is a_1, $(a_1-1)_{a_0+1}$ by (40) and is $[a_0, a_1]$, $a_1-1=\rho$, and therefore is $\pi+\rho$. Assume (65) when $n=m$, m odd. Then let $b_1, \ldots, b_i$ and $c_1, \ldots, c_j$ denote the elements of π and ρ, respectively. Write a for a_{m+1}. By assumption, $[a_0+1, a_1, \ldots, a_m]$ is $b_1, \ldots, b_i, c_1, \ldots, c_j$. By its definition in (42), $[a_0+1, a_1, \ldots, a_m, a]$ is

$$a, (a-1)_{c_j}, a, \ldots, (a-1)_{c_1}; a, (a-1)_{b_i}, a, \ldots, (a-1)_{b_1} .$$

The part preceding the semicolon is $[a_1-1, a_2, \ldots, a_m, a]$ and the part following it is $[a_0, a_1, \ldots, a_m, a]$. Hence $\sigma=\rho+\pi$ when $n=m+1$.

Assume (65) when $n = m$, m even. In the preceding discussion we interchange letters b and c and i and j and find that $\sigma = \pi + \rho$ when $n = m+1$.

In particular, let $a_n = 2$. Let $[a_0, \ldots, a_n : 2]$ denote the period obtained by writing each term of $[a_0, \ldots, a_n, 2]$ twice consecutively. Then (65) shows that the periods

(66) $[a_0, \ldots, a_{n-1} : 2]$; $[a_1 - 1, a_2, \ldots, a_n : 2]$; $[a_0 + 1, \ldots : 2]$.

are of the types

(67) $2, 2, a, \ldots, a, 1, 1$; $2, 2, \beta, \ldots, \beta, 1, 1$;

       $2, 2, a, \ldots, a, 1, 1, 2, 2, \beta, \ldots, \beta, 1, 1$ or

       $2, 2, \beta, \ldots, \beta, 1, 1, 2, 2, a, \ldots, a, 1, 1$,

according as n is odd or even. Let

(68) $(2, 2, a, \ldots, a, 1, 1,)$; $(2, 2, \beta, \ldots, \beta, 1, 1)$;

       $(2, 2, a, \ldots, a, 1, 1, 2, 2, \beta, \ldots, \beta, 1, 1)$

denote the continued fractions whose partial quotients are the sets (67) for the first[1] alternative. For $i = 1, 2, 3$, let P_i/Q_i denote their ultimate convergents (i.e., the fractions themselves), and P_i'/Q_i' designate their penultimate convergents, each in its lowest terms. Then the Q_i have the values (63). By V and VIII,

$$P_i Q_i' - P_i' Q_i = +1 \qquad (i = 1, 2, 3) ,$$
$$P_3 = P_1 P_2 + P_1' Q_2 , \qquad P_3' = P_1 P_2' + P_1' Q_2' ,$$
$$Q_3 = Q_1 P_2 + Q_1' Q_2 , \qquad Q_3' = Q_1 P_2' + Q_1' Q_2' .$$

By (53), $P_i + Q_i' = 3 Q_i$ $(i = 1, 2, 3)$. Hence

$$P_i' Q_i + P_i^2 + 1 = P_i (P_i + Q_i') = 3 P_i Q_i ,$$
$$3 Q_1 Q_2 Q_3 = 3 Q_1 Q_2 (Q_1 P_2 + Q_1' Q_2) = Q_1^2 (P_2' Q_2 + P_2^2 + 1) + Q_2^2 Q_1' (P_1 + Q_1')$$
$$= Q_1^2 + (Q_1 P_2 + Q_2 Q_1')^2 + Q_2 [P_2' Q_1^2 + Q_2 Q_1' P_1 - 2 Q_1 P_2 Q_1']$$
$$= Q_1^2 + Q_3^2 + Q_2^2 + a Q_1 Q_2 ,$$
$$a = P_2' Q_1 + Q_2 P_1' - 2 P_2 Q_1'$$
$$= (P_2' Q_1 + Q_1' Q_2') + (P_1 P_2 + P_1' Q_2) - Q_1' (P_2 + Q_2') - P_2 (P_1 + Q_1')$$
$$= Q_3' + P_3 - 3 Q_1' Q_2 - 3 P_2 Q_1 = Q_3' + P_3 - 3 Q_3 = 0 .$$

This completes the proof of Theorem 76. We shall now prove the converse:

[1] For the second alternative the proof is similar.

THEOREM 77. *Every number in a triple of positive, integral solutions of* (61) *is a Markoff number.*

We require three lemmas and a theorem.

LEMMA 4. *The only integral solutions of* (61) *with* $x = y > 0$ *are*

$$(69) \qquad (x, y, z) = (1, 1, 1) \text{ or } (1, 1, 2) .$$

For $x = y$, (61) implies $2x^2 + z^2 = 3x^2 z$, $z = lx$, $2 + l^2 = 3lx$, $(2l - 3x)^2 = 9x^2 - 8$. Thus $9x^2 - 8 = u^2$, where u is an integer > 0. Since $3x + u$ and $3x - u$ have the product 8 and difference $2u$, they are 4 and 2, whence $u = 1$, $x = 1$. Thus $l = 1$ or 2.

LEMMA 5. *We have the inequalities*

$$(70) \qquad Q(a_0 + 1, a_1, \ldots, a_{n-1}, 2) > Q(a_0, a_1, \ldots, a_{n-1}, 2) ,$$

$$(71) \qquad Q(a_0, \ldots, a_{n-1}, 2) > Q(a_1, a_2, \ldots, a_{n-1}, 2) \text{ if } a_0 > 0 .$$

These follow from $Q_3 = Q_1 P_2 + Q_1' Q_2$ above. We give another proof. The period $[a_0 + 1, a_1, \ldots, a_{n-1} : 2]$ contains the same set of quotients as $[a_0, \ldots, a_{n-1} : 2]$ in the same order, but with further numbers 1 and 2 interspersed among them. Evidently P and Q for the former period exceed P and Q respectively for the latter period in view of I in § 49.

From (70) with a_0 replaced by $a_0 - 1$, $a_0 - 2$, $\ldots$, we get (71).

LEMMA 6. *If* n, $a_0 + 1$, a_1, $\ldots$, a_n *are positive integers, and* $a_n = 2$, *then*

$$(72) \quad Q(a_0 + 2, a_1, \ldots, a_n) + Q(a_0, \ldots, a_n)$$
$$= 3Q(a_1 - 1, a_2, \ldots, a_n) Q(a_0 + 1, a_1, \ldots, a_n) ,$$

$$(73) \quad Q(1, a_0 + 1, a_1, \ldots, a_n) + Q(a_1 - 1, a_2, \ldots, a_n)$$
$$= 3Q(a_0, \ldots, a_n) Q(a_0 + 1, a_1, \ldots, a_n) .$$

In (64) for the values (63), take $a_0 = 0$, replace n by $n + 1$, a_1 by $a_0 + 1$, a_i by a_{i-1} for $i = 2, \ldots, n + 1$; we get

$$(74) \quad Q^2(a_0 + 1, a_1, \ldots, a_n) + Q^2(a_0, a_1, \ldots, a_n) + Q^2(1, a_0 + 1, a_1, \ldots, a_n)$$
$$= 3QQQ.$$

Subtract (64) from this. Also subtract (64) from the result obtained by replacing a_0 by $a_0 + 1$ in (64). In the respective cases, the common factors

$$Q(1, a_0 + 1, a_1, \ldots, a_n) - Q(a_1 - 1, a_2, \ldots, a_n)$$
$$Q(a_0 + 2, a_1, \ldots, a_n) - Q(a_0, a_1, \ldots, a_n)$$

may be cancelled since they are not zero by (70) and (71). We obtain (73) and (72), respectively.

The latter serve as recursion formulas to compute all $Q(a_0, \ldots, a_n)$ in terms of $Q(1, 2) = 5$ and (62). When $n = 1$, we agree to interpret $Q(a_1 - 1, a_2, \ldots, a_n)$ as 1; then (72) becomes

$$(75) \qquad Q(a+2, 2) = 3Q(a+1, 2) - Q(a, 2) .$$

This gives $Q(2, 2) = 3 \cdot 5 - 2 = 13$, $Q(3, 2) = 34$, $Q(4, 2) = 89$, $Q(5, 2) = 233$, $Q(6, 2) = 610$. Next, (73) for $n = 1$ is

$$(76) \qquad Q(1, a+1, 2) = 3Q(a, 2)Q(a+1, 2) - 1 ,$$

which gives $Q(1, 1, 2) = 29$, $Q(1, 2, 2) = 194$. Then (73) for $n = 2$ gives $Q(1, 1, 1, 2) = 3 \cdot 5 \cdot 29 - 2 = 433$. By (72) with $n = 2$, $a_0 = 0$ or 1, $a_1 = 1$, gives $Q(2, 1, 2) = 169$, $Q(3, 1, 2) = 985$. We see that all further $Q(a_0, \ldots, a_n)$ exceed 1000.

By (63) these lie in the following triples of solutions of (64):

$$(77) \quad \left\{ \begin{array}{c} (1, 2, 5) , \quad (1, 5, 13) , \quad (2, 5, 29) , \quad (1, 13, 34) , \quad (1, 34, 89) , \\ (2, 29, 169) , \quad (5, 13, 194) , \quad (1, 89, 233) , \quad (5, 29, 433) , \\ (1, 233, 610) , \qquad (2, 169, 985) \end{array} \right.$$

These may be found more simply by the next theorem.

THEOREM 78. *Any integral solution (a, b, c) of (61) with $c \geqq a \geqq 1$, $c \geqq b \geqq 1$, generates two new solutions*

$$(a, c, b') , \quad b' = 3ac - b > c ; \quad (b, c, a') , \quad a' = 3bc - a > c ,$$

which are distinct unless $a = b$. Repetitions of this generating process, starting with $(1, 1, 1)$, will yield all sets of solutions of (61) in positive integers. The numbers forming a set are relatively prime in pairs.

We see that $(1, 1, 1)$ generates only $(1, 1, 2)$, which generates only $(1, 2, 5)$. The latter generates $(1, 5, 13)$ and $(2, 5, 29)$. A few repetitions give all the triples (77), but no further ones with each entry < 1000.

Let (x, y, z) be any solution of (61) in positive integers. Except for the special solutions (69), we may assume that $x < y < z$. For $t = 3xy - z$, (x, y, t) is a solution of (61), whence $3xyt > 0$, $t > 0$. Then z and t are roots of

$$f(w) \equiv w^2 - 3xyw + x^2 + y^2 = 0 .$$

Since $f(y) < 3y^2 - 3xy^2 \leqq 0$, y lies between the roots z and t, whence $t < y < z$. Hence (x, y, z) yields a solution (x, t, y) in smaller positive integers. But (x, t, y) generates $(x, y, 3xy-t=z)$.

If x, y, z have a common factor $d > 1$, then x, y, t have the factor d, etc., until we reach $1, 2, 5$.

THEOREM 79. *Except* $(1, 1, 1)$ *and* $(1, 1, 2)$, *every triple of positive integral solutions of* (61) *is of type* (63) *with* $a_n = 2$.

We employ the generating process in Theorem 78 starting with $(1, 2, 5)$, which is the case $a = 0$ of

$$(1, \quad Q(a, 2), \quad Q(a+1, 2)) .$$

By (75) and (76), this generates the two triples

$$(1, Q(a+1, 2), \quad 3Q(a+1, 2) - Q(a, 2) = Q(a+2, 2)) ,$$

$$(Q(a, 2), \quad Q(a+1, 2), \quad 3Q(a, 2)Q(a+1, 2) - 1 = Q(1, a+1, 2)) .$$

The former is of the type from which we started. Hence it remains only to start with a triple of the latter type, which is the case $n = 2$, $a_0 = 0$, $a_1 = a+1$, $a_2 = 2$ of (63).

Hence we start with (63) with $n \geqq 2$, $a_n = 2$. Using (72) and (73), we see that it generates

$$(Q_1, Q_3, Q(1, a_0+1, a_1, \ldots, a_n)) ,$$

$$(Q_2, Q_3, Q(a_0+2, a_1, \ldots, a_n)) .$$

The latter is derived from (63) by replacing a_0 by a_0+1. The former is derived from (63) just as we obtained (74).

As a corollary, we have Theorem 77.

51. The main theorem. The calculation of the forms (56) is now simple. We employ (68) and the notations and formulas following it. Thus $P = P_3$, $Q = Q_3$. We have

$$Q_2 + Q_1 P_3 = Q_2 + Q_1(P_1 P_2 + P_1' Q_2) = Q_2(1 + Q_1 P_1') + Q_1 P_1 P_2$$
$$= Q_2 P_1 Q_1' + Q_1 P_1 P_2 = P_1 Q_3 .$$

But Q_3 is prime to Q_1 and Q_2 by Theorem 78. Hence in (56),

$$(78) \qquad P \equiv -\frac{Q_2}{Q_1} \equiv \frac{Q_1}{Q_2} \pmod{Q} , \qquad Q^2 + Q_1^2 + Q_2^2 = 3QQ_1Q_3 .$$

By (53) and a preceding result, $2Q < P < 3Q$. Hence P is uniquely determined by Q, Q_1, Q_2.

Write p for $P - 2Q$ and replace x by $x - 2y$. Then (56) becomes $Qx^2 + (2p - 3Q)xy + \ldots$, $0 < p < Q$. If $p > \frac{1}{2}Q$, write $\pi = Q - p$, change the sign of the middle term, and replace x by $x - 2y$; we get (79). If $p < \frac{1}{2}Q$, write $\pi = p$.

Theorem 80. *If the lower bound of an indefinite form f of discriminant D^2 exceeds $\frac{1}{3}D$, then f is properly or improperly equivalent to a form proportional to*

$$(79) \qquad Qx^2 + (2\pi - 3Q)xy + (\rho - 3\pi)y^2 , \qquad \rho Q = 1 + \pi^2 ,$$

where Q, π, ρ are positive[1] integers and $\pi \leqq \frac{1}{2}Q$. With Q are associated positive integers u and v such that

$$Q^2 + u^2 + v^2 = 3Quv , \qquad Q > u \geqq v .$$

Then $\pm \pi$ is the absolutely least residue of u/v modulo Q.

By (77) the following list is complete for $Q < 1000$:

Q	2	5	13	29	34	89	169	194	233	433	610	985
π	1	2	5	12	13	34	70	75	89	179	233	408
ρ	1	1	2	5	5	13	29	29	34	74	89	169

The triples continuing (77) are (13, 34, 1325), (1, 610, 1597), (5, 194, 2897), (1, 1597, 4181), (2, 985, 5741), (5, 433, 6466), (13, 194, 7561), (34, 89, 9077). Hence

Q	1325	1597	2897	4181	5741	6466	7561	9077
π	507	610	1120	1597	2378	2673	2923	3468

52. New notations. For an application to ternary forms we shall need a different formula for our quadratic form.

In (59), $a_1 = 2$, $a_m = 1$. Hence $p/q < (2, 1, 2) = 8/3$, $p/q \geqq (2, 2) = 5/2$, with equality if the period is 2_∞. We employ the negative of (60) with the middle coefficient changed in sign. Write $r - 3q'$ for $-p'$, and eliminate $p = 3q - q'$. We get

$$[q, 3q - 2q' , r - 3q'] , \qquad 1 = pq' - qp' = qr - q'^2 .$$

---

[1] With one exception. For $Q = \rho = 1$, $\pi = 0$, (79) is $x^2 - 3xy + y^2$ and becomes (1) when x is replaced by $x + 2y$.

Also, $q < 3q'$, $q \geqq 2q'$. We now write p for q, drop the accent from q', and obtain

$$(80) \qquad \phi(x,\, y) = px^2 + (3p - 2q)xy + (r - 3q)y^2 \, ,$$

$$(81) \qquad pr = 1 + q^2 \, , \qquad p < 3q \, , \qquad p \geqq 2q \, .$$

Here p, q, r are positive integers. We exclude the case $p = 2$, $q = r = 1$, which gives the form (2). Then $p > 2q$. Then (81) give

$$(82) \qquad 2r \leqq q < 3r \, .$$

The minimum of ϕ is p. But $\phi(0,\, 1) < 0$; hence

$$(83) \qquad 3q - r \geqq p.$$

Next, $\phi(5,\, -2) = 4r - 5p + 8q$. If it were $\geqq 0$ and hence $\geqq p$, then $4q + 2r \geqq 3p > 6q$, $2r \geqq 2q$, contrary to (82$_1$). Hence

$$(84) \qquad p \geqq 2q + r \, .$$

Conditions (82)–(84) imply inequalities (81) and that ϕ is reduced.

CHAPTER VIII

MINIMA OF INDEFINITE, TERNARY, QUADRATIC FORMS

53. Summary. Markoff[1] obtained the first three minima, but made the serious error[2] indicated in § 62. This error is avoided in the present new proof, which is so arranged that we first obtain a short proof of the first minimum and then obtain not only the first three minima, but also the fourth minimum. This proof employs only the first three minima of indefinite, binary, quadratic forms, which were found by a short, elementary proof in *Introd.*, Chap. XI, but are of course included in the elaborate theory of the preceding Chap. VII.

The latter theory is presupposed in the supplementary discussion (§ 64), which proceeds below the fourth minimum as far as is possible by known methods.

Finally the theory is extended to forms which do not attain their lower bounds. This new investigation was made by A. Oppenheim, who also aided materially in the revision of Markoff's proof.

54. Associated binary form. Let d be the determinant of

$$(85) \qquad F = ax^2 + by^2 + cz^2 + 2ryz + 2sxz + 2txy \ .$$

Let B, C, R denote the cofactors of b, c, r in d:

$$(86) \qquad B = ac - s^2 \ , \qquad C = ab - t^2 \ , \qquad R = st - ar \ .$$

In § 7, we gave the identity

$$(87) \qquad aF - (ax + ty + sz)^2 = f = Cy^2 - 2Ryz + Bz^2 \ .$$

We call f the binary form *associated* with F.

THEOREM 81. *Let T be any transformation which expresses y and z as linear functions of y_1 and z_1. If T replaces f by f_1 and F by F_1, then f_1 is associated with F_1. In particular, F is equivalent to a form whose associated form is any assigned binary form equivalent to f.*

---

[1] *Math. Annalen*, LVI (1903), 233–51.

[2] Reproduced by Bachmann, *Arith. quad. Formen*, II (1923), 529. His objections (footnotes to pp. 530–31) to other parts of Markoff's proof are obviously without point.

Let $F_1 = a_1x_1^2 + \ldots + 2t_1x_1y_1$, where $x_1 = x$, $a_1 = a$. Differentiation of $F = F_1$ with respect to x gives $ty + sz = t_1y_1 + s_1z_1$. Hence T replaces (87) by the like identity in which all letters have the subscript 1. Hence f_1 is associated with F_1. To prove the last part of the theorem, let the coefficients of T be integers of determinant unity.

A theorem on determinants gives $R^2 - BC = -ad$. Hence the discriminant of f is $-4ad$, and

$$(88) \qquad Cf = (Cy - Rz)^2 + adz^2 .$$

THEOREM 82. *F has the same associated form as the form F' derived from F by any transformation of type*

$$(89) \qquad x = x' + uy' + vz' , \qquad y = y' , \qquad z = z' .$$

Give to F' the notation (85) in accented letters. Differentiation of $F = F'$ with respect to x gives

$$ax + ty + sz = a'x' + t'y' + s'z' .$$

Since $a' = a$, the theorem follows by applying transformation (89) to (87).

55. Theorem 83. *If a real, indefinite, ternary, quadratic form ϕ of determinant d has a minimum m, then $m^3 \leqq \frac{2}{3} |d|$.*

This will follow if proved for $\phi / \sqrt[3]{d}$, of determinant 1.

Let $|a|$ be the minimum of an indefinite form g of determinant unity which represents a. We exclude the case $a = 0$ since the theorem then requires no proof. By Theorem 81, g is equivalent to a form F with the notation (85) such that $f = [C, -2R, B]$ in (87) has the discriminant $-4a$ and is reduced (or is any chosen form of its class).

The case $a > 0$. By (88) with $d = 1$, Cf is a positive binary form. Since F is indefinite, (87) shows that C is negative. But (85) is unaltered if we interchange y and z, b and c, s and t, whence B and C are interchanged. Hence also B is negative. Let F become Y when $y = 0$, and become Z when $z = 0$. These forms

$$(90) \qquad Y = ax^2 + 2sxz + cz^2 , \qquad Z = ax^2 + 2txy + by^2$$

have the positive discriminants $-4B$ and $-4C$, respectively, and hence are indefinite. Any number represented by Y is represented by F and hence is $\geqq a$, since a is the minimum of F. Since Y represents a, a is the minimum of Y, and similarly of Z. Hence the forms

$$(91) \qquad Y / \sqrt{-4B} , \qquad Z / \sqrt{-4C}$$

of discriminant 1 have the respective minima

$$(92) \qquad a/\sqrt{-4B} , \qquad a/\sqrt{-4C} .$$

First, let both numbers (92) be $< \sqrt{1/8}$. By Theorem 62, each is $\leqq 5/\sqrt{221}$, whence $a^2 \leqq (25/221)\sqrt{16BC}$. Since $-f$ is a reduced, positive, binary form, it is known that $CB \leqq \frac{4}{3}a$. Hence

$$a^3 \leqq \frac{64}{3}\left(\frac{25}{221}\right)^2 < \frac{2}{7} .$$

Hence the theorem is true in this case.

Second, let at least one of the numbers (92) be $\geqq \sqrt{1/8}$. By Theorem 62, the corresponding form (91) is equivalent to $\sqrt{1/5}\, u$ or $\sqrt{1/8}\, v$, where

$$u = x^2 + xy - y^2 , \qquad v = x^2 + 2xy - y^2 .$$

The minimum (92) is therefore $\sqrt{1/5}$ or $\sqrt{1/8}$. Hence Y (or Z) is equivalent to au or av, each of which has the term $-ay^2$. Thus $-a$ is represented properly by Y(or Z) and hence by F. This case therefore falls under the next one.

The case $a < 0$. Since the discriminant of f is $-4a > 0$, f is indefinite. Since f may be chosen as any form of its class, and hence as any one of its chain of reduced forms (5), we may take f to be $\Phi_{2j} = A_{2j}y^2 + B_{2j}yz - A_{2j+1}z^2$, where the A's are all positive and j is any assigned integer. Thus

$$C = A_{2j} > 0 , \qquad B = -A_{2j+1} < 0 .$$

We use the notations (9). Then

$$K_i = F_i + S_i = 2\sqrt{-a}/A_{i+1} .$$

Hence

$$(93) \qquad K_{2j-1} = 2\sqrt{-a}/C , \qquad K_{2j} = -2\sqrt{-a}/B .$$

Consider the forms (90). The minimum of $-Z$ is $-a$ and its discriminant is $-4C$, whence $-Z$ is a positive form. Hence (*Introd.*), $-a \leqq \sqrt{4C/3}$, and by (93_1),

$$(94) \qquad K_{2j-1}^2 \leqq \frac{-64}{9a^3} .$$

Let M_j denote the minimum of the negative of the first form (91):

$$(95) \qquad M_j = -a/\sqrt{-4B} .$$

Elimination of B by means of (93_2) gives

$$(96) \qquad -a^3 K_{2i}^2 = 64 M_j^4 , \qquad M_j \leq \sqrt{1/5} ,$$

where the inequality follows from Theorem 62.

To this point our proof applies also to the more general Theorem 84. In completing the simpler proof of our present Theorem 83, we may evidently take

$$(97) \qquad -a^3 > \tfrac{2}{3} .$$

This with (96) gives

$$(98) \qquad K_{2i} < \tfrac{4}{5}\sqrt{6} , \qquad K_{2i}^2 < 96/25 , \qquad K_{2i} < 2 .$$

But $g_{2i} < F_{2i} < K_{2i} < 2$, *whence every* $g_{2i} = 1$. By (94) and (97),

$$(99) \qquad K_{2j-1}^2 < 32/3 .$$

When $g = g_{2j-2} \leq 2$, $1/S_{2j-1} = (g, \ldots) < g+1 < 3$. When $h = g_{2j} \leq 2$,

$$F_{2j-1} = (g_{2j-1}, h, \ldots) > g_{2j-1} + \tfrac{1}{3} , \qquad K_{2j-1} > g_{2j-1} + \tfrac{2}{3} .$$

But if $g_{2j-1} \geq 3$, then $K_{2j-1} > 11/3$, contrary to (99). *Hence every* $g_{2j-1} \leq 2$.

Suppose that $M_i < \sqrt{1/5}$ for a certain i. By Theorem 62, $M_i \leq \sqrt{1/8}$. Then (96) and (97) give $K_{2i}^2 < \tfrac{3}{2}$. But for $t = g_{2i+1}$,

$$F_{2i} = (1, t, 1, \ldots) > (1, t, 1) \geq (1, 2, 1) = \tfrac{4}{3} ,$$

while $1/S_{2i} = (g_{2i-1}, \ldots) < 3$, whence $K_{2i} > 5/3$, a contradiction. Hence every $M_j = \sqrt{1/5}$. By (96), the K_{2j} are all equal.

In the following proof we omit the subscripts on S_{2i-1}, g_{2i-1}, and F_{2i}.

$$S_{2i} = (0, g, g_{2i-2}, \ldots) = 1/(g, 1/S) , \qquad K_{2i} = F + 1/(g+S) ;$$
$$\sigma \equiv g_{2i-2} + S_{2i-2} = (g_{2i-2}, g_{2i-3}, \ldots) = 1/S ,$$
$$K_{2i-2} = F_{2i-2} + S_{2i-2} = \sigma + (0, g, F) = \frac{1}{S} + \frac{F}{gF+1} .$$

We shall now prove that

(100) $$\frac{gF+1}{gS^{-1}+1} \cdot K_{2i-2} = K_{2i} .$$

Replace the second factor by the preceding sum. Hence the product is

$$\frac{gF+1}{g+S} + \frac{FS}{g+S} = F + \frac{1}{g+S} = K_{2i} .$$

But $K_{2i-2} = K_{2i}$. Hence (100) gives

(101) $$F = S^{-1} , \qquad (g_{2i}, g_{2i+1}, \ldots) = (g_{2i-2}, g_{2i-3}, \ldots) .$$

Since g_{2i} is uniquely determined as the greatest integer $\leqq F$, etc., we have

(102) $$g_{2i} = g_{2i-2}, \qquad g_{2i+1} = g_{2i-3} \qquad \text{for every } i .$$

In the second equation, the subscripts differ by 4. Hence every g_{4j+1} is equal to $g_1 = g$, every g_{4j+3} is equal to $g_3 = h$. Since every $g_{2j} = 1$, F_0 is the periodic continued fraction $F_0 = (\overset{*}{1}, g, 1, \overset{*}{h})$. Here g and h have only the values 1 or 2.

If $g = h = 1$, $F_0 = (1, F_0)$, $F^2 - F - 1 = 0$, $F_0 = \frac{1}{2}(\sqrt{5}+1)$, $S_0 = (0, F_0) = \frac{1}{2}(\sqrt{5}-1)$, $K_0 = \sqrt{5} > 2$, contrary to (98).

If $g = h = 2$, $F_1 = (\overset{**}{21}) = (2, 1, F_1)$, $F_1^2 - 2F_1 - 2 = 0$, $F_1 = \sqrt{3}+1$, $S_1 = (0, \overset{*}{1}, \overset{*}{2})$, $1/S_1 = (1, 2, 1/S_1)$, $S_1^2 + 2S_1 - 2 = 0$, $S_1 = \sqrt{3}-1$, $K_1 = 2\sqrt{3}$, contrary to (99).

If $g = 1$, $h = 2$, $F \equiv F_0 = (1, 1, 1, 2, F) = \frac{8F+3}{5F+2}$, $5F^2 - 6F - 3 = 0$, $F_0 = \frac{1}{5}(\sqrt{24}+3)$, $K_0 = \frac{2}{5}\sqrt{24}$. Then $-a^3 = 2/3$ by (96), contrary to (98).

If $g = 2$, $h = 1$, $F_2 = (\overset{*}{1}, 1, 1, \overset{*}{2})$ plays the rôle of F_0 in the last case. This completes the proof of Theorem 83.

56. Theorem 84. *The indefinite forms of determinant d:*

$$f_1 = -\sqrt[3]{\tfrac{2}{3}d}(x^2+xy+y^2-2z^2) , \qquad f_2 = \sqrt[3]{\tfrac{2}{5}d}(x^2+xy-y^2-2z^2) ,$$

$$f_3 = -\sqrt[3]{\tfrac{1}{3}d}(x^2+y^2-3z^2) , \qquad f_4 = -\sqrt[3]{\tfrac{1}{25}d}(2x^2+2xy-2y^2+5z^2)$$

have the respective minima $m_1, \ldots, m_4$, whose cubes are the products of $|d|$ by $2/3$, $2/5$, $1/3$, $8/25$, respectively. If a real, indefinite, ternary, quadratic form has a minimum m and has the determinant d, and is not equivalent to *one of $f_1, \ldots, f_{k-1}$, then $m \leqq m_k$ for $k = 2, 3, 4$. If not equivalent to one of $f_1, \ldots, f_4$, then $m < m_4$.*

It suffices to take $d = 1$. We may employ the proof of Theorem 83 as far as (97), which is now replaced by

$$(103) \qquad\qquad -a^3 > 8/25 \ .$$

This with (96) gives

$$(104) \qquad\qquad K_{2j} < \sqrt{8} \ , \qquad K_{2j} < 2.8285 \ .$$

Hence every $g_{2j} \leqq 2$. By (94) and (97),

$$(105) \qquad\qquad K_{2j-1} < \tfrac{5}{3}\sqrt{8} \ , \qquad K_{2j-1} < 4.7141 \ .$$

As below (99), every $g_{2j-1} \leqq 4$. Suppose that $g_{2j-1} = 4$ for a certain j. If also $g_{2j} = 1$, then $F_{2j-1} > (4, 1, 1) = 4\tfrac{1}{2}$, while $S_{2j-1} > \tfrac{1}{3}$, as below (99), whence $K_{2j-1} > 4.8$, contrary to (105). Hence $g_{2j} = 2$. Similarly, if $g_{2j-2} = 1$, then $1/S_{2j-1} = (1, \ldots) < 2$, $F_{2j-1} > (4, 2, 1) = 4\tfrac{1}{3}$, $K_{2j-1} > 4.8$. Hence $g_{2j-2} = 2$. Thus

$$1/S_{2j-1} < (2, g_{2j-3}, 3) \leqq (2, 1, 3) = 11/4 \ ,$$
$$F_{2j-1} > (4, 2, g_{2j+1}, 3) > (4, 2, 1, 3) = \tfrac{48}{11} \ , \qquad K_{2j-1} > \tfrac{52}{11} > 4.72 \ ,$$

contrary to (105). *Hence every $g_{2j-1} \leqq 3$.*

By Theorem 62, $M_j = \sqrt{1/5}$, $\sqrt{1/8}$ or $\leqq \sqrt{25/221}$. These radicals are in descending order of magnitude. Except in the two cases

$$(106) \qquad\qquad \text{Every } M_j = \sqrt{1/5} \ ,$$

$$(107) \qquad\qquad \text{Every } M_j \leqq \sqrt{1/8} \ ,$$

at least one M_j is $\leqq \sqrt{1/8}$ and at least one is $\sqrt{1/5}$. If two or more consecutive M's are $\sqrt{1/5}$, we have (108) or (109) for a certain i:

$$(108) \qquad\qquad M_{i-1} \leqq \sqrt{1/8} \ , \qquad M_i = M_{i+1} = \sqrt{1/5} \ ;$$
$$(109) \qquad\qquad M_{i-1} = M_i = \sqrt{1/5} \ , \qquad M_{i+1} \leqq \sqrt{1/8} \ .$$

In the contrary case there is an i for which

$$(110) \qquad M_{i-1} \leqq \sqrt{1/8} \ , \qquad M_i = \sqrt{1/5} \ , \qquad M_{i+1} \leqq \sqrt{1/8} \ .$$

We mark by accents the cases in which each $\leqq$ is $<$.

57. Case (109′): $M_{i-1} = M_i = \sqrt{1/5}$, $M_{i+1} \leq \sqrt{25/221}$. By (96) for $j = i-1, i, i+1$, we have

$$(111) \qquad K_{2i-2} = K_{2i}, \qquad K_{2i} = \frac{M_i^2}{M_{i+1}^2} K_{2i+2} \geq \tfrac{221}{125} K_{2i+2} .$$

We saw that the first equality gives (101), which implies $F_{2i} = 1/S_{2i-1}$, and (102) for the present i. The inequality (111) shows that the reciprocal of the first fraction in (100), with i replaced by $i+1$, is $\geq 221/125$, whence

$$(112) \qquad 1/S_{2i+1} \geq \tfrac{221}{125} F_{2i+2} + \tfrac{96}{125} 1/g_{2i+1} .$$

But $F_{2i+3} = (g_{2i+3}, \ldots) < 4$. Hence $F_{2i+2} = (g_{2i+2}, F_{2i+3}) > 1\tfrac{1}{4}$. Since $g_{2i+1} \leq 3$, (112) gives

$$(113) \qquad 1/S_{2i+1} > \tfrac{221}{100} + \tfrac{32}{125} = 2.466 .$$

But $1/S = (g_{2i}, \ldots) < 3$. Hence $g_{2i} = 2$. If $g = g_{2i-1} \geq 2$,

$$(114) \qquad 1/S_{2i+1} = (2, g, 1/S_{2i-1}) < (2, g, 3) \leq (2, 2, 3) = \tfrac{17}{7} < 2.43 ,$$

contrary to (113). Hence $g_{2i-1} = 1$. Since $F_{2i+1} < 4$,

$$(115) \qquad \begin{cases} F_{2i} = (2, F_{2i+1}) > 2\tfrac{1}{4} , & 1/S_{2i} = (1, 1/S_{2i-1}) = (1, F_{2i}) \\ \quad < (1, 2\tfrac{1}{4}) = \tfrac{13}{9} , & S_{2i} > \tfrac{9}{13} > 0.69 , \qquad K_{2i} > 2.94 , \end{cases}$$

contrary to (104). This excludes case (109′).

58. Case (108′): $M_i = M_{i+1} = \sqrt{1/5}$, $M_{i-1} \leq \sqrt{25/221}$. Then[1]

$$(116) \qquad K_{2i+2} = K_{2i} \geq \tfrac{221}{125} K_{2i-2} .$$

Hence the fraction in (100) is $\geq 221/125$, whence

$$(117) \qquad F_{2i} \geq \frac{221}{125} \cdot \frac{1}{S_{2i-1}} + \frac{96}{125} \cdot \frac{1}{g_{2i-1}} .$$

But $1/S_{2i-1} = (g_{2i-2}, \ldots) > (g_{2i-2}, 4) \geq 1\tfrac{1}{4}$. Hence

$$F_{2i} > \tfrac{221}{100} + \tfrac{32}{125} = 2.466 ,$$

---

[1] This is the reverse of § 57 and follows from it.

as in (113). But every $F_{2i} < 3$. Hence $g_{2i} = 2$. If $g = g_{2i+1} \geqq 2$, we see that, as in (114),

$$F_{2i} = (2, g, F_{2i+2}) < (2, g, 3) \leqq (2, 2, 3) < 2.43 \ ,$$

contrary to $F_{2i} > 2.466$. Hence $g_{2i+1} = 1$. By (100), with i replaced by $i+1$, the equality in (116) gives

(118) $$F_{2i+2} = 1/S_{2i+1} \ , \qquad g_{2i+2} = g_{2i} = 2 \ .$$

As in (115),

$$F_{2i+2} = (2, F_{2i+3}) > 2\tfrac{1}{4} \ , \quad 1/S_{2i+2} = (1, 1/S_{2i+1}) = (1, F_{2i+2}) < (1, 2\tfrac{1}{4}) = \tfrac{13}{9} \ ,$$

and $K_{2i+2} > 2.94$, contrary to (104).

59. Case (110′): $M_i = \sqrt{1/5}$, M_{i-1} and M_{i+1} both $\leqq \sqrt{25/221}$. The inequalities in (111) and (116) hold, and hence also (112) and (117). The second parts of the proofs in cases (109′) and (108′) apply here and give $g_{2i} = 2$, $g_{2i-1} = g_{2i+1} = 1$. Thus

$$F_{2i} > (2, 1, 1) = 2\tfrac{1}{2} \ , \qquad 1/S_{2i} < (1, 1) \ , \qquad S_{2i} > \tfrac{1}{2} \ , \qquad K_{2i} > 3 \ ,$$

contrary to (104).

We have now excluded (108)–(110) when each $\leqq$ is $<$, whence they fall under case

(119) $$M_i = \sqrt{1/8} \text{ for a certain } j \ .$$

Case (107) falls under either (119) or

(120) $$\text{Every } M_j < \sqrt{1/8} \ .$$

Hence there remain only the cases (106), (119), and (120).

60. Case (106): Every $M_j = \sqrt{1/5}$. By (96) the K_{2j} are all equal. Hence we have (102). Hence every g_{4j+3} is equal to $g_3 = g$ and every g_{4j+1} is equal to $g_5 = h$. Also every g_{2i} is equal to $g_2 = s$. Hence F_2 is the periodic continued fraction $(\overset{*}{s}, g, s, \overset{*}{h})$, where $s = 1$ or 2.

If $g > h$, we use $F_0 = (\overset{*}{s}, h, s, \overset{*}{g})$ as a new F_2 without disturbing our identification (§ 55) of f with a Φ_{2j} of even subscript. Hence we may take $g \leqq h$.

I. Let[1] $s = 1$. Then

$$F_2 = (1, g, 1, h, F_2) = \frac{[h(g+2)+g+1]F_2+g+2}{[h(g+1)+g]F_2+g+1} ,$$

$$[h(g+1)+g]F_2^2-h(g+2)F_2-g-2=0 , \qquad F_2 = \frac{h(g+2)+\sqrt{D}}{2h(g+1)+2g} ,$$

where $D = h^2(g+2)^2+4(g+2)[h(g+1)+g]$ is the discriminant of the quadratic equation. By (7), $1/F_2$ and $-1/S_2$ are the first and second roots of the form Φ_2 with which f may be identified. Hence $-S_2$ is the second root of the quadratic equation satisfied by F_2, whence $-S_2$ is derived from our value of F_2 by changing the sign before $\sqrt{D}$. Hence

$$K_2 = F_2 + S_2 = \sqrt{D}/(hg+h+g) .$$

Since $F_1 = (h, 1, g, 1, F_1)$, we see as before that F_1 and $-S_1$ are the roots of

$$(g+2)x^2-h(g+2)x-g(h+1)-h=0 ,$$

whose discriminant is the same D, whence

$$K_1 = F_1 + S_1 = \frac{\sqrt{D}}{g+2} , \qquad \frac{K_2}{K_1} = \frac{g+2}{hg+h+g} .$$

By (94) and (96) for $j = 1$, $K_2/K_1 \geqq 3/5$. Hence

$$2g+10 \geqq 3h(g+1) .$$

But $h \geqq g$. Hence $10 \geqq 3g^2+g$, $g = 1$, $12 \geqq 6h$, $h = 1$ or 2.

I₁. Let $g = h = 1$. Then $F_2^2-F_2-1=0$, $K_2 = \sqrt{5}$, and $a = -4/5$ by (96). We saw that $1/F_2$ is a root of $\Phi_2 = f$. Hence f, whose discriminant is $-4a$, is proportional to $[1, 1, -1]$, whose discriminant is 5. Thus f is the product of $[1, 1, -1]$ by $\sqrt{-4a/5} = 4/5$. Division of (87) by a^2 gives

$$\frac{F}{a} = \left(x+\frac{t}{a}y+\frac{s}{a}z\right)^2 + \tfrac{5}{4}(y^2+yz-z^2) .$$

Its values for $y = 0$, $z = 1$; $y = -1$, $z = 1$; $y = 1$, $z = 2$, are $v_i^2-5/4$, where

$$v_1 = x_1+\frac{s}{a} , \qquad v_2 = x_2-\frac{t}{a}+\frac{s}{a} , \qquad v_3 = x_3+\frac{t}{a}+\frac{2s}{a} .$$

---

[1] In case I we make no assumption like (103) on a.

We can evidently choose an integer x_1 so that $\frac{1}{2} \leq v_i < \frac{3}{2}$. Then $-1 \leq v_i^2 - 5/4 < 1$. Unless the equality holds, $|F/a| < 1$, contrary to the hypothesis that F has the minimum $|a|$. Hence $v_i = \frac{1}{2}$ and

$$\frac{s}{a} - \frac{1}{2} , \qquad \frac{-t}{a} + \frac{s}{a} - \frac{1}{2} , \qquad \frac{t}{a} + \frac{2s}{a} - \frac{1}{2}$$

are all integers, which is false.

I_2. Let $g = 1$, $h = 2$. Then

$$5F_2^2 - 6F_2 - 3 = 0 , \qquad F_2 = \tfrac{1}{5}(\sqrt{24} + 3) , \qquad K_2 = \tfrac{3}{5}\sqrt{24} , \qquad a^3 = -\tfrac{2}{3} .$$

Here f is the product of $[3, 6, -5]$ by $\sqrt{-4a/96}$, and

$$\frac{F}{a} = \left(x + \frac{t}{a} y + \frac{s}{a} z \right)^2 + \tfrac{1}{4}(3y^2 + 6yz - 5z^2) .$$

Its values for $y = 1$, $z = 0$, and $y = 0$, $z = 1$, are

$$v = (x + t/a)^2 + \tfrac{3}{4} , \qquad (x + s/a)^2 - \tfrac{5}{4} .$$

As in I_1, $s/a - \frac{1}{2}$ is an integer n. For $0 \leq |x + t/a| \leq \frac{1}{2}$, we have $|v| < 1$ unless $|x + t/a| = \frac{1}{2}$, and then $t/a + \frac{1}{2}$ is an integer m. Write X for $x + my + nz$. Then

$$F/a = X^2 - Xy + Xz + y^2 + yz - z^2 = (X+z)^2 + (y+z)^2 - (X+z)(y+z) - 2z^2 .$$

This is equivalent to $x^2 + Y^2 - xY - 2z^2$. Write $Y = y + x$. We see that F is equivalent to f_1 in the theorem with $d = 1$.

II. Let $s = 2$. Then

$$F_2 = (2, g, 2, h, F_2) = \frac{[h(4g+4)+2g+1]F_2 + 4g+4}{[h(2g+1)+g]F_2 + 2g+1} ,$$

$$[h(2g+1)+g]F_2^2 - 4h(g+1)F_2 - 4(g+1) = 0 , \qquad F_2 = \frac{2h(g+1)+2\sqrt{\Delta}}{h(2g+1)+g} ,$$

where $\Delta = h^2(g+1)^2 + (g+1)[h(2g+1)+g]$, and 16Δ is the discriminant of the quadratic equation. As in I,

$$K_2 = 4\sqrt{\Delta}/[h(2g+1)+g] ,$$

$$f = \psi\sqrt{-4a/(16\Delta)} , \qquad \psi = 4(g+1)y^2 + 4h(g+1)yz - [h(2g+1)+g]z^2 .$$

If $g=1$, the condition for $K_2<3$ is $17h^2-42h-23>0$ and fails when $h=1$ or 2. Since $g\leqq h\leqq 3$, the only cases are II_1 and II_2 below. By (96),

$$-a^3=\frac{64}{25K_2^2}=\frac{4[h(2g+1)+g]^2}{25\Delta}\,.$$

Division of (87) by a^2 gives

(121) $$\frac{F}{a}=\left(x+\frac{t}{a}y+\frac{s}{a}z\right)^2+l\psi\,,\qquad l=\frac{5}{4[h(2g+1)+g]}\,.$$

Its values for $y=0$, $z=1$; $y=-h$, $z=1$; $y=1$, $z=0$, are

(122) $$\left(x+\frac{s}{a}\right)^2-\frac{5}{4}\,,\qquad \left(x-\frac{ht}{a}+\frac{s}{a}\right)^2-\frac{5}{4}\,,\qquad \left(x+\frac{t}{a}\right)^2+r\,,\qquad r=\frac{5(g+1)}{h(2g+1)+g}\,.$$

As in I_1, the first two require that

(123) $$n=\frac{s}{a}-\tfrac{1}{2}\,,\qquad \frac{s}{a}-\frac{ht}{a}-\tfrac{1}{2}$$

be integers, whence ht/a is an integer.

II_1. Let $h=3$. Then $g\leqq 3$. Thus $t/a=u$ or $u\pm\tfrac{1}{3}$, where u is an integer. In (122$_3$), take $x=-u$; we get r or $r+1/9$, which are positive. But $r+1/9<1$ if $21<11g$ and hence if $g=2$ or 3. Then $F<|a|$, whereas $|a|$ is the minimum of F. Hence $g=1$, and $a^3=-2/7$, contrary to (103).

II_2. Let $g=h=2$. Then $-a^3=\tfrac{8}{25}$. Since $r=\tfrac{5}{4}$, (122$_3$) is of no service. Here $l\psi=\tfrac{5}{4}(y^2+2yz-z^2)$. For $y=1$, $z=-1$, $F/a=(x+t/a-s/a)^2-\tfrac{5}{2}$. If t/a is an integer, $x+t/a$ takes the value $s/a+\tfrac{3}{2}$ by (123), and then $F/a=-\tfrac{1}{4}$. Since $2t/a$ is integral, this proves that $t/a+\tfrac{1}{2}$ is an integer m. For $X=x+my+nz$,

$$F=-\sqrt[3]{1/25}(2X^2-2Xy+2Xz+3y^2+4yz-2z^2)\,.$$

The transformation $y=-Z$, $z=Y-Z$ of determinant unity replaces this by f_4 (in capital letters) of our theorem.

61. Reduced, binary, quadratic forms.

THEOREM 85. *Let $f(x, y)=ax^2+bxy+cy^2$ be a positive reduced form with the minimum a. Then for any integers x and y, $f\geqq c$ if $y\neq 0$, while $f\leqq c$ if $y=0$, $x^2\leqq c/a$.*

Since f is reduced, $-a<b\leqq a\leqq c$. If $y\neq 0$,

$$f-c\geqq ax^2+bxy+a(y^2-1)\geqq a[x^2-|xy|+y^2-1]\,.$$

The quantity in brackets is $(|x|-|y|)^2+|xy|-1$ and hence is >-1.

Corollary. *If v is a value of f and if v/a is not an integral square, then $v \geqq c$.*

A *parallel* transformation is one of type $x = X + lY$, $y = Y$.

Theorem 86. *If the indefinite form $f = ax^2 + bxy + cy^2$ has the minimum $a > 0$, it can be reduced by a parallel transformation.*

The transformation replaces f by $F = AX^2 + BXY + CY^2$, where

$$A = a , \qquad B = 2al + b , \qquad C = al^2 + bl + c .$$

The discriminant $b^2 - 4ac$ is positive; let D denote its positive square root. Write u for $(D - b)/(2a)$, v for $(D + b)/(2a)$. Then $f = a(x - uy)(x + vy)$ vanishes when $x = u$, $y = 1$. Since the minimum of f is $a > 0$, u is not an integer. Take l to be the largest integer $< u$, whence $u - 1 < l < u$. Then

$$D - b - 2a < 2al < D - b , \qquad 0 < D - B < 2A .$$

Since a is the minimum $|C| \geqq a = A$. Also, $B^2 - 4AC = D^2$. Hence

$$|D + B| = \frac{4A|C|}{D - B} > \frac{4A^2}{2A} = 2A .$$

In case $D + B < 0$, this gives $-D - B > 2A > D - B$, contrary to $D > 0$. Hence $D + B \geqq 0$, $D + B > 2A$. By definition, F is then reduced.

62. Case (119): a certain M_j is $\sqrt{1/8}$. For Y in (90), we saw that $-Y/\sqrt{-4B}$ has the minimum (95), which is now $\sqrt{1/8}$, and hence is equivalent to $\sqrt{1/8}\,[1, 2, -1]$ by (2). Hence $-Y$ is equivalent to $-a[1, 2, -1]$ and its minimum is $-a$. By Theorem 86, there exists a parallel transformation which reduces $-Y$. By Theorem 82, C, R, B have the same values after this transformation as before. The chain of $[1, 2, -1]$ contains only the further form $[-1, 2, 1]$. Hence $-a[1, 2, -1]$ is not equivalent to a different reduced form whose first coefficient is positive. It is therefore identical with the reduced form of $-Y$. We may therefore take $Y = a(x^2 + 2xz - z^2)$. In particular, $c = -a = \sqrt{-\frac{1}{2}B}$ in (90).

As a convenient change of notation, take

$$a = c' , \quad b = b' , \quad c = a' , \quad r = t' , \quad s = s' , \quad t = r' ,$$

and interchange x and z. Then F becomes a form F' of type (85) with accents on the coefficients. Thus F' has the minimum a', while

$$(124) \qquad a' = \sqrt{-\tfrac{1}{2}B'} , \qquad B' = a'c' - s'^2 .$$

As in case $a > 0$, $f' = [C', =2R', B']$ is a negative form.[1] To F' we apply a transformation on y and z such that the resulting form, denoted by[2] F in (85), has for its associated binary form f one equivalent to any chosen form of the class containing f'. We choose it so that the positive form $-h$, of discriminant $-4a$, is reduced, where $h = By^2 + 2Ryz + Cz^2$ is derived from f by replacing y by z and z by $-y$. Hence

$$(125) \qquad B < -2R \leqq -B \leqq -C \; , \qquad BC \leqq \tfrac{4}{3}a \; , \qquad a' = a \; .$$

Thus f', f, h are equivalent. Since $-B'$ is represented by $-f'$ and hence by $-h$, which has the minimum $-B$, we have $-B' \geqq -B$.

For $y = \lambda w$, $z = \mu w$, F' becomes ψ:

$$\psi = a'x^2 + 2(s'\mu + t'\lambda)xw + Kw^2 \; , \qquad K = b'\lambda^2 + 2r'\lambda\mu + c'\mu^2 \; .$$

The discriminant of ψ is seen to be $-4f'(\lambda, \mu)$. Since B is represented by h and hence by f', integers λ and μ may be chosen so that $f'(\lambda, \mu) = B$. Since every number represented by ψ is represented by F', the minimum of ψ is a'. Thus $\psi/\sqrt{-4B}$ has discriminant unity and minimum $a'/\sqrt{-4B}$. By (124) and $-B' \geqq -B$, $a' \geqq \sqrt{-\tfrac{1}{2}B}$. Hence the minimum is $\geqq \sqrt{1/8}$, and therefore is either $\sqrt{1/8}$ or $\sqrt{1/5}$ by Theorem 62. Since $a' = a$, this gives

$$(126) \qquad\qquad a = \sqrt{-\tfrac{1}{2}B} \quad \text{or} \quad a = \sqrt{-\tfrac{4}{5}B} \; .$$

I. Let $a = \sqrt{-\tfrac{1}{2}B}$. First, let $-C > -B$. Then (92_2) is $< \sqrt{1/8}$ and hence is $\leqq \sqrt{25/221}$, being the minimum of the binary form (91_2) of discriminant unity. Using (125), we get

$$a^4 \leqq (-\tfrac{1}{2}B)(-4C) \cdot \tfrac{25}{221} \leqq 2 \cdot \tfrac{4}{3}a \cdot \tfrac{25}{221} \; ,$$

$$a^3 \leqq \tfrac{200}{663} = 0.30166 < 0.32 = \tfrac{8}{25} \; ,$$

and the theorem is true in this case. Hence by (125) there remains only the case $C = B$. Both numbers (92) are now $\sqrt{1/8}$. Hence both Y and Z are equivalent to $a[1, 2, -1]$.

By Theorem 86, certain parallel transformations reduce Y and Z without altering the other. By Theorem 82, each replaces F by a form hav-

---

[1] But not necessarily reduced, as assumed without proof by Markoff (and Bachmann). But it is not reduced in case II_2.

[2] This F is not our earlier F.

ing the same B, R, C as F. Hence we may assume that both Y and Z are reduced. As at the beginning of Case (119),

$$Y = a(x^2 + 2xz - z^2) , \qquad Z = a(x^2 + 2xy - y^2) .$$

Hence

$$F = a(x^2 + 2xz - z^2 + 2xy - y^2 + 2\rho yz$$
$$= a[(x+y+z)^2 - 2z^2 - 2y^2 + 2gyz] , \qquad g = \rho - 1 .$$

Replacing x by $x - y - z$, we get the equivalent form aG, where

$$G = x^2 - 2z^2 - 2y^2 + 2gyz .$$

We may take $g \geqq 0$ after changing the signs of x and y if necessary. Since aG has determinant unity,

$$a^3(4 - g^2) = 1 , \qquad g < 2 .$$

For $x = y = z = 1$, $G = 2g - 3$. Since aG has the minimum a, $|2g - 3| \geqq 1$. But $2g - 3 \geqq 1$ contradicts $g < 2$. Hence $3 - 2g \geqq 1$, $g \leqq 1$. For $x = 5$, $y = 3$, $z = -1$, $G = 5 - 6g$. If this were $\geqq 1$, then $g \leqq 2/3$, $4 - g^2 \geqq 32/9$, $a^3 \leqq 9/32$, $a^3 < 0.2813$. Hence $6g - 5 \geqq 1$, $g \geqq 1$. Thus $g = 1$, $a^3 = \frac{1}{3}$, $-G = X^2 + Y^2 - 3Z^2$, where

$$X = x + y + z , \qquad Y = -x + y - 2z , \qquad Z = -x - z$$

define a transformation of determinant unity. Hence aG is equivalent to f_3 of our theorem.

II. Let $a = \sqrt{\dfrac{-4}{5}B}$. By (124), $a = \sqrt{-\tfrac{1}{2}B'}$. Hence $-B'$ is the product of $-B$ by $8/5$. We saw that $-B'$ is represented by the reduced positive form $-h = [-B, -2R, -C]$. Hence $-B' \geqq -C$ by the corollary to Theorem 85. The discussion which led to (126) now holds also when B is replaced by C and proves

$$(127) \qquad a = \sqrt{-\tfrac{1}{2}C} \qquad \text{or} \qquad a = \sqrt{\dfrac{-4}{5}C} .$$

II$_1$. Let (127$_1$) hold. The numbers (92) are $\sqrt{1/5}$ and $\sqrt{1/8}$, respectively, whence Y and Z are equivalent to $a[1, 1, -1]$ and $a[1, 2, -1]$, respectively. As before, we may take them equal respectively. Thus

$$F = a(x^2 + xz - z^2 + 2xy - y^2 + 2\rho yz) .$$

Replacing x by $x-y$, we get $a\psi$, where

$$\psi = x^2 - 2y^2 + xz - z^2 + 2gyz , \qquad 2g = 2\rho - 1 .$$

We may take $g \geqq 0$ after changing the signs of x and z if necessary. Since $a\psi$ has determinant unity,

$$a^3(\tfrac{5}{2} - g^2) = 1 , \qquad g^2 < \tfrac{5}{2} .$$

The values of ψ for $x = y = z = 1$ and $x = 3$, $y = 1$, $z = -1$ are $2g - 1$ and $3 - 2g$, which must be numerically $\geqq 1$. Since

$$3 - 2g > 3 - 2\sqrt{5/2} > -1 ,$$

$3 - 2g \geqq +1$, $g \leqq 1$. By $|2g - 1| \geqq 1$, either $g \geqq 1$ or $g \leqq 0$. Hence $g = 0$ or 1, $a^3 = 2/5$ or $2/3$, respectively. When $g = 0$, we interchange y and z and get f_2. When $g = 1$,

$$-\psi = z^2 - z(2y + x) + (2y + x)^2 - 2(y + x)^2 .$$

Replacing x by $x - 2y$, we get $z^2 - zx + x^2 - 2(y - x)^2$. Now replace y by $y + x$ and then y by z and z by $-y$. We get f_1.

II$_2$. Let (127_2) hold. The numbers (92) are both $\sqrt{1/5}$, whence Y and Z are both equivalent to $a[1, 1, -1]$, and may be taken equal to it. Thus $F = a\psi$,

$$\psi = x^2 + xz - z^2 + xy - y^2 + 2gyz .$$

Since F has determinant 1,

$$a^3(\tfrac{3}{2} + \tfrac{1}{2}g - g^2) = 1 , \qquad -1 < g < \tfrac{3}{2} .$$

For $y = z = 1$, $\psi = 2g + x^2 + 2x - 2$. Taking $x = 0$ or 1, we get $2g - 2$ or $2g + 1$. If $2g - 2 \geqq 1$, $g \geqq 3/2$, a contradiction. Hence $2 - 2g \geqq 1$, $g \leqq 1/2$. If $-2g - 1 \geqq 1$, $g \leqq -1$, a contradiction. Hence $2g + 1 \geqq 1$, $g \geqq 0$. For $x = z = 1$, $y = 2$, $\psi = 4g - 1$. According as $\psi \geqq 1$ or $-\psi \geqq 1$, $g \geqq \tfrac{1}{2}$ or $g \leqq 0$. Hence $g = 0$ or $1/2$, and $a^3 = 2/3$.

The transformation $x = -X - Y$, $y = Y$, $z = -Z$ has determinant unity and replaces ψ with $g = 0$ by ψ with $g = 1/2$. To the latter ψ apply the transformation $x = X$, $y = X + Y$, $z = X + Z$ of determinant 1; we get $2X^2 - Y^2 - Z^2 + YZ$. The transformation $X = z$, $Y = y$, $Z = -x$ has determinant 1 and replaces this by $-(x^2 + xy + y^2 - 2z^2)$. Hence F is equivalent to f_1.

63. Case (120): every $M_j < \sqrt{1/8}$. Then every $M_i \leq \sqrt{25/221}$. By (96) and (103),

(128)
$$K_{2i} < \tfrac{250}{221}\sqrt{2} < 1.6 .$$

Hence every $g_{2j} = 1$. If a certain $g_{2i-1} = 1$,

$$1/S_{2i} = (1, \ldots) < 2 , \qquad F_{2i} = (1, g_{2i+1}, \ldots) > (1, 4) ,$$

since every $g_{2i+1} \leq 3$. Hence $K_{2i} > 1\tfrac{3}{4} > 1.6$. Hence every g_{2j-1} is 2 or 3.

    I. Let every $g_{2j-1} = 3$. Then

$$F = F_0 = (1, 3, F) = \frac{4F+1}{3F+1} , \qquad 3F^2 - 3F - 1 = 0 , \qquad F_0 = \tfrac{1}{6}(\sqrt{21}+3) ,$$

$$K_0 = \tfrac{1}{3}\sqrt{21} , \qquad f = \sqrt{-4a/21} \; [1, 3, -3,] ,$$

$$\frac{F}{a} = \left(x + \frac{t}{a} y + \frac{s}{a} z\right)^2 + u(y^2 + 3yz - 3z^2) , \qquad u = \sqrt{\frac{-4}{21a^3}} .$$

Its values for $y = 1$, $z = 0$; $y = z = 1$; $y = 4$, $z = -1$, are

$$\left(x + \frac{t}{a}\right)^2 + u , \qquad \left(x + \frac{t}{a} + \frac{s}{a}\right)^2 + u , \qquad \left(x + \frac{4t}{a} - \frac{s}{a}\right)^2 + u .$$

Since $|F/a| \geq 1$, the squares of

$$l_1 = x_1 + \frac{t}{a} , \qquad l_2 = x_2 + \frac{t}{a} + \frac{s}{a} , \qquad l_3 = x_3 + \frac{4t}{a} - \frac{s}{a}$$

are $\geq 1 - u$ for all integers x_i. But

$$-a^3 \geq \tfrac{8}{25} > \tfrac{7^3}{1200} , \qquad u < \tfrac{40}{49} , \qquad \sqrt{1-u} > \tfrac{3}{7} .$$

    We can choose integers x_i so that $|l_i| \leq \tfrac{1}{2}$. Hence there exist values ± 1 of c_1, c_2, c_3 and values of d_1, d_2, d_3 such that $0 \leq d_i < 1/14$ for which each $c_i l_i$ is $> 3/7$ and $\leq 1/2$ and hence is $\tfrac{1}{2} - d_i$. Then $l_i = c_i(\tfrac{1}{2} - d_i)$,

$$5x_1 - x_2 - x_3 = \tfrac{1}{2}A + E , \qquad A = 5c_1 - c_2 - c_3 , \qquad E = -5c_1 d_1 + c_2 d_2 + c_3 d_3 .$$

But $|E| < 7(1/14) = 1/2$ and A is odd. Hence $\tfrac{1}{2}A + E$ is not an integer, while $5x_1 - x_2 - x_3$ is one.

II. Let a certain g_{2i+1} be 2. Then

$$F_{2i} = (1, 2, 1, g, 1, \ldots) , \qquad g = g_{2i+3} .$$

II$_1$. Let $g = 2$. Then $F_{2i} > (1, 2, 1, 2, 1) = 15/11 > 1.3636$. If $g_{2i-1} = 2$, then $1/S_{2i} = (2, \ldots) < 3$, $K_{2i} > 1.6969$, contrary to (128). If $g_{2i-1} = 3$,

$$1/S_{2i} < (3, 1, 4) = 19/5 , \qquad S_{2i} > 0.2631, \qquad K_{2i} > 1.6267 ,$$

contrary to (128).

II$_2$. Hence $g = 3$. Thus the pair 1, 2 is followed by the pair 1, 3. Hence $g_{2i-1} = 3$ and $S_{2i} > 0.2631$, as just proved. Also,

$$F_{2i} > (1, 2, 1, 3, 1) = \tfrac{19}{14} > 1.3571 , \qquad K_{2i} > 1.6202 ,$$

contrary to (128). This completes the proof of Theorem 84.

64. Supplement to Theorem 84. We shall reduce the former limit $\sqrt[3]{8/25}$ as much as possible by our methods. But the refinement secured is not needed in our later study of quaternary forms.

THEOREM 87. *If an indefinite form F of determinant 1 has a minimum $\geq \sqrt[3]{2/7}$ and has every $M_j = \sqrt{1/5}$, then F is equivalent to f_1, f_4, or*

$$f_5 = - \sqrt[3]{2/7} (x^2 + xz + y^2 + yz - 3z^2) .$$

Let $|a|$ be the minimum of F in (85). By § 55, the case $a > 0$ reduces to the case $a < 0$. Hence let $-a^3 \geq 2/7$. Then (96) gives $K_{2i}^2 \leq 7 \cdot 32/25 < 9$, whence every $g_{2i} \leq 2$. By (94), $K_{2i-1} < 5$. As below (99), every $g_{2i-1} \leq 4$.

We proceed as in § 60. If $s = 1$, we proved that F is equivalent to f_1. Let $s = 2$. When $h = 3$, we proved that $g = 1$, $a^3 = -2/7$. For $y = 1$, $z = 3$, (121) becomes

$$(129) \qquad \frac{F}{a} = \left(x + \frac{t}{a} + \frac{3s}{a}\right)^2 - v , \qquad v = \frac{5[3h(2g-1) + 5g - 4]}{4[h(2g+1) + g]} .$$

For our case $g = 1$, $h = 3$, we get $v = 5/4$. Hence $t/a + 3s/a - \tfrac{1}{2}$ is an integer; likewise $n = s/a - \tfrac{1}{2}$ by (123). Hence t/a is an integer m. Write X for $x + my + nz$. Then

$$F/a - (X + \tfrac{1}{2}z)^2 = \tfrac{1}{8}\psi = \tfrac{1}{8}[8, 24, -10] .$$

Replacing X by x and y by $y - z$, we get f_5.

From $F_1 = (h, 2, g, 2, F_1]$ we get

$$F_1 = \frac{h(g+1)+\sqrt{\Delta}}{2(g+1)}, \qquad K_1 = \frac{\sqrt{\Delta}}{g+1}, \qquad \frac{K_2}{K_1} = \frac{4(g+1)}{2hg+h+g} \geq \frac{3}{5},$$

$17g+20 \geq 3h(2g+1)$. If $h=4$, this gives $8 \geq 7g$, $g=1$. Then $4t/a$ is an integer by the conclusion from (123). Thus $t/a = w$, $w \pm \frac{1}{4}$, or $w + \frac{1}{2}$, where w is an integer. In (122_3), $r = 10/13$; take $x = -w$; we get r, $r+1/16 < 1$, $r+1/4 > 1$. Hence $t/a = w + \frac{1}{2}$. Hence $v = 5/4$ in (129). Hence $t/a + 3s/a - \frac{1}{2}$ is an integer, whereas its value is $w + 3(n + \frac{1}{2})$.

THEOREM 88. *If an indefinite form of determinant 1 has a minimum $> \frac{2}{3}$, and is equivalent to no one of f_1, f_2, f_3, the case in which $\frac{1}{3} < M_j < \sqrt{1/5}$ for a certain j is excluded.*

The negative of the form (91_1) has the minimum M_j and hence is proportional to a form equivalent to ϕ in (80), whose discriminant is $9p^2 - 4$ and minimum is p. Hence

$$(130) \qquad -a/\sqrt{-4B} = p/\sqrt{9p^2-4} \leq \sqrt{1/8}, \qquad p \geq 2,$$

and Y is equivalent to $a\phi/p$. But ϕ represents $-p$ by Theorem 75. Hence Y is equivalent to a form with the first coefficient $-a$ and discriminant $-4N$. Hence after a linear transformation on y and z the given ternary form becomes a form F' of type (85) with accents on the coefficients. Thus F' has the minimum a'. In our new notations (130) becomes

$$(131) \qquad a'/\sqrt{-4B'} = p/\sqrt{9p^2-4}, \qquad p \geq 2, \qquad B' = a'c' - s'^2.$$

The discussion below (124) shows that $\psi/\sqrt{-4B}$ has discriminant unity and minimum $a'/\sqrt{-4B}$. By (131) and $-B' \geq -B$,

$$a' \geq \sqrt{-4B} \; p/\sqrt{9p^2-4}.$$

Hence that minimum is $\geq p/\sqrt{9p^2-4} > \frac{1}{3}$, and hence is of the form $P/\sqrt{9P^2-4}$ by the binary theory. Hence $P \leq p$. Since $a' = a$, this gives

$$(132) \qquad a = \frac{P\sqrt{-4B}}{\sqrt{9P^2-4}}, \qquad P \leq p.$$

I. Let $P \geq 5$. Then $P/\sqrt{9P^2-4} \leq 5\sqrt{221}$ and (132) gives $a^2 \leq -100B/221$. By (125),

$$a^4 \leq (\tfrac{100}{221})^2 BC \leq (\tfrac{100}{221})^2 \cdot \tfrac{4}{3} a, \qquad a^3 < \tfrac{2}{7},$$

contrary to hypothesis. Hence $P = 1$ or 2.

II. Let $P=2$. Then (132) becomes $a=\sqrt{-\tfrac{1}{2}B}$. If $C=B$, F is f_3 by I of § 62. There remains only the case $-C>-B$. Then, in (92$_2$), $a/\sqrt{-4C}$ is a minimum and is $<\sqrt{1/8}$.

II$_1$. Let it be $\leq \tfrac{1}{3}$. Then, by (125)

$$a^2 \leq \tfrac{1}{3}\sqrt{2BC} \leq \tfrac{1}{3}\sqrt{8a/3} \ , \qquad a \leq \tfrac{2}{3} \ .$$

II$_2$. Let it exceed $\tfrac{1}{3}$. Then it is the minimum of a Markoff form, whence (using p in a new sense)

$$a/\sqrt{-4C}=p/\sqrt{9p^2-4} \ , \qquad p>2 \ .$$

Hence Y and Z are equivalent to $a[1, 2, -1]$ and $a\phi/p$, respectively. By Theorem 74, the period of ϕ contains no form except ϕ whose first coefficient is p. But ϕ is reduced. Since Y and Z may be assumed reduced, they coincide with $a[1, 2, -1]$ and $a\phi/p$, respectively. By replacing x by $x-z$, we may take $Y=a(x^2-2z^2)$. Hence $F=aK$, where

$$(133) \qquad K=x^2-2z^2+\frac{3p-2q}{p}\, xy+\frac{r-3q}{p}\, y^2+2Gyz \ .$$

We may take $G \geq 0$ after changing the signs of x and y if necessary. Since aK has determinant unity,

$$(134) \qquad 1=a^3\left[\frac{9}{2}+\frac{2}{p^2}(q^2-rp)-G^2\right]=a^3\left(\frac{9}{2}-\frac{2}{p^2}-G^2\right) \ .$$

For $x=4$, $y=-1$, $z=1$, $K=2+(r+5q)/p-2G$. If $K<0$, then $-K\geq 1$, $2G\geq 3+(r+5q)/p>3+5/3$, since $p<3q$ by (81). Then $G>7/3$, $G^2>9/2$, and the final factor in (134) would be negative. Hence $K\geq 1$,

$$(135) \qquad 2G\leq 1+(r+5q)/p \ .$$

For $x=0$, $y=z=1$, the case $K\geq 1$ gives $2G\geq 3+(3q-r)/p$, which exceeds (135) since $p>r+q$ by (84). Hence $-K\geq 1$,

$$(136) \qquad 2G\leq 1+(3q-r)/p \ .$$

For $x=-3$, $y=z=1$, $K=2G-2+(r+3q)/p$. If $-K\geq 1$, then $-2G>0$ by $p<3q$. Hence $K\geq 1$,

$$(137) \qquad 2G\geq 3-(r+3q)/p \ .$$

For $x=4$, $y=1$, $z=-3$, $K=10-6G+(r-11q)/p$. When $-K\geqq1$, $6G>3[1+(3q-r)/p]$, contrary to (136), if $2p>5q-r$, which follows from (84) and (82): $2p\geqq4q+2r>4q+q-r$. Hence $K\geqq1$,

$$6G\leqq9+(r-11q)/p<3[3-(r+3q)/p]\ ,$$

contrary to (137), if $2r<q$. The latter is true by (82) unless $2r=q$, whence $r=1$, $q=2$, $p=5$ by (81$_1$). Then $6G\leqq24/5$. By (137), $2G\geqq8/5$. Hence $G=4/5$. Then for $x=-5$, $y=1$, $z=3$, $K=6G-5=-1/5$. Hence case II$_2$ is excluded.

III. Let $P=1$. By (132), $a=\sqrt{-4B/5}$. This with (131) and $a'=a$ shows that $-B'$ is the product of $-B$ by $(9p^2-4)/(5p^2)$, which is never an integer since $p\geqq2$. Since $-B'$ is represented by the reduced positive form $-h=[-B,\ -2R,\ -C]$, $-B'\geqq-C$ by the Corollary in § 61. The discussion which led to (132) now holds when B is replaced by C, and P by a new letter π, whence

$$(138)\qquad a=\pi\sqrt{-4C}/\sqrt{9\pi^2-4}\ .\qquad \pi\leqq p\ .$$

If $\pi=2$ or 1, we have (127), and the two cases were treated fully just following (127) and proved to lead only to f_1 or f_2.

Let $\pi>2$ and write p for π. As in II$_2$, $F=aL$,

$$L=x^2+xz-z^2+\frac{3p-2q}{p}\,xy+\frac{r-3q}{p}\,y^2-2gyz\ .$$

Since aL has determinant unity,

$$(139)\qquad a^3M=1\ ,\qquad M=\frac{2q-3p}{2p}\,g-g^2+\frac{9p^2+3pq+4q^2-5rp}{4p^2}\ .$$

Take $x=0$, $y=-1$, $z=1$. If $L\geqq1$, then $g\geqq h$, $h=1-(r-3q)/(2p)$. When $g\geqq h$,

$$\frac{dM}{dg}\leqq\frac{2q-3p}{2p}-2h=\frac{2r-7p-4q}{2p}<0$$

since $2r\leqq q$ by (82), whence M decreases as g increases. Thus $M\leqq M'$, where M' is the value of M for $g=h$:

$$(140)\qquad 4p^2M'=2r(p+2q)-r^2-14pq+q^2-p^2\ .$$

But $2r\leqq q$, $2q\leqq p$. Hence $M'<0$, $M<0$, contrary to (139). Hence $-L\geqq1$, $2pg\leqq3q-r$.

For $x=2$, $y=-1$, $z=1$, $L=2g-1+(r+q)/p$. Since $p>2q$, the case $L\geqq 1$ is contradicted by the preceding inequality. Hence $-L\geqq 1$,

$$(141) \qquad\qquad g=-G, \qquad 2pG\geqq r+q.$$

For $x=y=-1$, $z=1$, $L=(2p+r-5q)/p\ -2G$ is negative by (141) and $p<3q$. Hence $-L\geqq 1$,

$$(142) \qquad\qquad 2pG\geqq 3p+r-5q.$$

For $x=-1$, $y=z=1$, $L=(r-q-4p)/p+2G$. If $L\geqq 1$, then $G\geqq k$, $2kp=5p-r+q$. Since $2r\leqq q$, $dM/dG\leqq (3p-2q)/(2p)-2k<0$. Hence $M\leqq M'$, where M' is the value of M for $G=k$. We again get (140). Hence $-L\geqq 1$,

$$(143) \qquad\qquad 2pG\leqq 3p+q-r.$$

For $x=3$, $y=-1$, $z=1$, $L=2-2G+(r+3q)/p$. The case $-L\geqq 1$ contradicts (143). Hence $L\geqq 1$,

$$(144) \qquad\qquad 2pG\leqq p+r+3q.$$

For $x=0$, $y=z=1$, $L=2G+(r-3q-p)/p$. The case $L\geqq 1$ contradicts (144) since $p>2r$ by (81) and (82). Hence $-L\geqq 1$,

$$(145) \qquad\qquad 2pG\leqq 3q-r.$$

For $x=5$, $y=-2$, $z=1$, $L=(8q+4r)/p-1-4G$. When $L\geqq 1$, the value of G is less than that from (142) if $9q+r<4p$, which follows from (84) and (82_2). Hence $-L\geqq 1$, $pG\geqq 2q+r$, contrary to (145). Hence this case is excluded.

Lemma. *Every term 4 is followed and preceded by 2 if*

$$(146) \qquad\qquad -a^3\geqq (\tfrac{5\,6}{1\,0\,3})^2=0.295598+.$$

By (94), $K_{2j-1}\leqq 103/21$ for every j. Let $g_{2j-1}=4$ for a certain j. Suppose that $g_{2j}=1$. If $g_{2j+1}\geqq 2$, then $F_{2j+1}>2$, $F_{2j-1}>(4,1,2)=14/3$. But for every odd n, $g_{n-1}\leqq 2$ by the remark below Theorem 87, whence $1/S_n<g_{n-1}+1$, $S_n>\tfrac{1}{3}$. Hence $K_{2j-1}>5$. This contradiction gives $g_{2j+1}=1$. Then $F_{2j+1}>(1,3)$, $F_{2j-1}=(4,1,F_{2j+1})>(4,1,\tfrac{4}{3})=\tfrac{3\,2}{7}$, $K_{2j-1}>\tfrac{1\,0\,3}{2\,1}$.

This proves that $g_{2j}=2$. Next, let $g_{2j-2}=1$. Then $F_{2j-1}>(4,2,1)=13/3$. If $g_{2j-3}\geqq 2$, $1/S_{2j-1}<(1,2)$, $K_{2j-1}>5$. Hence $g_{2j-3}=1$,

$$1/S_{2j-1}<(1,1,3)=\tfrac{7}{4}, \qquad K_{2j-1}>\tfrac{1\,0\,3}{2\,1}.$$

Exclusion of case (109′): $M_{i-1} = M_i = \sqrt{1/5}$, $M_{i+1} \leq \sqrt{25/221}$ *for* (146).
We have (111) and (112). Now $g_{2i+3} \leq 4$ by the remark below Theorem 87,
whence $F_{2i+3} < 5$, and $F_{2i+2} > (1, 5)$. By (112), $1/S_{2i+1} > 2$. Hence $g_{2i} = 2$.

If $g_{2i+2} \geq 2$, then (112) gives $1/S_{2i+1} > 3$, a contradiction. Hence $g_{2i+2} = 1$.
By the Lemma, $g_{2i+3} \leq 3$, whence $F_{2i+3} < 4$, $F_{2i+2} > (1, 4)$. By the Lemma,
$g_{2i+1} \leq 3$, and (112) gives $1/S_{2i+1} > 2.466$. But if $g = g_{2i-1} \geq 2$,

$$1/S_{2i+1} = (2, g, 1/S_{2i-1}) < (2, g, 3) \leq (2, 2, 3) = \tfrac{17}{7} < 2.43 .$$

Hence $g_{2i-1} = 1$. Thus

$$(147) \quad \begin{cases} F_{2i+1} \leq (3, 1, F_{2i+3}) < (3, 1, 4) = 19/5 , \\[2pt] F_{2i} = (2, F_{2i+1}) > (2, \tfrac{19}{5}) = \tfrac{43}{19} , \qquad F_{2i} > 2.263 , \\[2pt] \dfrac{1}{S_{2i}} = \left(1, \dfrac{1}{S_{2i-1}}\right) = (1, F_{2i}) < (1, \tfrac{43}{19}) , \qquad S_{2i} > \tfrac{43}{62} > 0.693 , \end{cases}$$

whence $K_{2i} > 2.956$. But by (146) and (96), $K_{2j} \leq 103/35 < 2.943$.

Exclusion[1] *of case* $M_i = M_{i+1} = \sqrt{1/5}$, $M_{i-1} \leq \sqrt{25/221}$ *for* (146). We
have (116) and (117). Since $1/S_{2i-1} > (1, 5)$, (117) gives $F_{2i} > 2$, whence $g_{2i} =$
2. If $g_{2i-2} \geq 2$, then $1/S_{2i-1} > 2$, and (117) gives $F_{2i} > 3$, a contradiction.
Hence $g_{2i-2} = 1$. By the Lemma, $g_{2i-3} \leq 3$, $g_{2i-1} \geq 3$. Thus $1/S_{2i-1} > (1, 4)$.
Hence (117) gives $F_{2i} > 2.466$. If $g = g_{2i+1} \geq 2$,

$$F_{2i} = (2, g, F_{2i+2}) < (2, g, 3) \leq (2, 2, 3) = \tfrac{17}{7} < 2.43 .$$

Hence $g_{2i+1} = 1$. By (118),

$$g_{2i+2} = g_{2i} = 2 , \quad g_{2i+3} = g_{2i-1} \leq 3 , \quad g_{2i+4} = g_{2i-2} = 1 , \quad g_{2i+5} = g_{2i-3} \leq 3 .$$

Thus (147) hold when every subscript is increased by 2.

The case in § 59 is excluded as before.

Either every $M_j = \sqrt{1/5}$, or every $M_j \leq \tfrac{1}{3}$, or $\tfrac{1}{3} < M_j < \sqrt{1/5}$ for a certain j, or some of the M_j are $\sqrt{1/5}$ and all others are $\leq \tfrac{1}{3}$, with at least one
of each kind. The last case falls into the three subcases (108)–(110) with
$\sqrt{1/8}$ replaced by $\tfrac{1}{3}$. Since $M \leq \tfrac{1}{3}$ implies $M \leq \sqrt{25/221}$, those subcases
have just been excluded.

Hence there remains only the case in which every $M_j \leq \tfrac{1}{3}$. Assume (146).
By (96), $K_{2j} \leq 103/63 = 1.6349+$. Hence every $g_{2j} = 1$. Also, every $g_{2j-1} \geq 2$.
For, if a certain $g_{2i-1} = 1$, then

$$1/S_{2i} < 2 , \qquad F_{2i} > (1, 5) , \qquad K_{2i} > \tfrac{1}{2} + \tfrac{6}{5} = 1.7 .$$

---

[1] Follows from the preceding case by reversion.

If a certain $g_{2i-1} = 4$, then

$$F_{2i-1} > (4, 1, 2) = 1\tfrac{4}{3} , \qquad 1/S_{2i-1} < (1, 2) , \qquad K_{2i-1} > 1\tfrac{6}{3} ,$$

contrary to $K_{2i-1} < 5$ (below Theorem 87). Hence every g_{2j-1} is 2 or 3.

The case in which every g_{2j-1} is 3 was excluded in § 63.

Hence let $g_{2i+1} = 2$ for a certain i. Since F_{2i} is decreased when we increase a term in an even place from 2 to 3, $F_{2i} \geqq (1, 2, \phi)$, where ϕ has the period 1, 3, whence $\phi = (1, 3, \phi)$, $3\phi^2 - 3\phi = 1$. Also $1/S_{2i} \leqq k = (\overset{*}{3}, \overset{*}{1}) = (3, 1, k)$, $k^2 - 3k = 3$. Write $l = 1/k$. Then $S_{2i} \geqq l$, $3l^2 + 3l = 1$. Hence $\phi = \tfrac{1}{6}(\sqrt{21} + 3)$, $l = \tfrac{1}{6}(\sqrt{21} - 3) = \phi - 1$. Also, $(1, 2, \phi) = (3\phi + 1)/(2\phi + 1) = \tfrac{1}{5}(3\phi + 3)$. Hence $K_{2i} \geqq \tfrac{1}{5}(8\phi - 2) = \tfrac{1}{15}(6 + 4\sqrt{21}) = 1.62202$. This case will be excluded if $K_{2i} \leqq 1.622$, and hence by (96) if

$$-a^3 \geqq 64/[81(1.622)^2] = 0.300326 + .$$

THEOREM 89. *There exists no indefinite, ternary, quadratic form of determinant unity the cube of whose minimum lies between 0.300327 and 8/25 = 0.32.*

This gap exceeds the gap from 8/25 to 1/3 in Theorem 84.

65. Extension to forms without minima. This extension is due to A. Oppenheim and is here first published.

Let F be an indefinite form of determinant unity whose lower bound $L > 0$ is not attained, *i.e.*, L is not a value of $|F|$ for integral values of the variables not all zero. Then $|F|$ represents infinitely many numbers less than any assigned number exceeding L. Hence for any $\epsilon > 0$, there are infinitely many values of F such that

$$(148) \qquad\qquad L < |F| < (1 + \epsilon)L .$$

If $\epsilon < 3$, every such value is represented properly. For, if it be $F(gX, gY, gZ)$, where X, Y, Z are integers not all zero and g is an integer > 1, whence $g \geqq 2$, write V for $|F(X, Y, Z)|$. Then $V > L$ and

$$|F| = g^2 V \geqq 4V > 4L > (1 + \epsilon)L ,$$

contrary to (148). Hence the first coefficient of F may be taken as such a value.

THEOREM 90. *We can choose a value a of F as close numerically to L as we please such that, in any form*

$$(149) \qquad\qquad ax^2 + by^2 + cz^2 + 2ryz + 2sxz + 2txy$$

equivalent to F and having a as first coefficient, at least one of the ratios $a:t:b$ is irrational and at least one of the ratios $a:s:c$ is irrational.

The second part will follow from the first part by replacing y by z and z by $-y$. If the first part be false, there are infinitely many values a_i of F as close to L as we please such that F is equivalent to $F_i = a_i x_i^2 + \cdots + 2t_i x_i y_i$, where the ratios $a_i : t_i : b_i$ are all rational. There is a transformation

$$(150) \qquad \begin{pmatrix} l_1 & m_1 & n_1 \\ l_2 & m_2 & n_2 \\ l_3 & m_3 & n_3 \end{pmatrix}$$

with integral coefficients of determinant unity which replaces F_1 by F_2. By the coefficients of x_2^2, y_2^2, $2x_2 y_2$, we get

$$(151) \qquad a_2 = F_1(l_1, l_2, l_3) , \qquad b_2 = F_1(m_1, m_2, m_3) ,$$

$$(152) \qquad t_2 = a_1 l_1 m_1 + \ldots + c_1 l_3 m_3 + r_1(l_2 m_3 + l_3 m_2) + \ldots .$$

If $l_3 = 0$, then a_2 is a value of $[a_1, 2t_1, b_1]$ by (151_1). Since $a_1 : t_1 : b_1$ are rational, only a finite number of values of this binary form can satisfy inequality (148). Since they are values of F_1 and hence of F, we have a contradiction.

Hence $l_3 \neq 0$. Multiply (151) and (152) by m_3^2, l_3^2, $-2m_3 l_3$ and add. We get

$$(153) \qquad a_2 m_3^2 - 2t_2 m_3 l_3 + b_2 l_3^2 = a_1 N_2^2 - 2t_1 N_2 N_1 + b_1 N_1^2 ,$$

where N_i is the cofactor of n_i in the determinant of (150). Since F is not a zero form, the left member of (153) is not zero. Since $a_i : t_i : b_i$ are rational, $a_2 : a_1$ must be rational.

The matrix of the coefficients of s_1, r_1, c_1 in (151_1) and (152) is

$$\begin{pmatrix} 2l_1 l_3 & 2l_2 l_3 & l_3^2 \\ l_1 m_3 + l_3 m_1 & l_2 m_3 + l_3 m_2 & l_3 m_3 \end{pmatrix} .$$

Its three determinants are the products of l_3^2 by N_1, N_2, $2N_3$, which are not all zero since $\Sigma n_i N_i = 1$. Hence we can solve (151_1) and (152) for some two of s_1, r_1, c_1 in terms of the third and a_1, b_1, t_1, a_2, t_2. Hence two of s_1, r_1, c_1 are linear functions of a_1 and the third with rational coefficients. In other words,

$$(154) \qquad F_1 = a_1 G(x_1, y_1, z_1) + kz_1(\lambda x_1 + \mu y_1 + \nu z_1) ,$$

where λ, μ, ν and the coefficients of G are all rational.

If $a_1:k$ were rational, the coefficients of F_1 and hence those of F would be commensurable, and L would be attained by F. Hence $a_1:k$ is irrational.

In (154) take $x_1=l_1$, $y_1=l_2$, $z_1=l_3$ and apply (151$_1$). Thus

$$a_2 = a_1 G + k l_3 w \; , \quad G = G(l_1,\, l_2,\, l_3) \; , \quad w = \lambda l_1 + \mu l_2 + \nu l_3 \; .$$

But $a_2 = \rho a_1$, where ρ is rational. Thus $a_1(\rho - G) = k l_3 w$. If $w \neq 0$, k/a_1 would be rational. Hence $w=0$, $\rho = G$, $a_2 = a_1 G$. But only a finite number of values of $G(x,\, y,\, z)$ are such that $L < |a_1 G| < (1+\epsilon)L$, whereas there are infinitely many values of $|a_2|$ within those limits. This proves the theorem.

We are now in a position to extend Theorem 84 to any F. First, let F represent positive numbers as close to L as we please. Then we may take $a > 0$ in Theorem 90. Then f in (87) is a negative form which may be taken as a reduced form. Consider the form $Z = [a,\, 2t,\, b]$ of determinant $-4C$. Let M denote the lower bound of $|Z|$. Since the ratios $a:t:b$ are not all rational, Theorem 72 gives $M^2 \leq -\frac{4}{9}C$. Similarly, if N denotes the lower bound of $|Y|$, where $Y = [a,\, 2s,\, c]$, then $N^2 \leq -\frac{4}{9}B$. Evidently $L \leq M$, $L \leq N$. Hence

$$L^4 \leq M^2 N^2 \leq \tfrac{16}{81} BC \leq \tfrac{16}{81} \cdot \tfrac{4}{3}a < \tfrac{64}{243}(1+\epsilon)L \; ,$$

however small ϵ may be. Hence

$$L^3 \leq \tfrac{64}{243} < \tfrac{2}{7} \; .$$

Second, let no positive values of F satisfy (148) for a sufficiently small ϵ. Then $a < 0$. Employ the notations before (93). Then $M^2 \leq 4C/3$, $N^2 \leq -4B/9$, where M and N are now the lower bounds of $-Z$ and $-Y$.

We have $L \leq N \leq -a < (1+\epsilon)L$. Then, by (93$_2$),

$$K_{2j}^2 = \frac{-4a}{B^2} \leq \frac{-64a}{81N^4} < \frac{64(1+\epsilon)}{81L^3} \; .$$

Contrary to the desired result, let $L^3 \geq 8/25$. Hence for ϵ sufficiently small, $K_{2j} < 1.58$. Thus every $g_{2j} = 1$. By (93$_1$),

$$K_{2j-1}^2 = \frac{-4a}{C^2} \leq \frac{64}{9} \cdot \frac{-a}{M^4} < \frac{64}{9} \cdot \frac{(1+\epsilon)L}{L^4} < \frac{200}{9}(1+\epsilon) \; ,$$

since $L \leq M \leq -a < (1+\epsilon)L$. If $\epsilon < 1/8$, $K_{2j-1} < 5$. Write g for g_{2j-1}. Then

$$1/S_{2j-1} = (1,\, \ldots) < 2 \; , \quad F_{2j-1} = (g,\, 1,\, \ldots) > (g,\, 2) \; , \quad K_{2j-1} > g + 1 \; .$$

Hence every $g_{2j-1} \leqq 3$. If $h = g_{2i-1} \leqq 2$ for a certain i, then

$$1/S_{2i} = (h, \ldots) < 3 , \qquad F_{2i} > (1, 4) , \qquad K_{2i} > 1\tfrac{1}{4} + \tfrac{1}{3} > 1.58 ,$$

contrary to an earlier inequality.

Theorem 91. *If L is the lower bound of an indefinite ternary quadratic form f of determinant unity and if f represents neither[1] L nor $-L$, then $L^3 <$ 8/25.*

Hence if f has a lower bound whose cube is $\geqq 8|d|/25$, f is equivalent to one of $f_1, \ldots, f_4$ in Theorem 84.

---

[1] Or at most one of L and $-L$.

CHAPTER IX

MINIMA OF INDEFINITE, QUATERNARY, QUADRATIC FORMS

This interesting investigation was made by A. Oppenheim at the suggestion of the author, who added the proofs of Lemmas 3 and 4 on the basis of chapter viii and also certain details of service to the reader.

66. Five lemmas on ternary quadratic forms.

LEMMA 1. *If a real, indefinite, ternary, quadratic form F of determinant d has a minimum m, then either*

$$m^3 = \tfrac{2}{3}|d| \ , \qquad F \backsim F_1 = \sqrt[3]{\tfrac{2}{3}}d(x^2 - y^2 - z^2 + xy + xz) \ ,$$

$$or \ m^3 = \tfrac{2}{5}|d| \ , \qquad F \backsim F_2 = \sqrt[3]{\tfrac{2}{5}}d(x^2 - y^2 - z^2 + xy + 2xz + yz) \ ,$$

or $m^3 \leqq \tfrac{1}{3}|d|$.

For, by the end of § 62 with $g=0$, $F_1 \backsim f_1$. The forms f_i are defined in Theorem 84. Replacing x by $x+z$ in f_2, we get F_2.

LEMMA 2. *If F does not represent both m and $-m$, then $m^3 < \tfrac{1}{3}|d|$.*

For, f_1, f_2, and f_3 represent both m and $-m$.

LEMMA 3. *Let the first coefficient a of F be the minimum of F. Let f be the binary form (87) associated with F. Let f, $Y = F_{y=0}$, and $Z = F_{z=0}$ be reduced. If $d>0$ and $a^3 = \tfrac{2}{3}d$, then F is either F_1 or*

$$\sqrt[3]{\tfrac{2}{3}}d(x^2 - y^2 - z^2 + xy + xz + yz) \ .$$

The two forms may be united into

$$F = a[(x + \tfrac{1}{2}y + \tfrac{1}{2}z)^2 - \tfrac{5}{4}y^2 \mp \tfrac{1}{2}yz - \tfrac{5}{4}z^2] \ .$$

We employ (85)–(88). Since the discriminant of f is $-4ad < 0$, f is definite. If f were positive, F would be positive by (87), whereas it is indefinite. Hence f is a negative form. It suffices to prove Lemma 3 when $d=1$. If either of the numbers (92) is $\leqq \sqrt{1/8}$, then since the other is certainly $\leqq \sqrt{1/5}$, we have

$$a^2 \leqq \sqrt{16BC/40} \leqq \sqrt{16 \cdot \tfrac{4}{3}a/40} \ , \qquad a^3 \leqq \tfrac{8}{15} < \tfrac{2}{3} \ .$$

Hence each number (92) is $\sqrt{1/5}$, and Lemma 3 follows from II_2 in § 62.

LEMMA 4. *Make the initial assumptions in Lemma 3, but let* $d < 0$, $a^3 = -\frac{2}{3}d$, *and let C be the minimum of f. Then F is*

$$(155) \qquad \sqrt[3]{-\tfrac{2}{3}d}(x^2+y^2-z^2+xy+xz+2yz) .$$

Employ the quotients of F and a by $\sqrt[3]{d}$ as a new F and a new a. Now F has determinant unity and minimum $-a$, where $a^3 = -\frac{2}{3}$. Consider all such forms having $-a^3 \geqq \frac{2}{3}$, instead of (97). The cases (i) $g=1$, $h=2$ and (ii) $g=2$, $h=1$, which were formerly excluded at the end of § 55 must now be examined.

Case (i) is I_2 of § 60 with F_0 instead of F_2. Hence

$$F = a(X^2 - Xy + Xz + y^2 + yz - z^2) , \qquad X = x + my + nz ,$$

$$a^3 = -\tfrac{2}{3}, \; f = F_0 = \rho[3,\, 6,\, -5], \; \rho = \sqrt{-4a}/96.$$

By hypothesis, $-Y$ is reduced. Since $[1, 1, -1]$ is the only reduced form of discriminant 5 whose first coefficient is positive, we have $Y = a(x^2 + xz - z^2)$, whence $n = 0$. Similarly,

$$-Z = -a(\xi^2 + \xi y - y^2) , \qquad \xi = x + (m-1)y ,$$

is reduced and hence is $-a(x^2 + xy - y^2)$. Thus $m = 1$, and F is (155).

In case (ii), $F_0 = (1, 2, 1, 1, F_0)$, $5F_0^2 - 4F_0 - 4 = 0$, whence $f = \rho[4, 4, -5]$. But its first coefficient 4ρ is not its minimum since it represents $\rho(4 + 4 - 5)$.

LEMMA 5. *For the assumptions in Lemma 3, except that* $a^3 = \frac{2}{3}d$, *F is either*

$$(156) \qquad a(x^2 - y^2 - z^2 + xy + 2xz + yz)$$

or the form derived from (156) *by interchanging y and z.*

It suffices to prove this when $d = 1$.

Here $-f = -Bz^2 + 2Ryz - Cy^2$. To treat only one of two similar cases, let $-B \leqq -C$. Then $-f$ is a reduced, positive form of discriminant $-4a$, whence

$$(157) \qquad B < 2R \leqq -B \leqq -C , \qquad BC \leqq \tfrac{4}{3}a .$$

By Lemma 1, F is equivalent to a form which is the product of a by a form with integral coefficients. Hence, by (86),

$$B = -\tfrac{1}{4}\beta a^2 , \qquad C = -\tfrac{1}{4}\gamma a^2 , \qquad R = \tfrac{1}{4}\delta a^2 ,$$

where β, γ, δ are integers, $\beta>0$, $\gamma>0$. Since the discriminants of $F_{y=0}$ and $F_{z=0}$ are $-4B$ and $-4C$ and their minimum is a,

$$a^2 = -\tfrac{4}{5}B \text{ or } a^2 \le -\tfrac{1}{2}B; \qquad a^2 = -\tfrac{4}{5}C \text{ or } a^2 \le -\tfrac{1}{2}C .$$

If $a^2 \le -\tfrac{1}{2}B$, then (157) gives

$$a^2 \le -\tfrac{1}{2}C , \qquad a^4 \le \tfrac{1}{4}BC \le \tfrac{1}{3}a ,$$

contrary to $a^3 = \tfrac{2}{3}$. Hence $a^2 = -\tfrac{4}{5}B$ and $\beta=5$. But $R^2 - BC = -a$. Hence $5\gamma - \delta^2 = 40$, and δ is divisible by 5. By (157), $-5 < 2\delta \le 5$. Hence $\delta = 0$, $\gamma = 8$, $a^2 = -\tfrac{1}{2}C$.

We therefore have case II_1 of § 62 with $g=0$, $2\rho=1$. Thus F is (156) with y and z interchanged.

67. Quaternary forms. Consider an indefinite form

$$(158) \quad F = F(x, y, z, t) = ax^2 + by^2 + cz^2 + dt^2 + 2pxy + 2sxz + 2ryz$$
$$+ 2uxt + 2vyt + 2wzt$$

having a minimum $m>0$. If F represents $-m$, but not m, we apply our discussion to $-F$. Hence let F represent m. Then m is represented properly by F. After applying an integral transformation of determinant unity, we may take $d=m$. We have

$$(159) \qquad dF - (ux + vy + wz + dt)^2 = G(x, y, z) .$$

We assume[1] that G has a minimum $n>0$. Define a by

$$(160) \qquad \begin{cases} a = -n \text{ if } G \text{ represents } -n , \\ a = n \text{ if } G \text{ represents } n, \text{ but not } -n . \end{cases}$$

We call G the ternary form *associated* with F. As in Theorem 81, F is equivalent to a form with the same d whose associated form is any assigned ternary form equivalent to G. Hence we may take

$$(161) \qquad G = ax^2 + \beta y^2 + \gamma z^2 + 2\rho yz + 2\sigma xz + 2\pi xy ,$$

---

[1] Since this is certainly true if G is a negative form, the only omitted case is that in which $|G|$ is indefinite and does not represent its lower bound n. By Theorem 91, $n^3 < \tfrac{1}{4}g$, where g is the absolute value of the determinant of G. Then there are values a of G such that $|a^3| < \tfrac{1}{4}g$. After simple modifications the proofs in the text remain valid.

with a as in (160). By (159),

$$(162) \quad \begin{cases} \alpha = da - u^2 , & \beta = db - v^2 , & \gamma = dc - w^2 , \\ \rho = dr - vw , & \sigma = ds - uw , & \pi = dp - uv , \end{cases}$$

We have

$$(163) \quad \alpha G - (\alpha x + \pi y + \sigma z)^2 = df(y, z) , \quad f = Cy^2 - 2Ryz + Bz^2 ,$$

$$(164) \quad dC = \alpha\beta - \pi^2 , \quad dB = \alpha\gamma - \sigma^2 , \quad dR = \sigma\pi - \alpha\rho .$$

A simple computation shows that C, B, R are the cofactors of c, b, r in the determinant $\Delta \neq 0$ of F, and that the determinant of G is $d^2\Delta$. By (87),

$$(165) \quad \text{Disc. } f = 4(R^2 - BC) = -4a\Delta .$$

By Theorem 81, we may assume that f is a reduced form.

THEOREM 92. *Without altering d or a, we may assume that, when $a > 0$, each of*

$$(166) \quad \psi_1 = G_{y=0} , \quad \psi_2 = G_{z=0} , \quad \psi_3 = F_{y=z=0} , \quad \psi_4 = F_{x=z=0} , \quad \psi_5 = F_{x=y=0}$$

is a reduced form when it is indefinite, while if it is definite it is either reduced or is of type

$$(167) \quad [g, -h, g] , \quad 0 < h < g .$$

When $a < 0$, the same is true of ψ_3, ψ_4, ψ_5.

First, consider $\psi_2 = ax^2 + 2\pi xy + \beta y^2$, $a > 0$. Apply transformation

$$(168) \quad x = X + lY , \quad y = Y , \quad z = Z , \quad t = T .$$

In case ψ_2 is indefinite it can be reduced by a transformation (168) by Theorem 86. In case ψ_2 is definite, we use the notations in the proof of the theorem cited. There is a unique integer l such that $-a < 2al + b \leq a$, whence $-A < B \leq A$. Also $C \geq a$, since a is the minimum. The resulting form is reduced unless $B < 0$, $C = A$, and then it is of type (167). Transformation (168) leaves unaltered every $\psi_i (i \neq 2)$.

Second, consider ψ_3. We now use transformation $t = t' + lx$, which leaves x, y, z unaltered. Let it replace F by F'. Then $F'(0, y, z, t') = F(0, y, z, t)$. Hence ψ_4 and ψ_5 are unaltered. Since v, w, d are unaltered, while $u' = u + dl$, the linear function in (159) is unaltered and G is unaltered. As before, our transformation either reduces the positive form ψ_3 or replaces it by (167).

Our proof shows that all these reductions can be made simultaneously.

By means of a real linear transformation, F can be reduced to a sum of p squares and the negatives of n squares. Then $p-n$ is called the *signature* S of F. Since F is indefinite, the only possible cases are $+++-$, $++--$, $+---$. Hence by (159),

(169)   If $\Delta>0$, then $S=0$ and G is indefinite ;

(170)   If $\Delta<0$, either $S=2$ and G is indefinite,

          or $S=-2$ and G is a negative form .

When $S=2$, we may exclude the case in which F represents $-d$. For then $-F$ represents d, has determinant Δ, and has signature -2, and hence is treated in our case $S=-2$.

68. Case $S=0$, $a=-n$. The discriminant of $[a, 2u, d]$ is $-4a=4n$. Since it is indefinite and has the minimum d, Theorem 62 gives

(171) $$d^2 = \tfrac{4}{5}n \text{ or } d^2 \leqq \tfrac{1}{2}n .$$

Since G is indefinite, of minimum n, and of determinant $d^2\Delta$, Lemma 1 gives

(172) $$n^3 = \tfrac{2}{3}d^2\Delta \text{ or } n^3 \leqq \tfrac{2}{5}d^2\Delta .$$

If (171_2) holds, then

$$d^6 \leqq \tfrac{1}{8} \cdot \tfrac{2}{3}d^2\Delta , \qquad d^4 \leqq \tfrac{1}{12}\Delta .$$

If (171_1) holds, then either

$$d^6 \leqq (\tfrac{4}{5})^3 \cdot \tfrac{2}{5}d^2\Delta , \qquad d^4 \leqq \tfrac{128}{625}\Delta ,$$

or

(173) $$d^2 = \tfrac{4}{5}n , \qquad n^3 = \tfrac{2}{3}d^2\Delta , \qquad d^4 = \tfrac{128}{375}\Delta .$$

In case (173), Lemma 1 with x and z interchanged shows that we may take

$$G = n(z^2 - y^2 - x^2 + zy + xz) .$$

Division of (159) by d gives

$$F = d[(Ux + Vy + Wz + t)^2 + \tfrac{5}{4}(z^2 - y^2 - x^2 + zy + xz)] .$$

Take $x=1$, $y=z=0$. Since $|F|\geqq d$, $|(U+t)^2-\frac{5}{4}|\geqq 1$, $U-\frac{1}{2}$ must be an integer as in I_1 of § 60. By adding an integral multiple of x to t, we may take $U=\frac{1}{2}$, and similarly $V=\frac{1}{2}$ in view of the symmetry of F in x and y. Take $x=0$, $y=1$, $z=-1$; then $|(\frac{1}{2}-W+t)^2-\frac{5}{4}|\geqq 1$ and W is an integer. We may take $W=0$. But then $F=0$ for $x=3$, $y=0$, $z=t=1$, whereas F has a minimum $m>0$. Hence in the present case,

$$d^4 \leqq \tfrac{128}{625}\, \Delta\ .$$

69. Case $S=0$, $a=n$. Hence G is indefinite and does not represent $-n$. We may take $\Delta=1$. By Lemma 2,

$$(174)\qquad\qquad a^3=n^3<\tfrac{1}{3}|g|=\tfrac{1}{3}d^2\ .$$

The discriminant of f is $-4a$ by (165), whence f is definite. It is a negative form by (163), whence $B<0$, $C<0$. Since it is reduced,

$$(175)\qquad\qquad BC\leqq\tfrac{4}{3}a\ .$$

The ternary forms $F_{y=0}$ and $F_{z=0}$, of negative determinants B and C, represent $d>0$ and hence are indefinite and have the minimum d. Hence

$$(176)\qquad\qquad d^3=-\tfrac{2}{3}B\ ,\ \text{or}\ d^3\leqq-\tfrac{2}{5}B\ ,$$

$$(177)\qquad\qquad d^3=-\tfrac{2}{3}C\ ,\ \text{or}\ d^3\leqq-\tfrac{2}{5}C\ .$$

Let both (176_2) and (177_2) hold. Then by (174) and (175),

$$d^6\leqq\ \tfrac{4}{25}BC\leqq\tfrac{16}{75}a\ ,\qquad d^{16}\leqq\tfrac{1}{3}(\tfrac{16}{75})^3<(\tfrac{4}{15})^4\ ,$$

$$(178)\qquad\qquad d^4\leqq\tfrac{4}{15}\ .$$

Next, let (176_1) hold. For $\phi=F_{y=0}$,

$$(179)\qquad d\phi-(dt+ux+wz)^2=ax^2+2\sigma xz+\gamma z^2=\psi_1=G_{y=0}\ .$$

The discriminant of ψ_1 is $-4dB>0$. The coefficient d and a of ϕ and ψ_1 are their minima. The determinant of ϕ is B. Each of ψ_1, $\phi_{x=0}$, $\phi_{z=0}$ are reduced forms by Theorem 92. All conditions in Lemma 4 are satisfied. Hence ϕ is (155) with x and y replaced by t and x:

$$F_{y=0}=d(t^2+x^2-z^2+tx+tz+2xz)=d[(t+\tfrac{1}{2}x+\tfrac{1}{2}z)^2+\tfrac{3}{4}x^2+\tfrac{3}{2}xz-\tfrac{5}{4}z^2]\ .$$

Comparing the latter with (179) we have $a=\tfrac{3}{4}d^2$.

Hence if (176$_1$), but not (177$_1$), holds then

$$d^6 \leqq \tfrac{2}{3} \cdot \tfrac{3}{5} BC \leqq \tfrac{4}{15} \cdot \tfrac{4}{3} a = \tfrac{4}{15} d^2 \ ,$$

and hence (178) holds.

Next, let (177$_1$) hold. Interchanging y and z in the preceding case, we get

$$F_{z=0} = d(t^2 + x^2 - y^2 + tx + ty + 2xy) \ , \qquad a = \tfrac{3}{4} d^2 \ .$$

Then if (176$_1$) fails, we again get (178).

There remains only the case (176$_1$) with (177$_1$). Then

$$F = d(x^2 - y^2 - z^2 + t^2 + tx + ty + tz + 2xy + 2xz + 2hyz) \ ,$$
$$d^6 = \tfrac{4}{9} BC \leqq \tfrac{4}{9} d^2 \ , \qquad d^4 \leqq \tfrac{4}{9} \ .$$

Since F has determinant $\Delta = 1$,

$$\tfrac{3}{4} d^4 [4 - (h-1)^2] = 1 \ .$$

Hence $(h-1)^2 \leqq 1$, $0 \leqq h \leqq 2$.

When $x = t = 0$, $y = z = 1$, $F/d = 2h - 2$. Since $|F| \geqq d$, either $h \geqq 3/2$ or $h \leqq \tfrac{1}{2}$. When $x = 0$, $t = -1$, $y = z = 1$, $F/d = 2h - 3$. If $h \geqq 3/2$, then $2h - 3 \geqq 1$, $h \geqq 2$, whence $h = 2$. Hence either $h = 2$ or $0 \leqq h \leqq \tfrac{1}{2}$.

In the latter case, consider the binary section

$$y^2 + (2h+1)yz - z^2 \ ,$$

obtained from F/d by taking $x = 0$, $t = y$. Its minimum is 1 (since that of F is d). Its discriminant is

$$(2h+1)^2 + 4 \leqq 8 \ .$$

By Theorem 62, the discriminant is either 5 or 8, whence $h = 0$ or $h = \tfrac{1}{2}$, respectively. Taking $x = -y = z = t = 1$, we get $F/d = 1 - 2h$, which excludes $h = 1/2$.

Hence $h = 0$ or 2, and $d^4 = 4/9$. If $h = 0$, we get

(180) $$F = d(x^2 - y^2 - z^2 + t^2 + tx + ty + tz + 2xy + 2xz) \ .$$

The form given by $h = 2$ is derived from (180) by replacing z by $-z$, and x by $x + 2z$. Since (180) is unaltered by the interchange of y and z, the two forms are properly equivalent.

It remains to show that d is actually the minimum of (180). This is evidently true if F is not a zero form. But $4F/d$ is equal to

$$(2x+2y+2z+t)^2+3t^2-2(2y+z)^2-6z^2 ,$$

and the form $H = X^2+3T^2-2Y^2-6Z^2$ is not a zero form. For, $H \equiv 0 \pmod 3$ requires that $X = 3\xi$, $Y = 3\eta$, whence H is the triple of $T^2+3\xi^2-2Z^2-6\eta^2$, which is of type H. Another proof was given in the second footnote of § 39.

Theorem[1] 93. *If an indefinite, quaternary, quadratic form F has a positive determinant Δ and a minimum m, then $m^4 \leq \frac{4}{5}\Delta$. If $m^4 = \frac{4}{5}\Delta$, then F is equivalent to (180), where $d = m$. If F is not equivalent to (180), then $m^4 \leq \frac{4}{15}\Delta$.*

70. Case $S = -2$. By (9), G is a negative form and $\Delta < 0$. We may take $\Delta = -1$. Evidently $a = -n$ and $-a \leq -\beta$, $-a \leq -\gamma$.

The form $[a, 2u, d]$ is indefinite, of minimum d, and of discriminant $-4a$, whence either

$$(181) \qquad\qquad d^2 = -\tfrac{4}{5}a ,$$

or

$$(182) \qquad d^2 \leq -\tfrac{1}{2}a , \qquad d^2 \leq -\tfrac{1}{2}\beta , \qquad d^2 \leq -\tfrac{1}{2}\gamma .$$

The forms $[a, 2\pi, \beta]$, $[a, 2\sigma, \gamma]$, and $f = [C, -2R, B]$ are reduced forms of discriminants $-4dC$, $-4dB$, $-4a$. They are all definite since f is a positive form by (163). Hence

$$(183) \qquad a\beta \leq \tfrac{4}{3}dC , \qquad a\gamma \leq \tfrac{4}{3}dB , \qquad BC \leq -\tfrac{4}{3}a ,$$
$$-a\beta\gamma \leq (\tfrac{4}{3})^3 d^2 .$$

In case (182) we have

$$d^6 \leq -\tfrac{1}{8}a\beta\gamma \leq \tfrac{8}{27}d^2 , \qquad d^4 \leq \tfrac{8}{27} .$$

Henceforth, let $d^4 > 8/27$. Then (181) holds. Since $F_{y=0}$ and $F_{z=0}$ have the minimum d and determinants B and C, we have either

$$(184) \qquad\qquad d^3 = \tfrac{2}{3}C$$

---

[1] By the method of § 84, Oppenheim gave another proof with the final inequality replaced by the cruder one $m^8 \leq \frac{16}{135} \Delta^2$, in *Proc. Nat. Acad. Sc.*, XV (1929), 724–27.

or

(185) $$d^3 \leqq \tfrac{2}{5}C \text{ and } d^3 \leqq \tfrac{2}{5}B ,$$

since $0 < C \leqq B$ in the reduced positive f. By (185), (183), and (181),

$$d^6 \leqq \tfrac{4}{25}BC \leqq - \tfrac{4}{25} \cdot \tfrac{4}{3} a = \tfrac{4}{25} \cdot \tfrac{4}{3} \cdot \tfrac{5}{4} d^2 = \tfrac{4}{15} d^2 , \qquad d^4 \leqq \tfrac{4}{15} < \tfrac{8}{27} ,$$

which excludes (185). Hence (184) holds. As in the case of (179), the binary form associated with $F_{z=0}$ is reduced. Hence by Lemma 3,

(186) $$F_{z=0} = d[(t + \tfrac{1}{2}y + \tfrac{1}{2}x)^2 - \tfrac{5}{4}y^2 \mp \tfrac{1}{2}yx - \tfrac{5}{4}x^2] .$$

Also, by $F_{y=0}$,

(187) $$d^3 = \tfrac{2}{3}B \text{ or } d^3 = \tfrac{2}{5}B \text{ or } d^3 \leqq \tfrac{1}{3}B .$$

If the third case holds, then

$$d^6 \leqq \tfrac{2}{9}BC \leqq - \tfrac{2}{9} \cdot \tfrac{4}{3} a = \tfrac{2}{9} \cdot \tfrac{4}{3} \cdot \tfrac{5}{4} d^2 , \qquad d^4 \leqq \tfrac{10}{27} .$$

Case (184) *and* (187₁). By (179) and Lemma 3,

$$F_{y=0} = d[(t + \tfrac{1}{2}x + \tfrac{1}{2}z)^2 - \tfrac{5}{4}x^2 \mp \tfrac{1}{2}xz - \tfrac{5}{4}z^2] .$$

Using also (186), we get

$$F = d[(t + \tfrac{1}{2}x + \tfrac{1}{2}y + \tfrac{1}{2}z)^2 - \tfrac{5}{4}x^2 - \tfrac{5}{4}y^2 - \tfrac{5}{4}z^2 + (2h - \tfrac{1}{2})yz \mp \tfrac{1}{2}xz \mp \tfrac{1}{2}xy] ,$$

for four combinations of signs. Let F' be the form with both signs $-$. For the signs $+$, $-$, we change the sign of z and then replace t by $t+z$. For the signs $-$, $+$, we change the sign of y and replace t by $t+y$. For the signs $+$, $+$, we change the sign of x and replace t by $t+x$. Hence all cases are reduced to F' by a proper or improper transformation. Hence let both signs be $-$. Then

$$F = d(t^2 + tx + ty + tz - x^2 - y^2 - z^2 + 2hyz) .$$

Since its determinant is $\Delta = -1$, we have

(188) $$(1+h)(7-5h)d^4 = 4 , \qquad -1 < h < 7/5 .$$

The binary $y^2 - 2hyz + z^2$ obtained from $-F/d$ by taking $x = t = 0$ must have the minimum 1. If $h = 1$, it is a zero form. If $h^2 > 1$, it is indefinite, whence its discriminant $4h^2 - 4$ is $\geqq 5$ by Theorem 62. This contradicts (188). Hence $h^2 < 1$. Then the binary is definite and $1 \leqq \frac{1}{3}(4 - 4h^2)$, whence $-\frac{1}{2} \leqq h \leqq \frac{1}{2}$.

The binary $y^2 + (2h+1)yz - z^2$ obtained from F/d by taking $x = 0$, $t = y$, is indefinite, of minimum 1, and of discriminant $(2h+1)^2 + 4 \leqq 8$. By Theorem 62, the discriminant is 5 or 8, whence $h = 0$ or $h = 1/2$, respectively. But $F(-1, 1, 1, 1) = (2h-1)d = 0$ if $h = 1/2$. Hence $h = 0$ and F is

$$F_1 = d(-x^2 - y^2 - z^2 + t^2 + xt + yt + zt) , \tag{189}$$

where $d^4 = 4/7$. Since F_1 is unaltered by the improper transformation which interchanges x and y, we conclude that every F is properly equivalent to F_1. Since

$$4F_1/d = 7t^2 - (2x - t)^2 - (2y - t)^2 - (2z - t)^2 ,$$

and, if $t \neq 0$, $7t^2$ is not a sum of three squares, F_1 is not a zero form. Hence F_1 has the minimum d.

Case (184) *and* (187$_2$). Then by (179), all the assumptions in Lemma 5 are satisfied, whence

$$\frac{1}{d} F_{y=0} = t^2 - x^2 - z^2 + tx + 2tz + xz = (t + \tfrac{1}{2}x + z)^2 - \tfrac{5}{4}x^2 - 2z^2 .$$

Using also (186), we get

$$F = d[(t + \tfrac{1}{2}x + \tfrac{1}{2}y + z)^2 - \tfrac{5}{4}(x^2 + y^2) - 2z^2 \mp \tfrac{1}{2}xy + (2h - 1)yz] . \tag{190}$$

We may discard the lower sign by changing the sign of x and replacing x by $x + t$. Then

$$F = d(-x^2 - y^2 - z^2 + t^2 + xz + 2hyz + xt + yt + 2zt) .$$

Since its determinant is -1,

$$[5(2h - 1)^2 - 48]d^4 = -16 , \qquad 5(2h - 1)^2 < 48 . \tag{191}$$

The form $y^2 + (1 - 2h)yz + 2z^2$, obtained from $-F/d$ by taking $x = 0$, $t = -z$, has the minimum 1 and discriminant $(1 - 2h)^2 - 8$. If the latter is > 0, the form is indefinite and the discriminant is $\geqq 5$ by Theorem 62, whence $(2h - 1)^2 \geqq 13$, contrary to (191). Hence $(1 - 2h)^2 < 8$ and the form is definite, whence $1 \leqq \frac{1}{3}[8 - (1 - 2h)^2]$,

$$(1 - 2h)^2 \leqq 5 . \tag{192}$$

Consider the form $\psi = y^2 - 2hyz + z^2$, of minimum 1, obtained from $-F/d$ by taking $x = t = 0$. If $h^2 > 1$, ψ is indefinite and $4(h^2 - 1) \geq 5$, $h^2 \geq 9/4$, whence $h \geq \frac{3}{2}$ or $h \leq -\frac{3}{2}$. The latter gives $(1 - 2h)^2 \geq 16$, contrary to (192). Hence $2h \geq 3$, and $2h - 1 \leq \sqrt{5}$ by (192). Then $4(h^2 - 1) \leq (1 + \sqrt{5})^2 - 4 < 8$, whence, by Theorem 62, $4h^2 - 4 = 5$, $h = 3/2$. By (159), G is proportional to the part of (190) after the first square, and hence to $(5x + y)^2 + \rho$, $\rho = 24y^2 - 40yz + 40z^2$, whence f is proportional to ρ. But this positive form ρ is not reduced, contrary to hypothesis.

Hence $h^2 < 1$. Now ψ is definite, whence $1 \leq \frac{1}{3}(4 - 4h^2)$, $-1 \leq 2h \leq 1$. Next, $\chi = y^2 + 2(1 - h)yz + z^2$, which is derived from $-F/d$ by taking $x = 0$, $t = -y$, has minimum 1.

First, let $(1 - h)^2 > 1$. Then h is negative and χ is indefinite, whence its discriminant $4(1 - h)^2 - 4$ is ≥ 5, and $1 - h \geq 3/2$, $2h \leq -1$. Thus $2h = -1$ and G is proportional to $(5x + y)^2 + M$, $M = 24y^2 + 40yz + 40z^2$, whence f is not reduced.

Second, let $(1 - h)^2 < 1$, whence $0 < h < 2$. Since χ is now definite, $3 \leq 4 - 4(1 - h)^2$, whence $(2 - 2h)^2 \leq 1$. This with $-1 \leq 2h \leq 1$ gives $2h = 1$. Then $F(-1, 1, 1, 1) = 0$.

Hence this case is excluded.

THEOREM 94. *If an indefinite, quaternary, quadratic form F has a minimum m and the signature -2, then its determinant Δ is negative and $m^4 \leq -\frac{4}{7}\Delta$. If $m^4 = -\frac{4}{7}\Delta$, then F is equivalent to F_1 in (189), where $d = m$. But if F is not equivalent to F_1, then $m^4 \leq -\frac{10}{17}\Delta$.*

71. Case $S = 2$. By (170), $\Delta < 0$ and G is indefinite. We saw below (170) that we may exclude the case in which F represents $-d$. We may take $\Delta = -1$.

First, let G represent $-n$. By (160), $a = -n$. The section $[a, 2u, d]$ of F does not represent $-d$. Its discriminant is $-4a = 4n$. It is indefinite and of minimum d. Since it is not equivalent to the binary form (1) or (2), we have $d^2 < 4n/8$. Since G has the determinant $-d^2$ and minimum n, Lemma 1 gives $n^3 \leq \frac{2}{3}d^2$. Hence

$$d^6 < \frac{1}{8}n^3 \leq \frac{1}{12}d^2 , \qquad d^4 < \frac{1}{12} .$$

Second, suppose that G does not represent $-n$. Then $a = n$ is the minimum of G. By Lemma 2, $a^3 < \frac{1}{3}d^2$.

The discriminant of f is $-4a\Delta = 4a$; write D for its positive square root. We may identify the indefinite reduced f with any form Φ_{2i} of the chain to which it belongs. By (5) and (163),

$$C = A_{2i} > 0 , \qquad B = -A_{2i+1} < 0 .$$

Consider the continued fractions (9). By (10),

$$(193) \qquad\qquad K_i = F_i + S_i = D/A_{i+1} .$$

Now $G_{y=0}$ has discriminant $-4dB$ and hence is indefinite, has the minimum a, and does not represent $-a$. Also, $G_{z=0}$ has discriminant $-4dC$ and is a reduced positive form of minimum a. Hence

$$(194) \qquad a^2 < \tfrac{25}{221}(-4dB) = \rho dA_{2i+1} , \qquad a^2 \leqq \tfrac{4}{3}dA_{2i} ,$$

where $\rho = 100/221$. Finally, $F_{y=0}$ has determinant B and minimum d, is indefinite, and does not represent $-d$. By Lemma 2,

$$(195) \qquad\qquad d^3 < -\tfrac{1}{3}B = \tfrac{1}{3}A_{2i+1} = \tfrac{2}{3}\sqrt{a}/K_{2i} .$$

Elimination of A_{2i+1} gives $a^{3/2} < 2\rho d/K_{2i}$. From this and the cube of (195), we get

$$d^9 < 2(\tfrac{2}{3})^3 \rho d/K_{2i}^4 , \qquad d^4 < \left(\frac{2}{K_{2i}}\right)^2 \sqrt{\rho/27} .$$

Hence $d^4 < \tfrac{1}{3}$ if $2/K_{2i} \leqq \sqrt{3/\rho}$, and therefore if $K_{2i} > 1.247$. We have our desired result $d^4 < \tfrac{1}{3}$ except when $K_{2i} \leqq 1.247$. In the latter case, $g_{2i} = 1$. Write $g = g_{2i+1}$, $h = g_{2i-1}$. Then

$$F_{2i} > (1, g, 1) , \qquad 1/S_{2i} = (h, \ldots) < h+1 ,$$
$$K_{2i} > 1+v , \qquad v = 1/(1+g) + 1/(h+1) .$$

Hence $K_{2i} \leqq 1.247$ gives $v < 0.247$. But if both g and h are $\leqq 7$, then $v \geqq 1/8 + 1/8 = 0.25$. Hence at least one of g and h is $\geqq 8$. The case $g \geqq 8$ is reduced to the case $h \geqq 8$ by replacing i by $i-1$ and hence identifying f with Φ_{2i-2} instead of Φ_{2i}. Hence we may take $h \geqq 8$, whence $K_{2i-1} > 8$. Then by (194_2) and by (193) with i replaced by $2i-1$,

$$a^2 \leqq \tfrac{4}{3}d \cdot 2\sqrt{a}/K_{2i+1} , \qquad a^3 < d^2/9 ,$$

where the last follows from the square of the first.

Since $[a, 2u, d]$ has discriminant $-4a < 0$, it is a positive reduced form of minimum d. Hence $d^2 \leqq 4a/3$. Cubing this, we see that

$$d^6 < (\tfrac{4}{3})^3 d^2/9 , \qquad d^4 < 64/243 < \tfrac{1}{3} .$$

Hence in all cases, $d^4 < \frac{1}{3}$ when $\Delta = -1$. This proves that if $S=2$ and if F represents its minimum d, but not $-d$, then $d^4 < -\frac{1}{3}\Delta$.

For the excluded case in which F represents $-d$, $-F$ has $S=-2$ and Theorem 94 applies to $-F$ and yields a like theorem concerning an F of signature 2 which represents $-d$, with F_1 replaced by $-F_1$. Since $1/3 < 10/27$, the latter theorem holds also if F does not represent $-d$.

Hence Theorem 94 holds also for signature $+2$ if we replace F_1 by $-F_1$. Combining the two theorems, we get

Theorem 95. *If an indefinite, quaternary, quadratic form F has a minimum m and negative determinant Δ, then $m^4 \leqq -\frac{4}{7}\Delta$. If $m^4 = -\frac{4}{7}\Delta$, F is equivalent to $\pm F_1$, where F_1 is* (189) *with $d=m$. But if F is equivalent to neither F_1 nor $-F_1$, then[1] $m^4 \leqq -\frac{10}{27}\Delta$.*

By the method of § 65, we readily show that if F does not attain its lower bound L, then $L^4 < 4\Delta/15$ when $\Delta > 0$, while $L^4 < -\frac{1}{3}\Delta$, when $\Delta < 0$, and hence extend Theorems 93 and 95 to the case in which F does not have a minimum.

---

[1] A further discussion shows that $m^4 < -\frac{1}{3}\Delta$.

CHAPTER X

TABULATION OF REDUCED, INTEGRAL, TERNARY,
QUADRATIC FORMS WHICH ARE INDEFINITE,
BUT NOT ZERO FORMS

72. It suffices to consider forms whose determinant d is positive. For, if $d < 0$, we multiply the form by -1.

Markoff[1] tabulated the forms with $d \leq 50$. We shall explain his method and supply essential details. The table was computed anew by A. E. Ross and extended to $d = 83$ except for[2] $d = 68$ and 81. The preliminary material was written by the author.

It suffices to treat integral forms $F = ax^2 + \ldots$ whose minimum is $m = |a|$. Unless F is equivalent to one of the forms $f_1, \ldots, f_4$ in Theorem 84, $m^3 < 8d/25$, whence $m < 3$ if $d < 85$. We see that f_i of minimum m_i has integral coefficients and determinant $d < 85$ only when $m_1 = 2$, $d = 12$; $m_2 = 2$, $d = 20$; $m_3 = 1$, $d = 3$; $m_3 = 2$, $d = 24$; $m_3 = 3$, $d = 81$; $m_4 = 2$, $d = 25$. Hence when $d < 85$, we have $m = 1$ or 2 except for forms equivalent to $-3x^2 - 3y^2 + 9z^2$.

Hence let $|a| = 1$ or 2. By Theorem 81, we may assume that the associated binary form f in (87) is reduced. By the remark before (88), the determinant of f is $-ad$. Without altering f, we can choose u and v in (89) to simplify s and t in $ax + ty + sz$ of (87).

If $a = \pm 1$, we can therefore take $t = s = 0$. Then $F = \pm x^2 \pm f$. Write $\phi = -f$. If $a = +1$, $F = x^2 - \phi$, where ϕ has determinant $-d$ and hence is a positive form. If $a = -1$, $F = -x^2 + \phi$, where ϕ has determinant d and is indefinite.

If $a = \pm 2$, we may assume that each of t and s is 0 or 1. Write $\phi = \pm f$. Then F is $F_1, \ldots,$ or F_4, where

$$F_i = \pm 2l_i^2 - \tfrac{1}{2}\phi \ , \quad l_1 = x \ , \quad l_2 = x + \tfrac{1}{2}y \ , \quad l_3 = x + \tfrac{1}{2}z \ , \quad l_4 = x + \tfrac{1}{2}y + \tfrac{1}{2}z \ .$$

In case F represents -2, it is treated under the case $a = -2$.

[1] *Mém. Imp. Acad. Sc. St. Pétersbourg* (ser. 8), XXIII, 1909, No. 7, 22 pp. The table was recomputed by the author.

[2] The entries for $d = 68$ are $A = x^2 - 3y^2 - 2yz - 23z^2$ and $B = x^2 - 7y^2 - 6yz - 11z^2$, having primitive adjoints, $C = x^2 - 6y^2 - 4yz - 12z^2$ with an even adjoint, and the even $D = -2x^2 - 2xy - 2xz - 2y^2 + 22z^2$. But the equivalence of A and B is not decided.

Let $a=2$. Then no one of 0, 1, -1, -2 is represented by F. The form $\phi=\alpha y^2+2\beta yz+\gamma z^2$ is a reduced positive form of determinant $-2d$. Hence $\alpha^2\leq 8d/3$. Let $d\leq 84$. Then $\alpha<15$. In F_2 and F_4, α is odd, $\alpha=2A-1$, $A\leq 7$. For $z=0$, $y=1$, they become

$$\psi(A)=2x^2+2x+1-A\ .$$

For $x=0$, $\psi(1)=0$, $\psi(2)=-1$, $\psi(3)=-2$. For $x=1$, $\psi(4)=1$, $\psi(5)=0$, $\psi(6)=-1$, $\psi(7)=-2$. This excludes F_2 and F_4. In F_1 and F_3, α is even, $\alpha=2A$, $A\leq 7$. For $z=0$, they become $2x^2-Ay^2$, which takes the values

$A=$	1	2	3	4	5	7
$x=$	0	1	1	1	3	2
$y=$	1	1	1	1	2	1
$2x^2-Ay^2=$	-1	0	-1	-2	-2	1

It remains to consider the case $A=6$, $\alpha=12$. Since ϕ is a reduced positive form of discriminant $-8d$, $\alpha\gamma=12\gamma\leq\frac{1}{3}\cdot 8d$, $\gamma<19$, $\gamma\geq 12$.

For F_1, γ is even, $\gamma=2C$, $C=6$, 7, 8, or 9. Take $y=0$; then $F_1=2x^2-Cz^2$. As before, $C\neq 7$. For $C=8$ or 9, F_1 represents 0 or -1. Hence let $C=6$, $\gamma=12$. Since ϕ is reduced, $0\leq 2\beta\leq 12$. Since the determinant of ϕ is even, $\beta=2B$, $0\leq B\leq 3$. Now $F_1=2x^2-6y^2-2Byz-6z^2$. According as $B=1$, 2, or 3, $F_1(2,1,-1)=-2$, $F_1(2,1,-1)=0$, or $F_1(3,1,1)=0$. Hence $B=0$, $F_1=2(x^2-3y^2-3z^2)$, which represents no one of 0, ± 1, -2.

For $F_3=2(x+\frac{1}{2}z)^2-\frac{1}{2}\phi$, $\gamma=13$, 15, or 17. When $\gamma=13$, $F_3(1,0,1)=-2$. When $\gamma=17$, $F_3(3,0,2)=-2$. Hence $\gamma=15$, $-12<2\beta\leq 12$, $\beta=2B$, $-3<B\leq 3$. Since we may change the signs of x and z, we may take $B\geq 0$. For $B=0$, 1, or 2, $F_3(2,1,1)=-1$, $F_3(3,1,-1)=1$, or $F_3(4,2,1)=1$. Hence $B=3$. Since $F_3\not\equiv 1\pmod 3$, $F_3\not\equiv 1$ or -2. Write $X=2x+z$, $Y=2y+z$. Then $6F_3=3X^2-9Y^2-36z^2$. Thus $6F_3\not\equiv -6\pmod 8$, $F_3\not\equiv -1$. Also, $F_3\neq 0$ since $F_1\neq 0$.

Hence $a=2$ is excluded except for the special forms F_1, F_3.

If $F=-x^2+\phi$ does not represent zero, neither α nor γ is a square. The indefinite binary form ϕ is chosen as the principal form rather than as one of the chain of reduced forms.

Of the forms $x^2-\phi$, we therefore need consider only those which represent neither -1 nor 0. In the reduced, positive, binary form ϕ, neither α nor γ is of type w^2 or $1+w^2$.

When $a=-2$, there are corresponding restrictions on the indefinite form ϕ of determinant $2d$.

Use was made of the tables of binary quadratic forms due to A. Cayley,[1] A. E. Cooper,[2] and H. N. Wright.[3] Cayley's tables of indefinite forms were recomputed and extended to 200 by Ross.

From the resulting list of ternary forms F we exclude those which represent 0, or -1 for $x^2 - \phi$, or ± 1 for $a = -2$. This was usually accomplished by small values of x, y, z. But -1 is represented by $x^2 - 3y^2 - 2yz - 18z^2$ for $x = 99$, $y = 52$, $z = -13$; by $x^2 - 6y^2 - 4yz - 11z^2$ for $x = 18$, $y = 5$, $z = -5$; and by $x^2 - 7y^2 - 11z^2$ for $x = 43$, $y = 15$, $z = 5$.

That none of the remaining forms represent zero was verified by Theorem 23 after completing squares.

Certain forms were proved equivalent by finding an appropriate integral transformation of determinant unity. The transformation

$$(3x + 5y + 33z , \qquad 3x + 4y + 29z , \qquad x + y + 8z) ,$$

which replaces x, y, z by the respective functions in parenthesis, transforms $-x^2 + 2y^2 + 2yz - 16z^2$ into $-x^2 - y^2 + 33z^2$. Again,

$$(3x + 7y + 57z , \qquad 10x + 17y + 149z , \qquad 3x + 5y + 44z)$$

replaces $-x^2 + 2y^2 + 2yz - 28z^2$ by $-x^2 - y^2 + 57z^2$. Also,

$$(8x + 4y + 79z , \qquad 11x + 7y + 116z , \qquad -3x - 2y - 32z)$$

replaces $-x^2 + 3y^2 + 2yz - 26z^2$ by $-x^2 - y^2 + 79z^2$. Theorem 47 proves the equivalence of the forms in each of the following pairs:

$$d = 41 , \quad x^2 - 3y^2 - 2yz - 14z^2 , \quad x^2 - 6y^2 - 2yz - 7z^2 ;$$
$$d = 63 , \quad x^2 - 3y^2 - 21z^2 , \quad x^2 - 6y^2 - 6yz - 12z^2 ;$$
$$d = 65 , \quad -x^2 + 5y^2 - 13z^2 , \quad -x^2 + 2y^2 + 2yz - 32z^2 ;$$
$$d = 66 , \quad -2x^2 - 2y^2 + 2yz + 16z^2 , \quad -2x^2 - 2xy - 2y^2 + 22z^2 .$$

In the following tables, no two forms of the same determinant d are equivalent. This was usually proved by congruential tests applied to F or to its adjoint, but occasionally by showing that $x^2 - \phi \neq -1$. For example, let F_1, F_2, F_3 denote the successive entries under $d = 54$ in Table III. Since $F_1 \not\equiv -1$ (mod 3), $F_1 \neq -1$ and F_1 is equivalent to neither F_2 nor F_3. The

---

[1] *Jour. für Math.*, LX (1862), 357–69; *Coll. Math. Papers*, V, 141–53. From -100 to $+99$.

[2] *Annals of Math.*, XXVI (1924–25), 309–16. From -101 to -200.

[3] *University of Cal. Publications in Math.*, I (1914), No. 5. From -1 to -150.

adjoints of the latter are the primitive $-54x^2-54y^2+z^2$ and the imprimitive $-54x^2-18y^2+3z^2$, respectively, whence F_2 and F_3 are not equivalent.

Next, let $F_1, \ldots, F_5$ be the successive entries under $d=72$ in Table III. The only imprimitive one of these is F_4. The adjoints of the others are

$$A_1 = -72x^2+24y^2-3z^2 , \quad A_2 = -72x^2-24y^2+3z^2 , \quad A_3 = -72x^2+12y^2-6z^2$$

and the properly primitive $A_5 = 33x^2-14y^2-12z^2+12yz+12xz-6xy$. But $A_3 \equiv 0 \pmod 6$, $A_2 \equiv 3z^2$, $A_1(0, 0, 1) \equiv 1 \pmod 4$. Hence no two of the F_i are equivalent.

I. d A PRIME p OR DOUBLE A PRIME p, $d \leq 83$.
Single class of indefinite, non-zero forms of determinant d.

$d=p$	$p \equiv 3 \pmod 4$	$-x^2-y^2+pz^2$
"	$p=8n+5$	$-x^2+2y^2+2yz-(4n+2)z^2$
"	$p=24n+17$	$x^2-3y^2-2yz-(8n+6)z^2$
$d=2p$	$p \equiv 3 \pmod 4$	$-x^2-y^2+2pz^2$
"	$p=8n+5$	$-x^2+2y^2-pz^2$
"	$p=24n+17$	$-x^2+3y^2+2yz-(16n+11)z^2$

II. d A PRODUCT OF TWO DISTINCT ODD PRIMES p AND q; $d<83$.
Three classes of indefinite, non-zero forms of determinant d.

$p \equiv 7 \pmod 8$ $q \equiv 5 \pmod 8$ $d=8n+3$	$-x^2-y^2+pqz^2$ $-x^2+2y^2+2yz-(4n+1)z^2$ $-x^2-2y^2+2yz+(4n+1)z^2$
$p \equiv 3 \pmod 8$ $q \equiv 5 \pmod 8$ $d=8n+7$	$-x^2-y^2+pqz^2$ $-x^2+2y^2+2yz-(4n+3)z^2$ $-x^2-2y^2+2yz+(4n+3)z^2$
$p=3$ $q \equiv 17 \pmod {24}$ $d=24n+3$	$-x^2-y^2+pqz^2$ $-x^2+3y^2-qz^2$ $-x^2-3y^2+qz^2$
$p \equiv 3 \pmod 8$ $q \equiv 7 \pmod 8$ $d=8n+5$	$-x^2-y^2+pqz^2$ $-x^2+2y^2+2yz-(4n+2)z^2$ $-x^2-2y^2+2yz+(4n+2)z^2$
$p=3$ $q \equiv 11$ or $19 \pmod {24}$ $d=24n+9$	$x^2-3y^2-qz^2$ $x^2-6y^2-6yz-(4n+3)z^2$, $-x^2-y^2+pqz^2$
$p \equiv 5 \pmod {24}$ $q \equiv 13 \pmod {24}$ $d=24n+17$	$x^2-3y^2-2yz-(8n+6)z^2$ $x^2-6y^2-2yz-(4n+3)z^2$ $-x^2+2y^2+2yz-(12n+8)z^2$

III. d NOT p, $2p$, OR pq, p AND q DISTINCT ODD PRIMES.

Every indefinite, non-zero form of determinant d is equivalent to one and only one of the forms listed at the right of d.

4	no forms	54	$x^2-3y^2-18z^2$
8	no forms		$-x^2-y^2+54z^2$
9	$x^2-3y^2-3z^2$		$-x^2-3y^2+18z^2$
12	$-x^2-y^2+12z^2$	56	$x^2-3y^2-2yz-19z^2$
	$-x^2+2y^2-6z^2$		$-x^2-y^2+56z^2$
	$-2x^2-2y^2-2xy+4z^2$		$-x^2-4y^2+4yz+13z^2$
16	No forms		$-x^2-2y^2+28z^2$
18	$-x^2+3y^2-6z^2$		$-2x^2-2y^2+14z^2$
20	$x^2-3y^2-2yz-7z^2$	60	$-x^2-3y^2+20z^2$
	$-x^2+2y^2-10z^2$		$-x^2+2y^2-30z^2$
	$-2x^2-2xy-2xz-2y^2+6z^2$		$-x^2-2y^2+30z^2$
24	$x^2-3y^2-8z^2$		$-x^2-4y^2+4yz+14z^2$
	$-x^2-y^2+24z^2$		$-2x^2-2xy-2y^2+20z^2$
	$-x^2-3y^2+8z^2$		$-2x^2-2xz-2y^2+2yz+14z^2$
	$-x^2+2y^2-12z^2$		$-2x^2-2xy-2xz-4y^2+8z^2$
	$-2x^2-2y^2+6z^2$		$x^2-3y^2-20z^2$
25	$-2x^2-2xy+2y^2-5z^2$		$x^2-8y^2-4yz-8z^2$
27	$x^2-6y^2-6yz-6z^2$		$-x^2-y^2+60z^2$
	$-x^2-y^2+27z^2$		$-x^2+3y^2-20z^2$
	$-x^2+3y^2-9z^2$	63	$x^2-3y^2-21z^2$
28	$-x^2-y^2+28z^2$		$-x^2-y^2+63z^2$
	$-x^2-2y^2+14z^2$		$-x^2-2y^2+2yz+31z^2$
	$-2x^2-2xz-2y^2+2yz+6z^2$		$-x^2+3y^2-21z^2$
30	$-x^2-y^2+30z^2$		$-2x^2-2xy-2y^2+21z^2$
	$-x^2+2y^2-15z^2$	64	No forms
	$-x^2-2y^2+15z^2$	66	$-x^2-y^2+66z^2$
	$-2x^2-2xy-2y^2+10z^2$		$-x^2+3y^2-22z^2$
32	No forms		$-x^2-3y^2+22z^2$
36	$x^2-3y^2-12z^2$		$-2x^2-2y^2+2yz+16z^2$
	$x^2-6y^2-6z^2$	70	$-x^2-y^2+70z^2$
	$-2x^2-2xy-2y^2+12z^2$		$-x^2+2y^2-35z^2$
40	$x^2-7y^2-6yz-7z^2$		$-x^2-2y^2+35z^2$
	$-x^2+3y^2+2yz-13z^2$		$-2x^2-2xy+2y^2-14z^2$
	$-x^2-3y^2+2yz+13z^2$	72	$-x^2+3y^2-24z^2$
	$-x^2+2y^2-20z^2$		$-x^2-3y^2+24z^2$
	$-2x^2+4y^2+4yz-4z^2$		$-x^2+6y^2-12z^2$
42	$-x^2-y^2+42z^2$		$2x^2-6y^2-6z^2$
	$-x^2+2y^2-21z^2$		$2x^2+2xz-6y^2-6yz-7z^2$
	$-x^2-2y^2+21z^2$	75	$-x^2-y^2+75z^2$
	$-2x^2-2y^2-2yz+10z^2$		$-x^2+2y^2+2yz-37z^2$
44	$-x^2-y^2+44z^2$		$-x^2+5y^2-15z^2$
	$-x^2+2y^2-22z^2$		$-x^2-5y^2+15z^2$
	$-2x^2-2y^2-2xz-2yz+10z^2$		$-2x^2-2xy+2y^2-15z^2$
45	$x^2-3y^2-15z^2$	76	$-x^2-y^2+76z^2$
	$-x^2+2y^2+2yz-22z^2$		$-x^2+2y^2-38z^2$
	$-x^2-2y^2+2yz+22z^2$		$-2x^2-2xz-2y^2+2yz+18z^2$
	$-x^2+3y^2-15z^2$	78	$-x^2-y^2+78z^2$
	$-x^2+6y^2+6yz-6z^2$		$-x^2+2y^2-39z^2$
48	$x^2-6y^2-8z^2$		$-x^2-2y^2+39z^2$
	$x^2-8y^2-8yz-8z^2$		$-2x^2-2xy-2xz+2y^2-16z^2$
	$-x^2-y^2+48z^2$	80	$x^2-3y^2-2yz-27z^2$
	$-x^2+2y^2-24z^2$		$x^2-7y^2-4yz-12z^2$
	$-x^2+3y^2-16z^2$		$x^2-8y^2-8yz-12z^2$
	$-x^2-4y^2+12z^2$		$-x^2+2y^2-40z^2$
	$-2x^2-2y^2+12z^2$		$-x^2-2y^2+40z^2$
	$-2x^2-2xy-2y^2+16z^2$		$-x^2+8y^2+8yz-8z^2$
49	$x^2-7y^2-7z^2$		$-2x^2+4y^2-10z^2$
50	$-x^2+5y^2-10z^2$		$-2x^2-2xy-2xz-2y^2+26z^2$
52	$x^2-7y^2-4yz-8z^2$		
	$-x^2+2y^2-26z^2$		
	$-2x^2-2xy+2y^2+2yz-10z^2$		

PART III

MISCELLANEOUS INVESTIGATIONS OF QUADRATIC FORMS

The final three chapters are independent of each other and of the earlier chapters. They present recent researches of especial interest concerning the geometrical reduction of positive forms, the determination of all universal zero forms, and the representation as sums of squares.

CHAPTER XI

REDUCED, POSITIVE, QUADRATIC FORMS; THEIR MINIMA

73. Literature. L. A. Seeber[1] devoted 132 pages of his book to inequalities which are satisfied by one and only one reduced, positive, ternary, quadratic form of a class. In a review of that book, Gauss[2] represented binary and ternary, positive, quadratic forms by lattices, and remarked that the importance and difficulty of Seeber's problem justified the great length of its treatment.

Eisenstein[3] noted that Seeber's quadratic inequalities may be replaced by linear ones and stated that Seeber's inequalities are equivalent to those in Theorem 103. He tabulated the primitive reduced forms of determinants ≤ 100.

Dirichlet[4] introduced the notion of reduced parallelograms and parallelopipeds and sketched a method of finding inequalities which segregate a single form from its class. But since he did not know the simplified inequalities, and did not attempt a complete solution, it is not surprising that his provisional suggestions would handicap rather than aid. He took r, s, t either all negative or all ≥ 0 (contrary to our § 80) and was led to six determinations of N instead of our three in (21)–(23). The resulting complexity would make his method prohibitive.

The author's simpler method is developed completely and is here first published. Facts stated by Dirichlet are here proved in full detail. Incidentally we obtain all automorphs of a reduced form; our results agree with those found by Eisenstein[5] by direct computations.

The table of all reduced forms for $d \leq 50$ was computed by Mr. Ross in nine hours and found to agree with Eisenstein's table[6] (for $d \leq 100$).

[1] *Untersuchungen über die Eigenschaften der positiven ternären quadratischen Formen*, Freiburg, 1831.

[2] *Göttingische gelehrte Anzeigen*, 1831, No. 108; reprinted in *Jour. für Math.*, XX (1840), 312–20; *Werke*, II, 188–96.

[3] *Jour. für Math.*, XLI (1851), 141–90.

[4] *Ibid.*, XL (1850), 209–27; *Werke*, II, 21–48. French translation in *Jour. de Math.*, (ser. 2), IV (1859), 209–32.

[5] *Jour. für Math.*, XLI (1851), 227–39.

[6] Extended to $d = 200$ by Borissow, St. Petersburg, 1890.

The minimum of all positive quadratic forms in four variables of determinant d is shown in § 84 to be $\leq \sqrt[4]{4d}$.

74. All equivalent, positive, binary, quadratic forms are represented by the same point lattice. Let $f = ax^2 + by^2 + 2txy$ be a positive form. Take

$$(1) \qquad OP = \sqrt{a}, \qquad OQ = \sqrt{b}, \qquad \cos POQ = t/\sqrt{ab}.$$

Consider the infinitude of parallels to OP such that the distance between any two consecutive parallels is that of Q from OP. Together with the analogous parallels to OQ they are said to form a *line lattice l*. Their intersections form a *point lattice L*.

The parallelogram $OPRQ$ determined by OP and OQ is called a *fundamental parallelogram* of lattice L since the points of L coincide with the vertices of the parallelograms, each congruent to $OPRQ$, which together fill the plane without overlapping (so that the plane may be paved with blocks each a duplicate of $OPRQ$). In particular, O, P, R, Q are the only points of L which are on or within $OPRQ$.

Lattice L consists of all points E having the co-ordinates $OF = x\sqrt{a}$ and $FE = y\sqrt{b}$ referred to axes containing OP and OQ, where each of x and y ranges over all integers. Then f is the square of the distance from O to E since

$$(2) \qquad OE^2 = OF^2 + FE^2 - 2 \cdot OF \cdot FE \cos(\pi - POQ) = f.$$

If $-\Delta$ is the (negative) determinant of f, the perpendicular from Q to OP is readily verified to be of length $\sqrt{\Delta/a}$. Hence the area of $OPRQ$ is $\sqrt{\Delta}$.

Let A and B denote the vectors from O to P and Q, respectively. Then the vector from O to E is $xA + yB$. Choose two such vectors

$$(3) \qquad U = aA + \gamma B, \qquad V = \beta A + \delta B.$$

Then

$$(4) \qquad x_1 U + y_1 V = xA + yB$$

holds if and only if

$$(5) \qquad x = ax_1 + \beta y_1, \qquad y = \gamma x_1 + \delta y_1.$$

Let P_1 and Q_1 be the points such that the vectors from O to P_1 and Q_1 are U and V, respectively. The parallelogram determined by OP_1 and OQ_1 is a fundamental parallelogram of a point lattice L_1.

Henceforth let a, β, γ, δ be integers. For any integers x_1 and y_1, (5) yield integers x and y. Hence every point of L_1 is a point of L. The converse is true if and only if $a\delta - \beta\gamma = \pm 1$, since for any integers x and y, (5) then yield integers x_1 and y_1. Then L and L_1 coincide.

THEOREM 96. *To any integral transformation (5) of determinant ± 1 corresponds a change from one fundamental parallelogram of any point lattice to another, and conversely.*

Let (5) replace f by $\underline{f_1} = a_1 x_1^2 + b_1 y_1^2 + 2t_1 x_1 y_1$. Evidently, $a_1 = f(a, \gamma)$, $b_1 = f(\beta, \delta)$, whence $OP_1 = \sqrt{a_1}$, $OQ_1 = \sqrt{b_1}$. By (4), E has the co-ordinates $x_1\sqrt{a_1}$ and $y_1\sqrt{b_1}$ referred to axes containing OP_1 and OQ_1. The sum (2) with subscripts 1 inserted must be identical with f_1. Hence $\cos P_1OQ_1 = t_1/\sqrt{a_1 b_1}$. We therefore have (1) with subscripts 1 inserted.

THEOREM 97. *Let an integral transformation (5) of determinant ± 1 replace f by f_1. Then f and f_1 determine the same point lattice. In other words, all properly or improperly equivalent, positive, binary, quadratic forms are represented by the same point lattice.*

75. Reduced fundamental parallelograms. Consider any point lattice L in the plane. Choose any point O of L. If P is any further point of L, the *symmetrical* point P' determined so that O bisects PP' is also in L. Choose P so that OP is a minimum. All points of L lie on lines parallel to OP. Choose one of the two parallels nearest to OP. Of the lattice points on that parallel, let Q be the one (or one of the two) nearest to O. Since we may replace Q by its symmetrical point Q', we may assume that angle POQ is $\leq 90°$. Since we may view the plane from either side of it, we may regard Q as above OP, as in Fig. 1.

On the parallel QR to OP, let S denote the first lattice point to the left of Q. Then

$$(6) \qquad PQ = OS \geq OQ \geq OP .$$

Employ notations (1). Then $t \geq 0$ and

$$(7) \qquad PQ^2 = a + b - 2t \geq OQ^2 = b ,$$

whence

$$(8) \qquad b \geq a \geq 2t \geq 0 , \qquad ab \geq 4t^2 .$$

Let d denote the distance between the parallels OP and SQR. The square of the area of parallelogram $OPRQ$ is

$$(9) \qquad ad^2 = \Delta = ab - t^2 \geq \tfrac{3}{4}ab$$

by (8). Hence $2d \geqq \sqrt{3b} = \sqrt{3}OQ$. Thus the distance from O to every point of the second parallel (above SQR) exceeds OQ, whence OQ is the minimum distance from O to all points of L not on OP.

We shall call $OPRQ$ a *reduced* fundamental parallelogram of lattice L if OP is the minimum distance from O to all points of L and if OQ is the minimum distance from O to all points of L which are not on line OP. We call OP and OQ the first and second minima, respectively.

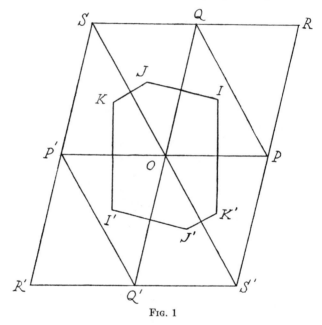

Fig. 1

We proved that every point lattice L has a reduced fundamental parallelogram $OPRQ$ in which $POQ \leqq 90°$. No side of it exceeds a diagonal. First, we have (6). Second, since OR is opposite to $OPR \geqq 90°$, $OR > PR = OQ$.

The congruent parallelogram $OPS'Q'$ is reduced, has no side exceeding a diagonal, but has $POQ' \geqq 90°$.

Conversely, if $OPRQ$ is a fundamental parallelogram of any point lattice L such that no side exceeds a diagonal and such that $OP \leqq OQ$, then $OPRQ$ is reduced. Since this will follow if the like result is proved for $OPS'Q'$, we may assume that $POQ \leqq 90°$ and use Fig. 1. Then no angle of triangle OPQ is obtuse and likewise for the congruent triangle OQS. Hence the perpendicular from O to SQR meets it between S and Q inclusive. By the definition of $OPRQ$ as fundamental parallelogram, no lattice point lies between O and P or between Q and R, and hence none lies between S and Q. Hence every lattice point of line SQR, except Q and possibly S, is further from O than Q is. It follows as before that OQ is the minimum distance from O to lattice points not on line OP. Also, OP is the minimum distance from O to lattice points. Hence $OPRQ$ is reduced.

THEOREM 98. *A fundamental parallelogram $OPRQ$ of a point lattice is reduced if and only if no side exceeds a diagonal, and $OP \leq OQ$.*

In the selection of a reduced parallelogram $OPRQ$ for a lattice L with $POQ \leq 90°$, we evidently have only the following choices for P and Q:

I. If $OP < OQ < PQ$, P and Q are unique.[1]

II. If $OP < OQ = PQ$, the first minimum occurs only at P, and the second only at Q and S.

III. If $OP = OQ < PQ$, the two minima are equal and occur only at P and Q.

IV. If $OP = OQ = PQ$, we may replace P and Q by any two of the points P, Q, S.

76. Reduced, binary forms.[2] Start with any positive, binary, quadratic form B and its point lattice L (§ 74). Choose a reduced fundamental parallelogram of L whose angle at O is $\leq 90°$. Hence B is properly or improperly equivalent to a form $f = [a, 2t, b]$ satisfying inequalities (8). If B is improperly equivalent to f, B is properly equivalent to $[a, -2t, b]$. If $a = b$, the latter becomes f when we replace x by y and y by $-x$. Hence every positive form B is properly equivalent to $[a, 2\tau, b]$ with $b \geq a \geq 2|\tau|$, and $\tau \geq 0$ if $a = b$.

First, let $b > a > 2t \geq 0$. We have case I. Hence the only reduced parallelograms of the lattice for f are the four in Fig. 1 with the common vertex O. Comparison of $OPRQ$ with itself yields the identity transformation. Comparison of it with the other three yields transformations which merely change the signs of x or y or both. Hence if the transformed form is properly equivalent to f it coincides with f; while, if it is improperly equivalent to f, it is $g = [a, -2t, b]$.

Second, let $b > a = 2t$. We have case II. We now have a new reduced parallelogram $OPQS$. The vectors from O to P and S are $U = A$ and $V = B - A$, respectively. Now (4) gives $x = x_1 - y_1$, $y = y_1$, which replaces f by the equivalent form g. If we replace S by its opposite point S', we obtain a transformation which is derived from the preceding by replacing y_1 by $-y_1$, whence we obtain f as the form improperly equivalent to f.

---

[1] Except that either may be replaced by its opposite point.

[2] This interesting geometrical theory, omitted by Dirichlet, is not needed in the rest of this chapter.

In the first (or second) case, g (or f) is the only one of our forms which is improperly equivalent to f and hence properly equivalent to g. This saves repeating our discussion with g in place of f.

Third, let $b = a > 2t \geqq 0$. We have case III. But if we use OQ as the first minimum, the second is not $OS = PQ > OQ$ and hence is OP', and $QOP' > 90°$ contradicts $\tau \geqq 0$. Hence we need only compare $OPRQ$ with itself.

Fourth, let $b = a = 2t$. We have IV. An equivalent form must have the same minima a and b and hence same t. Hence we need not discuss the various transformations available.

THEOREM 99. *Every positive, binary, quadratic form is properly equivalent to one and only one of the reduced form $[a, 2\tau, b]$ having*

$$-a < 2\tau \leqq a \leqq b \text{ , with } \tau \geqq 0 \text{ if } a = b \text{ .}$$

77. The hexagon H. In Fig. 1, draw the perpendicular bisectors of OP, OQ, OS, OP', OQ', and OS'. The first two intersect at a point I within[1] triangle OPQ since its angles are $\leqq 90°$. Similarly for the congruent triangles $OQS, \ldots, S'OP$. We obtain the convex hexagon $H = IJKI'J'K'$ whose vertices are all at the same distance ρ from O.

THEOREM 100. *The interior of hexagon H is the locus of all points nearer to O than to any other point of lattice L.*

This is evidently true for the points P, Q, S, P', Q', S'. It will follow for any new lattice point N if we prove that $ON \geqq 2\rho$, since every point within H is within the circumscribed circle of radius ρ and hence is then on the same side as O of the perpendicular bisector of ON, whence it is nearer to O than to N. The radius of the circle circumscribing triangle POQ is ρ. Hence

$$2\rho = PQ/\sin POQ, \qquad \sqrt{\Delta} = OP \cdot OQ \sin POQ \text{ .}$$

By multiplication, squaring, and using (7), we get

$$(10) \qquad\qquad 4\rho^2 \Delta = ab(a + b - 2t) \text{ .}$$

Thus by (8) and (9),

$$2\rho \leqq \sqrt{8b/3} < \sqrt{3b} \leqq 2d \text{ ,}$$

which states that the distance from O to all points of the second parallel exceeds 2ρ.

---

[1] On PQ if $POQ = 90°$; then J coincides with K, and J' with K', whence H is a rectangle.

It remains only to consider the first parallel SQR. Let G be the first of its lattice points to the left of S. Then

$$OG^2 = f(-2, 1) = 4a + b - 4t .$$

Its product by $\Delta = ab - t^2$ is the sum of $ab(a + b - 2t)$ and

$$4t^3 + b(a^2 - t^2) + ab(a - 2t) + a(ab - 4t^2) .$$

The latter is > 0 by (8). Hence $OG > 2\rho$ by (10).

Similarly, $OR^2 = f(1, 1) = a + b + 2t$. Then $\Delta \cdot OR^2$ is the sum of $ab(a + b - 2t)$ and

$$at(b - t) + tb(a - t) + 2(ab - t^2)t \geqq 0 .$$

Hence $OR \geqq 2\rho$. This completes the proof of Theorem 100.

By (8), (9), and (10),

$$4\Delta b - 4\rho^2 \Delta - 2ab^2 = ab(b - a) + 2bt(a - 2t) \geqq 0 .$$

Hence

(11)
$$2\Delta(b - \rho^2) \geqq ab^2 .$$

Since $\Delta \leqq ab$, this implies

(12)
$$\rho^2 \leqq \tfrac{1}{2}b .$$

78. Ternary forms, lattices, reduced parallelopipeds. Let

(13)
$$\phi = ax^2 + by^2 + cz^2 + 2ryz + 2sxz + 2txy$$

be a positive form of determinant d. By Theorem 8,

$$ab > t^2 , \qquad ac > s^2 , \qquad bc > r^2$$

and a, b, c, d are positive. Then

$$\cos \alpha = r/\sqrt{bc}, \ \cos \beta = s/\sqrt{ac}, \ \cos \gamma = t/\sqrt{ab}$$

determine three angles $< 180°$ which are the face angles of a trihedral angle, with vertex O, since

$$\cos^2 \alpha + \cos^2 \beta + \cos^2 \gamma - 2 \cos \alpha \cos \beta \cos \gamma < 1$$

is equivalent to $d > 0$. Let A_1, A_2, A_3 be the vectors whose lengths are the square roots of a, b, c which extend from O along the edges of the trihedal such that γ is the angle between A_1 and A_2, etc. The product of two vectors is defined to be the product of their lengths and the cosine of their included angle. Hence

$$(14) \quad A_1^2 = a, \quad A_2^2 = b, \quad A_3^2 = c, \quad A_1A_2 = t, \quad A_1A_3 = s, \quad A_2A_3 = r.$$

For all sets of integers x, y, z, the points with the vectors

$$V = xA_1 + yA_2 + zA_3$$

form a point lattice L. Evidently V^2 has the value (13). Employ a system of rectangular co-ordinates with the origin O. Let the point with the vector A_i have the co-ordinates c_{1i}, c_{2i}, c_{3i}. Then the point with the vector V has the co-ordinates ξ_1, ξ_2, ξ_3, where

$$\xi_i = c_{i1}x + c_{i2}y + c_{i3}z.$$

If the point with the vector W has the co-ordinates η_1, η_2, η_3, then $VW = \xi_1\eta_1 + \xi_2\eta_2 + \xi_3\eta_3$, since the cosine of their included angle is the quotient of that sum by the product of their lengths. In particular, $V^2 = \xi_1^2 + \xi_2^2 + \xi_3^2$, whence the form (13) is the square of the distance between O and the lattice point determined by x, y, z. Also,

$$A_iA_j = c_{1i}c_{1j} + c_{2i}c_{2j} + c_{3i}c_{3j}.$$

Hence if C is the determinant $|c_{ij}|$, C^2 has the element A_iA_j in the ith row and jth column. Thus (14) gives $C^2 = d$. By analytic geometry, C is the volume of the parallelopiped whose edges concurring in O are A_1, A_2, A_3. We call it a *fundamental parallelopiped* for the lattice L and denote it by $\{A_1, A_2, A_3\}$.

The analogs of Theorems 96 and 97 for space evidently follow by a like proof.

Start with any point lattice L in space and any point O of it. Choose any lattice point P such that OP is a minimum. Of all points of L not on OP choose a point Q as near to OP as possible and such that angle POQ is $\leq 90°$. Then $OQ \geq OP$ and parallelogram $OPRQ$ is reduced. In a plane nearest to OPQ, parallel to it, and containing a point of L, select a lattice point M as near to O as possible. The parallelopiped $F = \{P, Q, M\}$, having the edges OP, OQ, OM, is called a *reduced* fundamental parallelopiped of the lattice L. It has the following properties:

(i) no edge exceeds a diagonal,

(ii) no edge of a face exceeds a diagonal of it,

(iii) $OP \leqq OQ \leqq OM$.

We saw that (ii) is true for $OPRQ$ and hence for the upper face opposite to it. Each remaining diagonal is either a line joining O to a point of the plane U of the upper face or is parallel and equal to such a line. Hence it is $\geqq OM$.

Conversely, if F is any fundamental parallelopiped $\{P, Q, M\}$ of any point lattice L in space and if F has properties (i)–(iii), then F is reduced for L. By § 75, OP is the minimum distance from O to lattice points in the plane POQ, while OQ is the minimum distance from O to lattice points in that plane but not on line OP.

Consider the lattice points in the plane U of the upper face of F. By (i) and (ii), OM is not greater than any of the lines joining O to the eight lattice points of U which are vertices of four parallelograms with the common vertex M and one of which is the upper face (see Fig. 1 with O replaced by M). Hence the foot T of the perpendicular from O to U is not further from M than from any of those eight points. Hence T lies on or within the hexagon of Fig. 1. By Theorem 100, the distance from any lattice point in U from T is not less than MT, whence its distance from O is not less than OM. If ρ is the radius of the circle circumscribing the hexagon, so that $MT \leqq \rho$, evidently

(15)
$$OT^2 \geqq OM^2 - \rho^2 .$$

By (12), $\rho^2 \leqq \frac{1}{2}OQ^2 \leqq \frac{1}{2}OM^2$. Hence $OT \geqq \sqrt{\frac{1}{2}} \cdot OM$, and the distance from O to the second parallel plane is $\geqq \sqrt{2} \cdot OM > OM$. This proves the converse.

THEOREM 101. *A fundamental parallelopiped* $\{P, Q, M\}$ *of a lattice is reduced if and only if* (i)–(iii) *hold.*

79. Minima, Seeber's inequality. Our discussion shows that any positive, ternary, quadratic form is equivalent to a form ϕ whose fundamental parallelopiped F is reduced. Initially the equivalence may have been improper. But ϕ is improperly equivalent to itself under the transformation which replaces x, y, z by their negatives.

Let the squares of the lengths of the edges OP, OQ, OM of F be a, b, c. Then

(16)
$$a \leqq b \leqq c .$$

THEOREM[1] 102. *Any positive ternary form of determinant d is equivalent to a form* (13) *in which* $abc \leqq 2d$.

By § 78, $\sqrt{d}$ is the volume of F and hence is the product of its altitude h by its base. By (9), the square of the area of its base is $\Delta = ab - t^2$. By (15), $h^2 \geqq c - \rho^2$. Write $c = b + k$, where $k \geqq 0$. The theorem is true if $2\Delta(c - \rho^2) \geqq abc$ and hence if

$$2\Delta(b - \rho^2) - ab^2 \geqq k(ab - 2\Delta) \ .$$

The left member is $\geqq 0$ by (11), and $2\Delta - ab \geqq \frac{1}{2}ab$ since $ab \geqq 4t^2$ by (8).

By (16) and the theorem, $a^3 \leqq 2d$. But a is the minimum of ϕ.

COROLLARY. *The minimum of any positive, ternary, quadratic form of determinant d is* $\leqq g = \sqrt[3]{2d}$. *Also, g is actually the minimum of* $g\psi$ *of determinant d, where* $\psi = x^2 + y^2 + z^2 + xy + xz + yz$ *has the minimum 1 and determinant* $\frac{1}{2}$.

80. Reduced, positive, ternary, quadratic forms. By §79, any form is equivalent to a form (13) whose fundamental parallelopiped F_0 is reduced and has $POQ \leqq 90°$, whence $t \geqq 0$.

If r, s, t are all positive, we retain (13) and write F for F_0.

If $t = 0$, $r \leqq 0$, $s \leqq 0$, we retain (13).

If $t > 0$, $r < 0$, $s < 0$, we change the signs of x and y and see that F_0 is

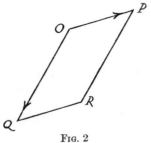

replaced by a congruent (and hence reduced) parallelopiped having the base $OP'R'Q'$ in Fig. 1. We rotate the base 180° about O and obtain a reduced parallelopiped, which we denote by $F = \{P, Q, M\}$. The new form (13) has r, s, t all positive.

If $r \leqq 0$, $s \geqq 0$, we change the signs of y and z and obtain a new (13) with r, s, t all $\leqq 0$. We write Q for the old Q' and obtain a reduced parallelopiped $F = \{P, Q, M\}$, whose base is shown in Fig. 2, while OM extends

FIG. 2

downwards from O in a positive direction, and $POQ \geqq 90°$. Then

$$OR^2 = f(1, 1) = a + b + 2t \geqq OQ^2 = b \ , \qquad a + 2t \geqq 0 \ .$$

Hence in (7) and I–IV, we replace PQ by OR, S by R, and t by $-t$, and obtain I'–IV'.

---

[1] Verified by L. A. Seeber for 600 cases in 1831. First proved by Gauss, *Göttingische gelehrte Anzeigen*, 1831; *Werke*, II, 188.

If $r \geq 0$, $s \leq 0$, we change the sign of y, write Q for Q' and have the same results as in the preceding case except that now OM extends upwards from O.

Finally, if $t = 0$, $r \geq 0$, $s \geq 0$, we change the sign of z. The new r, s, t are all ≤ 0. The base of F is now a rectangle, while OM extends downwards from O. Cases I'–IV' are the same as I–IV respectively, while the second and fourth cases are excluded.

We have now treated all possibilities.

Now r, s, t are either all positive and then we write $\sigma = +1$, or they are all ≤ 0 and then we write $\sigma = -1$. If $\sigma = 1$, we have cases I–IV. If $\sigma = -1$, we have cases I'–IV'.

For the moment, write O_1 for O and employ the lettering of Figs. 1 and 2 for the face of F parallel to its base. The diagonals of the lateral faces of F are equal to lines joining O_1 to P, P', Q, Q', whose x, y, z of §78 are ± 1, 0, 1 and 0, ± 1, 1. For the base, we have similarly x, y, $z = \pm 1$, 1, 0. Hence (ii) holds if and only if

$$a + b - 2\sigma t \geq b , \quad a + c - 2\sigma s \geq c , \quad b + c - 2\sigma r \geq c ,$$

which are equivalent to

(17) $$a \geq 2\sigma t , \quad a \geq 2\sigma s , \quad b \geq 2\sigma r .$$

The diagonals of F are equal to lines joining O_1 to R, R', S, S', whose x, y, z are the four sets ± 1, ± 1, 1. Hence (i) holds if and only if

$$a + b + c + 2\delta s + 2\epsilon r + 2\delta\epsilon t \geq c \qquad (\delta^2 = \epsilon^2 = 1) .$$

If $\sigma = +1$, whence r, s, t are all positive, these four inequalities all follow from (16) and (17). If $\sigma = -1$, the same is true except when $\delta = \epsilon = 1$ and then

(18) $$a + b + 2r + 2s + 2t \geq 0 \qquad (\text{if } r, s, t \text{ are } \leq 0) .$$

When referred to co-ordinate planes which are the faces of F containing O, let $N = (\xi, \eta, 1)$ be a lattice point in the face parallel to the base whose distance from O is $\sqrt{c}$. By the proof of Theorem 100, N can only be one of the nine vertices of the four juxtaposed parallelograms shown in Fig. 1. In other words, the only possible values of ξ and η are 0, ± 1.

We seek the points N distinct from M, whence $(\xi, \eta) \neq (0, 0)$, such that $F_1 = \{P, Q, N\}$ is a reduced parallelopiped. Denote the vectors from O to P, Q, N, M by $U = A$, $V = B$, W, C, respectively. Then $W = \xi A + \eta B + C$.

From $x_1U + y_1V + z_1W = xA + yB + zC$, we obtain the transformation

(19) $$x = x_1 + \xi z_1 , \qquad y = y_1 + \eta z_1 , \qquad z = z_1 .$$

This replaces ϕ in (13) by ϕ_1 with $a_1 = a$, $b_1 = b$, $t_1 = t$, and

(20) $$c_1 = \phi(\xi, \eta, 1) , \qquad r_1 = r + t\xi + b\eta , \qquad s_1 = s + a\xi + t\eta .$$

Using inequalities (16) and (17), we seek the cases in which $c_1 = c$. If $\eta = 0$, then $a + 2s\xi = 0$, which contradicts (17_2) if $\xi = \sigma$; we get

(21) $$\eta = 0 , \qquad \xi = -\sigma , \qquad a = 2\sigma s , \qquad r_1 = r - \sigma t , \qquad s_1 = -s .$$

If $\eta = \sigma$, then $a\xi^2 + b + 2\sigma r + 2\xi s + 2\xi\sigma t = 0$. This contradicts (17_3) if $\xi = 0$, and is evidently false if $\xi = \sigma = 1$. If $\xi = \sigma = -1$, $(a + 2t) + b - 2r - 2s > 0$. If $\xi = -\sigma$, $(a - 2\sigma s) + (b - 2t) + 2\sigma r > 0$. Finally, let $\eta = -\sigma$, whence $a\xi^2 + b - 2\sigma r + 2\xi s - 2\sigma\xi t = 0$. If $\xi = 0$,

(22) $$\eta = -\sigma , \qquad \xi = 0 , \qquad b = 2\sigma r , \qquad r_1 = -r , \qquad s_1 = s - \sigma t .$$

If $\xi = \sigma$, $(b - 2\sigma r) + (a - 2t) + 2\sigma s > 0$. If $\xi = -\sigma$, $(b - 2\sigma r) + (a - 2\sigma s) + 2t > 0$ unless $\sigma = -1$, and then

(23) $$\sigma = -1 , \qquad a + b + 2r + 2s + 2t = 0 , \qquad r_1 = r + t + b , \qquad s_1 = s + t + a ,$$

with $\xi = \eta = 1$. Then $r_1 = -s$, $s_1 = -r$ if $a = b$.

Conversely, $c_1 = c$ in the cases (21)–(23).

In case $a = 2\sigma t$, we employ the parallelopiped F_2 derived from F_1 by replacing OQ by OS or OR, according as $\sigma = 1$ or -1. Now $V = B - \sigma A$ and the new transformation is (19) with x_1 replaced by $x_1 - \sigma y_1$. Under that replacement, ϕ_1 becomes ϕ_2, which has the same a_1, b_1, c_1, s_1, and

(24) $$r_2 = r_1 - \sigma s_1 , \qquad t_2 = t_1 - \sigma a = -t .$$

LEMMA 1. *Every positive ternary form is equivalent to a form* (13) *having* r, s, t *either all* > 0 *or all* ≤ 0 *which satisfies conditions* (16)–(18), *and one or more of the following:*

(25) $$\sigma = 1: \quad s \leq 2r \text{ if } a = 2t , \quad t \leq 2r \text{ if } a = 2s , \quad t \leq 2s \text{ if } b = 2r ;$$

(26) $$\sigma = -1: \quad s = 0 \text{ if } a = -2t , \quad t = 0 \text{ if } a = -2s , \quad t = 0 \text{ if } b = -2r ;$$

(26_1) $$\sigma = -1: \quad a + 2s + t \leq 0 \text{ if } a + b + 2r + 2s + 2t = 0 .$$

We have already proved the first part of the lemma.

Let $\sigma = -1$, $a = -2s$. In (21) we change the signs of r_1, t_1 and obtain a form ϕ', equivalent to ϕ, for which $r' = -r-t$, $s' = -s$, $t' = -t$ are all positive when $t \neq 0$. This ϕ' has $\sigma = +1$ and satisfies conditions (16) and (17), since ϕ satisfies them and (18). This is evident except for $b - 2r' = b + 2r + 2t \geq 0$ by (18). Hence if $t \neq 0$, ϕ is equivalent to a form listed with those having $\sigma = +1$.

Similarly from (22), if $\sigma = -1$, $b = -2r$, we may take $t = 0$.

Let $\sigma = -1$, $a = -2t$. We employ (24) with $\xi = \eta = 0$ in (20). We change the signs of s_2 and r_2 and obtain ϕ' having $r' = -r-s$, $s' = -s$, $t' = -t$, all of which are positive when $s \neq 0$. Conditions (17) hold for ϕ'. Hence we may take $s = 0$.

Let (23) hold. Changing the signs of r_1, s_1, we get a form ϕ', equivalent to ϕ, having the same a, b, c, t, and

$$(27) \qquad r' = -r-t-b \, , \qquad s' = -s-t-a \, .$$

These are ≤ 0. For, by (16) and (17),

$$(28) \qquad b + 2r \geq 0 \, , \qquad b + 2t \geq a + 2t \geq 0 \, , \qquad b + r + t \geq 0 \, ,$$

by addition. The sum of the first two in (17) gives $a + s + t \geq 0$. Thus ϕ' has $\sigma = -1$ and satisfies (17) since $a + 2s' = b + 2r$, $b + 2r' = a + 2s$ by (23). By addition,

$$(29) \qquad a + b + 2r' + 2s' + 2t' = 0 \, .$$

Also,

$$(30) \qquad a + 2s' + t' = -a - 2s - t \, .$$

Hence $a + 2s + t \leq 0$ for one of ϕ, ϕ'.

Let $\sigma = 1$, $a = 2s$. In ϕ_1 satisfying (21) we change the signs of r_1, s_1 and get a form ϕ', equivalent to ϕ, having $r' = t-r$, $s' = s$, $t' = t$, which are all positive if $t > r$. If $t - 2r > 0$, then $t' - 2r' < 0$, whence one of ϕ, ϕ' has $t - 2r \leq 0$. The latter is automatically true in the remaining case $t \leq r$. Also ϕ' satisfies conditions (17).

Similarly by (22), if $\sigma = 1$, $b = 2r$, we get an equivalent form ϕ' with $r' = r$, $s' = t-s$, $t' = t$, which are all positive if $t > s$, whence $t' - 2s' = 2s - t$, and one of ϕ, ϕ' has $t \leq 2s$.

Let $\sigma = 1$, $a = 2t$. We employ (24) with $\xi = \eta = 0$ in (20). Changing the signs of r_2 and t_2, we obtain a form ϕ', equivalent to ϕ, for which $r' = s-r$,

$s'=s$, $t'=t$ are all positive when $s>r$. Conditions (17) hold for ϕ'. Since $s'-2r'=2r-s$, one of ϕ and ϕ' has $s \leqq 2r$.

This completes the proof of Lemma 1 when (25) and (26) are taken singly. We shall next prove (25) taken jointly.

First, let $a=2t=2s$. By means of a transformation altering only r, we just proved that we can take $s \leqq 2r$. Then $s=t \leqq 2r$.

Second, let $b=2r$, $a=2t$. By a transformation altering only s, we saw that we can take $t \leqq 2s$. By (17), $2t=a \geqq 2s$. By $a \leqq b$, $t \leqq r$. Hence $s \leqq t \leqq r \leqq 2r$.

Third, let $a=2s$, $b=2r$. No transformation is necessary. By (17), $2s = a \geqq 2t$. By $a \leqq b$, $s \leqq r$. Hence $t \leqq s \leqq 2s$, $t \leqq r \leqq 2r$.

Fourth, let the third case hold and also $a=2t$. Then $s=t \leqq 2r$.

Finally, we shall prove (26) taken jointly. Under the three hypotheses (26) we proved that $s=0$, $t=0$, or $t=0$, respectively, unless the form is equivalent to one with $\sigma=+1$; hence those facts can be used jointly. This excludes the case in which $a=-2t$ is taken jointly with $a=-2s$ or $b=-2r$, or with (26$_4$) which then gives $b+2r=0$.

Assume equation (26$_4$) and either (26$_2$) or (26$_3$). In either case, $a+2s=0$, $t=0$, whence $a+2s+t \leqq 0$.

LEMMA 2. *If $a=b$, we may take $|r| \leqq |s|$ without disturbing conditions* (25) *or* (26), *taken singly or jointly. In particular, $r=s$ if $a=b=2\sigma r$.*

If $a=b$, but no one of the equalities in (25) and (26) holds, then $|r| \leqq |s|$ holds either for ϕ or for the form derived from ϕ by interchanging x and y (and hence r and s).

If $a=b=2\sigma t$, we employ the parallelopiped $F_3=\{Q, \ S \text{ or } R', \ N\}$, according as $\sigma=1$ or $\sigma=-1$. Let U, V, W denote their respective vectors. Then $U=B$, $V=\sigma B-A$, $W=\xi A+\eta B+C$. The new transformation is (19) with x_1 replaced by $-y_1$, and y_1 replaced by $x_1+\sigma y_1$. Under the latter replacements, ϕ_1 becomes ϕ_3, which has the same a, b, c, and

$$(31) \qquad r_3=\sigma r_1-s_1, \qquad s_3=r_1, \qquad t_3=\sigma b_1-t_1=t.$$

First, let $\sigma=1$, $a=b$. When $a=2s$, (17) requires $2s=b \geqq 2r$. Next, let $b=2r$, $t \leqq 2s$. Then (17) hold if and only if $r \geqq t$, $r \geqq s$. Interchanging x and y and hence r and s, we obtain an equivalent form having $a=b=2s$, $t \leqq 2r$, $s \geqq t$, $s \geqq r$, which satisfies conditions (17) and (25$_2$). Since we list the new form, we may drop the given one unless the two are identical, which occurs if and only if $r=s$. Hence if $b=2r$, we may take $r \leqq s$.

Finally, let $a=2t$, $s \leqq 2r$, $r>s$. We apply (31) with $\xi=\eta=0$ in (20). Then $r_3=r-s$, $s_3=r$, $t_3=t$, which are all positive. If also $2s \leqq r$, then $s_3-2r_3=2s-r \leqq 0$, $r_3<s_3$, and ϕ_3 is the required form; it satisfies conditions

(17). There remains the case $2s>r>s$. We interchange r and s in ϕ and obtain an equivalent form ϕ' having $a=2t'$, $r'=s$, $s'=r$, $s'-2r'=r-2s<0$, $r'<s'$, which satisfies (17).

This proves Lemma 2 when $\sigma=1$.

Second, let $\sigma=-1$, $a=b$. For (23), $a+r+s+t=0$. Add $s-r$ and apply the inequality in (26_4). Hence $s-r\leq 0$.

If $a=-2s$, $t=0$, (18) gives $b+2r\geq 0$, whence $r\geq s$.

Let $b=-2r$, $t=0$. Then (17) and (18) all reduce to $a+2s\geq 0$, whence $s\geq r$. We interchange r and s and get $b=a=-2s$, $t=0$, $r\geq s$, and hence the form in the preceding case. Hence the given form may be discarded unless $r=s$. Hence if $b=-2r$, we may take $-r\leq -s$.

Finally, let $a=-2t$, $s=0$. Then (17) and (18) hold if and only if $r\geq t$. If $r\neq 0$, we change the signs of s_3 and t_3 in (31) with $\xi=\eta=0$ and obtain an equivalent form ϕ' having $r'=-r$, $s'=-r$, $t'=-t$ all positive. Then $b=a=2t'$, $s'=r'\leq t'$, whence $s'\leq 2r'$. This ϕ' has $\sigma=+1$, satisfies (17), and is listed in the first part of Lemma 2. Hence we discard the given form when $r\neq 0$.

LEMMA 3. *When $b=c$ we may discard the case $\sigma=-1$, $a=-2s$, and take $s=t\leq 2r$ if $\sigma=1$, $a=2s$; $s=t=0$ if $\sigma=-1$, $b=-2r$; $s\leq t\leq 2s$ if $\sigma=1$, $b=2r$; $t\leq s$ in case (26_4).*

When $b=c$, we employ parallelopiped $F_4=\{P,N,Q'\}$. The new transformation is $x=x_1+\xi y_1$, $y=-z_1+\eta y_1$, $z=y_1$, which is derived from (19) by replacing y_1 by $-z_1$ and z_1 by y_1. We obtain ϕ_4, whose only altered coefficients are $r_4=-r_1$, $s_4=-t_1$, $t_4=s_1$.

Let $\sigma=-1$, $a=-2s$. Then $t=0$ by (26). By (21), $r_4=-r$, $s_4=0$, $t_4=-s$. Thus ϕ' has $\sigma=-1$, $r'=r$, $s'=0$, $t'=s$, $a=-2t'$. Since $b+2r\geq 0$, (17), (18), and (26) hold for ϕ'. Since ϕ' is retained, we may drop ϕ.

Let $\sigma=1$, $a=2s$. Then $t\leq 2r$ by (25) and $s\geq t$, $b\geq 2r$ by (17). We take $\xi=\eta=0$ in (20). Then ϕ' has $\sigma=1$, $r'=r$, $s'=t$, $t'=s$, $a=2t'$, $s'\leq 2r'$, $t'\geq s'$, $b\geq 2r'$, whence (17) and (25) hold for ϕ'. Since $\phi'=\phi$ if and only if $s=t$ and since ϕ' is retained, we may drop ϕ when $s\neq t$.

If $b=c=2\sigma r$, we employ parallelopiped $F_5=\{P,M,N \text{ or } N'\}$, according as $\sigma=1$ or -1, where $N=(0,-\sigma,1)$ by (22). The vectors from O to these three points are $U=A$, $V=C$, $W=\sigma C-B$. The transformation is

$$(32) \qquad x=x_1, \qquad y=-z_1, \qquad z=y_1+\sigma z_1,$$

of determinant unity. It replaces ϕ in (13) with $c=b=2\sigma r$ by Φ having the coefficients a, b, c, and

$$(33) \qquad R=r, \qquad S=\sigma s-t, \qquad T=s,$$

since $C=b+c-2\sigma r=c$, $R=\sigma c-r=r$.

Let $\sigma = 1$, $b = 2r$, $s > r$. By (25), $t \leqq 2s$. If $s \geqq 2t$, Φ has $\sigma = 1$, $S < T \leqq 2S$, and Φ satisfies (17) when ϕ does. Hence we may take $s < 2t$. Then by F_4 with $\xi = \eta = 0$, we may interchange s and t. The new form satisfies (17) when ϕ does and satisfies (25) and has $s < t$.

Let $\sigma = -1$, $b = -2r$. Then $t = 0$ by (26). If $s \neq 0$, we use (33). Then ϕ' has $\sigma = 1$, $s' = -s$, $t' = -s$, $r' = -r$, $b = 2r'$, $s' = t'$, $t' \leqq 2s'$, whence (25) holds for ϕ'. Also (17) holds for ϕ' if for ϕ. Since ϕ' is listed, we may drop ϕ.

Consider case (26_4) with $b = c$. By (23), $N = (1, 1, 1)$. Employ parallelopiped $F_6 = \{P, M, N'\}$. The resulting transformation $x = x_1 - z_1$, $y = -z_1$, $z = y_1 - z_1$ of determinant unity replaces ϕ by Φ, whose only altered coefficients are

$$(34) \qquad R = -c - r - s , \qquad S = -a - s - t , \qquad T = s .$$

By (17) and $b - a \geqq 0$, we see that $R \leqq 0$, $S \leqq 0$. Hence $\phi' = \Phi$ has

$$(35) \qquad \sigma = -1 , \qquad r' = -b - r - s , \qquad s' = -a - s - t , \qquad t' = s ,$$

and satisfies (17) and (29). Also, $t' - s' = a + 2s + t \leqq 0$ by (26_4). Thus ϕ' satisfies Lemma 3 if

$$(36) \qquad a + 2s' + t' = -a - s - 2t \leqq 0 .$$

There remains only the case.

$$(37) \qquad t > s , \qquad -a - s - 2t > 0 .$$

Employ the parallelopiped $F_7 = \{P', N, M'\}$ with $N = (1, 1, 1)$, $b = c$, (26_4). The transformation is $x = y_1 - x_1$, $y = y_1$, $z = y_1 - z_1$, whose determinant is unity. It replaces ϕ by Φ, whose coefficients are a, b, c, and

$$(38) \qquad R = -c - r - s , \qquad S = s , \qquad T = -a - s - t ,$$

which are all $\leqq 0$. Thus $\phi' = \Phi$ has $\sigma = -1$ and satisfies (17) and (29). Also,

$$(39) \qquad a + 2S + T = s - t$$

is < 0 by (37), whence (26_4) holds for Φ. Next,

$$-a - S - 2T = a + s + 2t < 0 ,$$

by (37). Hence the proof by use of F_6 applies to Φ.

When $\sigma = 1$, $a = 2t$, (17) gives $s \leqq t$. We see that Lemma 3 implies

LEMMA 4. *If* $b=c$, *we may take* $|s| \leq |t|$ *without disturbing* (25) *or* (26), *taken singly or jointly.*

In case none of (25), (26) hold, then $|s| \leq |t|$ either for ϕ or for the form derived from ϕ by interchanging y and z (and hence s and t). We next prove

LEMMA 5. *If* $a=b=c$, *we may take* $\sigma r \leq \sigma s \leq \sigma t$ *without disturbing* (25) *or* (26), *taken singly or jointly. We may drop the case* $\sigma = -1$, $b = -2r$, *and take* $r = s = t$ *if* $\sigma = 1$, $b = 2r$.

When $a=b=c$, parallelopiped $F_8 = \{Q, N, P\}$ leads to the transformation derived from (19) by replacing x_1 by z_1, y_1, by x_1 and z_1 by y_1. Under these replacements, ϕ becomes Φ having

$$(40) \qquad\qquad R = s_1, \qquad S = t_1, \qquad T = r_1.$$

First, let no one of (25), (26) hold. We may take $\sigma s \leq \sigma t$ by Lemma 4. Suppose that $\sigma r > \sigma s$. Take $\xi = \eta = 0$. Then $\sigma R \leq \sigma S$. Since Lemma 5 holds for Φ if $\sigma S \leq \sigma T$, assume the contrary, whence $\sigma t > \sigma r$. We interchange r and s and obtain the desired result.

Let $\sigma = 1$, $b = 2r$. By Lemma 4, we may take $s \leq t \leq 2s$. Conditions (17) hold if and only if $r \geq t$, $r \geq s$. We apply F_8 with $N = M$, viz., $\xi = \eta = 0$. Then $R = s$, $S = t$, $T = r$ are all positive, whence $\phi' = \Phi$. Also, $R \leq S \leq T$, $S \leq 2R$, $b = a = 2T$. Thus (17) and (25$_1$) hold for Φ. Since Φ is in our final list under $a = b = c = 2T$, we may drop ϕ unless it coincides with Φ. But if $\phi \equiv \Phi$, $r = s = t$.

Let $\sigma = -1$, $b = -2r$. By Lemma 3, we may take $s = t = 0$. We use F_8 with the values $r_1 = -r$, $s_1 = t_1 = 0$ in (22). Then ϕ' has $\sigma = -1$, $r' = s' = 0$, $t' = r$, $a = -2t'$, and satisfies (17), (18), and (26$_1$). Since ϕ' is in our final list, we drop ϕ.

Let $\sigma = -1$, $a = -2t$. Then $s = 0$ by (26), and $r = 0$ by Lemma 2.

Let $\sigma = 1$, $a = 2t$. We may take $r \leq s$ by Lemma 2. By (17), $s \leq t$.

Let (26$_4$) hold. Then $a + r + s + t = 0$, whence $a + 2s + t = s - r \leq 0$. By Lemma 4, $-s \leq -t$.

Let $a = 2\sigma s$. By Lemma 3, $\sigma = +1$, $s = t$. By (17), $s \geq r$.

Lemmas 1–5 imply

Theorem 103. *Every positive, ternary, quadratic form is equivalent to a form* (13) *having* r, s, t *either all* > 0 *or all* ≤ 0 *and satisfying conditions* (16)–(28), (25), (26), *and*

$$(41) \qquad\qquad |r| \leq |s| \; if \; a = b, \qquad |s| \leq |t| \; if \; b = c,$$

all taken singly or jointly.

Such a form will be called *reduced.*

81. No two reduced forms are equivalent. The proof employs all possible reduced, fundamental parallelopipeds F_i.

F_5. We have $b = c = 2\sigma r$ and (33). If $\sigma = -1$, $s = t = 0$ by Lemma 3, whence $\phi' = \Phi = \phi$. If $\sigma = 1$, then $s \leq t$ and ϕ' has $\sigma = -1$, $s' = s - t$, $t' = -s$, $r' = -r$, $b = -2r'$, $t' = s' = 0$ by Lemma 3, contrary to $s > 0$.

F_6. We have $b = c$, $t \leq s$, (34), (35), (26_4). Since ϕ' is assumed to be reduced, we have (36). To it we add $a + 2s + t \leq 0$ from (26_4) and get $s - t \leq 0$. Hence $t = s$, $a + 3s = 0$. Then $b + 2r + s = 0$ by (26_4). Hence (35) gives $r' = r$, $s' = s$, $t' = t$, $\phi' = \phi$.

F_7. We have $b = c$, $t \leq s$, (38), (26_4). Since (39) is ≤ 0 by (26_4) for Φ, $t = s$. Also, $S - T = a + 2s + t \leq 0$. But the reduced Φ has $T \leq S$. Hence $T = S$, $a + 3s = 0$. Then $b + 2r + s = 0$ by (26_4). Hence $\phi' = \Phi = \phi$ by (38).

F_8. We have $a = b = c$ and (40).

First, let $\sigma = -1$. We may drop (21) and (22) by Lemmas 3 and 4. Hence $\xi = \eta = 0$. Then (40) gives $\phi' = \Phi$, $r' = s$, $s' = t$, $t' = r$. Since ϕ' is reduced, $-s' \leq -t'$, whence $-t \leq -r$. But $-r \leq -s \leq -t$, whence $r = s = t$, $\phi' = \phi$. In case (23), $a + r + s + t = 0$, $R = -r$, $S = t$, $T = -s$, whence ϕ' has $\sigma = -1$, $r' = r$, $s' = t$, $t' = s$, $-s' \leq -t'$, whence $t = s$, $\phi' = \phi$.

Second, let $\sigma = 1$. If $\xi = \eta = 0$, $\phi' = \Phi$ and $s' \leq t'$ gives $t \leq r$, whence $r \leq s \leq t$ give $r = s = t$, $\phi' = \phi$. For (21), $s = t$ by Lemma 3, and $R = -s$, $S = t$, $T = r - t \leq 0$. If $r \neq t$, ϕ' has $\sigma = 1$, $r' = s$, $s' = t$, $t' = t - r > 0$, $s' \leq t'$, contrary to $r > 0$. Hence $r = t$ and ϕ' has $\sigma = -1$, $r' = -s$, $s' = -t$, $t' = 0$, $|s'| < |t'|$, $s' = 0$, contrary to $t > 0$. For (22), $b = 2r$, $r = s = t$ by Lemma 3. Thus $R = 0$, $S = t$, $T = -r$. Hence ϕ' has $\sigma = -1$, $r' = 0$, $s' = -t$, $t' = -r$, $a = -2t'$, $s' = 0$ by (26), contrary to $t > 0$.

F_1. The discussion is long since a, b, c may be distinct. We have (20).

Case (21). First, let $\sigma = -1$. Then $t = 0$ by (26) and ϕ' has $\sigma = -1$, $r' = r$, $s' = s$, $t' = 0$, $\phi' = \phi$. Second, let $\sigma = 1$. Then $t \leq 2r$ by (25). If ϕ' has $\sigma = -1$, $s' = -s$, $a = -2s'$, $t' = 0$ by (26), contrary to $t' = -t \neq 0$. Hence ϕ' has $\sigma = 1$, $r' = t - r$, $s' = s$, $t' = t$, $t' - 2r' = 2r - t \geq 0$. But $a = 2s'$, $t' \leq 2r'$ by (25), whence $t' = 2r'$, $t = 2r$, $r' = r$, $\phi' = \phi$.

Case (22). We find that $\phi' = \phi$ by the proof in case (21) after interchanging a and b, r and s, also with accents.

Case (23). If $r_1 \leq 0$, $s_1 \leq 0$, we find by addition that $-r - s \leq 0$, $r = s = 0$, $a + b + 2t = 0$, whereas $a + 2t \geq 0$ by (17).

If $t = 0$, $a + 2s \leq 0$ by (26) and $a + 2s \geq 0$ by (17), whence $a + 2s = 0$, $b + 2r = 0$, $r_1 = -r$, $s_1 = -s$, $\phi' = \phi$.

Next, let $t \neq 0$. Thus $t_1 = t < 0$. If ϕ' has $\sigma = 1$, we must change the sign of t_1 and just one of r_1 and s_1. If we change the sign of r_1, we get $r' = -r - t - b > 0$, contrary to (28). If we change the sign of s_1, we get $s' = -s - t - a > 0$, contrary to the line below (28). Hence ϕ' has $\sigma = -1$. We must keep $t'=t$ and change the signs of both r_1 and s_1. We get (27). By $a+2s+t\leqq 0$ and the same in accents, and (30), we get $a+2s+t=0$, whence $b+2r+t=0$. Then (27) gives $r'=r$, $s'=s$, $\phi'=\phi$.

Case $\xi=\eta=0$. Then $\phi_1=\phi$. The case in which $\sigma=1$ for one of ϕ and ϕ', but $\sigma=-1$ for the other, is excluded since r_1, s_1, t_1 are then all $\neq 0$ and of like sign, while we are permitted only to change the signs of two of them. Hence $\phi'=\phi_1=\phi$.

F_2. We have $a=2\sigma t$ and (24). First, let $\xi=\eta=0$. If $\sigma=-1$, $s=0$ by (26) and we must change the signs of t_2 and s_2, whence $\phi'=\phi$. Next, let $\sigma=+1$, whence $s\leqq 2r$. If ϕ' has $\sigma=1$, we must change the signs of r_2 and t_2, whence $r'=s-r$, $t'=t$, $s'=s$. By (25$_1$), $s'\leqq 2r'$. Hence $2r\leqq s$, $2r=s$, $\phi'=\phi$. If ϕ' has $\sigma=-1$, we must change the signs of s_2 and r_2, whence $r'=s-r$, $t'=-t$, $s'=-s$. Then $a=-2t'$, $s'=0$ by (26$_1$), contrary to $s>0$.

Second, let one of (21)–(23) hold. This excludes $\sigma=-1$, whence $s=0$, $b\neq -2r$ by (26). Hence $\sigma=1$. For (21), $a=2s$, $s=t\neq 0$. By (24), $r_2=r$, $s_2=-s$, $t_2=-t$. We must change the signs of s_2 and t_2, whence $\phi'=\phi$. For (22), $b=2r$, $2t=a\geqq 2s$ by (17) and $t\leqq r$ by $a\leqq b$. By (22) and (24), $r_2=t-r-s$, $s_2=s-t$, $t_2=-t$ are all $\leqq 0$. Hence $\sigma=-1$ for $\phi'=\phi_2$. Since $a+2t_2=0$, (26) gives $s_2=0$, whence $b+2r_2=2(t-s)=0$, contrary to (26).

F_3. We have $a=b=2\sigma t$ and (31).

First, let $\xi=\eta=0$. If $\sigma=-1$, then $s=0$, whence $r=0$ by Lemma 2, and $\phi'=\phi_3=\phi$. If $\sigma=1$, $r_3=r-s\leqq 0$, $s_3=r>0$, $t_3=t>0$, whence ϕ' has $\sigma=-1$, $r'=r-s$, $s'=-r$, $t'=-t$, $a=-2t'$, $s'=0$ by (26), contrary to $r>0$.

Second, let one of (21)–(23) hold. This excludes $\sigma=-1$, whence $s=0$, $r=0$. Hence $\sigma=1$, $r\leqq s$. For (21), $s=t\neq 0$, $r_3=r$ and $t_3=t$ are positive, whence $\phi'=\phi_3$, $s_3=r-t>0$, contrary to $r\leqq s=t$. For (22), $r=t$ and $r=s$ by Lemma 2. Then $r_3=s_3=-r$, $t_3=t$, $\phi'=\phi$.

F_4. We have $b=c$, $r_4=-r_1$, $s_4=-t_1$, $t_4=s_1$.

Case (21). By Lemma 3, $\sigma=+1$, $a=2s$, $s=t\leqq 2r$. Now $r_4=t-r$, $s_4=-t$, $t_4=-s$. If ϕ' has $\sigma=-1$, then $\phi'=\phi_4$, $a=-2t_4$, $s_4=0$ by (26), contrary to $t>0$. Hence ϕ' has $\sigma=1$ and we must change the signs of s_4 and t_4 to get ϕ'. Then $a=2t'$, $s'\leqq 2r'$ by (25), whence $2r\leqq t$. Thus $t=2r$, $\phi'=\phi$.

Case (22). If $\sigma=-1$, then $b=-2r$, $s=t=0$ by Lemma 3, $r_4=r$, $s_4=t_4=0$, $\phi'=\phi_4=\phi$. But if $\sigma=1$, $b=2r$, $s\leqq t\leqq 2s$, $r_4=r$, $s_4=-t$, $t_4=s-t$. If $s\neq t$, $t_4<0$ and ϕ' has $\sigma=1$, $r'=r$, $s'=t$, $t'=t-s$, $s'>t'$, contrary to Lemma 3. Hence $s=t$, ϕ' has $\sigma=-1$, $r'=-r$, $s'=-t$, $t'=0$, $b=-2r'$, $s'\neq 0$, contrary to Lemma 3.

Case (23). Then $r_4=-r-t-b$, $s_4=-t$, $t_4=s+t+a$. By (17), $a+2t+a+2s\geqq 0$ or $t_4\geqq 0$, and $a+2t+b+2r+b-a\geqq 0$ or $r_4\leqq 0$. Hence ϕ' has $\sigma=-1$, $r'=-r-t-b$, $s'=t$, $t'=-s-t-a$. Then (29) holds, and $s'-t'=a+s+2t$. But $a+2s+t\leqq 0$ by (26$_4$) and $t-s\leqq 0$; adding, we get $a+s+2t\leqq$

0, whence $s' \leq t'$. But $t' \leq s'$. Hence $s' = t'$ or $a+s+2t=0$. Thus the sum of $a+2s+t$ and $t-s$ is zero and each is ≤ 0, whence each is zero. Then $b+2r+t=0$ by (26_4) and $\phi' = \phi$.

Case $\xi = \eta = 0$. Then ϕ' has $r' = r$, $s' = t$, $t' = s$, whence $s = t$, $\phi' = \phi$.

We have now treated all the F_i employed in § 80. In the next set of parallelopipeds, we shall give the replacements to make in (19) to obtain the new transformation. Under these replacements, ϕ_1 becomes a form Φ having the coefficients a, b, c, R, S, T.

$\{Q, P', M\}$, $a = b$. Replace x_1 by $-y_1$, y_1 by x_1. Then $R = -s_1$, $S = r_1$, $T = -t_1$. For (21) and $\sigma = -1$, $\phi' = \Phi$, $-R \leq -S$ gives $-s \leq -r$, whence $r = s$, $\phi' = \phi$. For (21) and $\sigma = 1$, $R = s$, $S = r-t$, $T = -t$. If ϕ' has $\sigma = -1$, then $r' = -s$, $b = -2r'$, $t' = 0$, by (26), contrary to $t > 0$. Hence ϕ' has $\sigma = 1$, $r' = s$, $s' = t-r$, $t' = t$, $r' \leq s'$ or $t \geq r+s \geq 2r$. Hence $t = 2r$ by (25) and $s \leq r$, $s = r$. By (17), $a \geq 2t = 4r$, contrary to $a = 2s = 2r$. For (22), $r = s$ by Lemma 2. For (22) and $\sigma = 1$, we interchange r's and s's in the last case and see that ϕ' has $\sigma = 1$, $r' = t-s$, $s' = r$, $t' = t$, $a = 2s'$, $t' \leq 2r'$ by (25), whence $2s \leq t$. But $t \leq 2s$ by (25), whence $t = 2s$. By (17), $a \geq 2t = 4s$, contrary to $a = b = 2r = 2s$. For (22) and $\sigma = -1$, $t = 0$, $R = -s$, $S = -r$, $T = 0$; we change the signs of R and S and get $\phi' = \phi$. For (23), $R = r$, $S = -s$, $T = -t$; we must change the signs of S and T. For $\xi = \eta = 0$, $r' = s$, $s' = r$, $t' = t$, $-r' \leq -s'$, $r = s$, $\phi' = \phi$.

$\{S'$ or $R, Q, N\}$, according as $\sigma = 1$ or -1, $a = b = 2\sigma t$. Replace y_1 by $y_1 - \sigma x_1$. Here $R = r$, $S = s_1 - \sigma r_1$, $T = -t$. First, let $\xi = \eta = 0$. If $\sigma = -1$, $r = s = 0$, $R = S = 0$, $T = -t$, $\phi' = \phi$. If $\sigma = 1$, ϕ' has $\sigma = -1$, $r' = -r$, $s' = r-s$, $t' = -t$, $a = -2t'$, $s' = 0$ by (26), $-r' \leq -s'$, $r' = 0$, contrary to $r > 0$. Second, let one of (21)–(23) hold. Then $\sigma = 1$. For (21), $t = s$, $R = r-t$, $S = -r$, $T = -t$, and ϕ' has $\sigma = -1$, $a = -2T$, $S = 0$, contrary to $r > 0$. For (22), $R = -r$, $S = s$, $T = -t$, $\phi' = \phi$ and $r = s$ by Lemma 2.

$\{S'$ or $R', P, N\}$, according as $\sigma = 1$ or -1, $a = b = 2\sigma t$. Replace x_1 by $\sigma x_1 + y_1$, and y_1 by $-x_1$. Here $R = s_1$, $S = \sigma s_1 - r_1$, $T = t$. First, let $\xi = \eta = 0$. If $\sigma = -1$, $r = s = 0$, $\phi' = \phi$. If $\sigma = 1$, ϕ' has $\sigma = 1$, $\phi' = \Phi$, $R \leq S$, contrary to $r > 0$. Second, let one of (21)–(23) hold. Then $\sigma = 1$. For (21), $s = t > 0$, $R = -s$, $S = -r$, ϕ' has $\sigma = 1$, $r' = s$, $s' = r$, $r' \leq s'$, $s \leq r$, $s = r$, $\phi' = \phi$. For (22), $r = t$, $R = s-t \leq 0$ by (17), $S = s$, $T = t$, ϕ' has $\sigma = -1$, $a = -2t'$, $s' = 0$, contrary to $s > 0$.

$\{N, P, Q\}$, $a = b = c$. Replace x_1 by y_1, y_1 by z_1, z_1 by x_1. Here $R = t$, $S = r_1$, $T = s_1$.

First, let $\sigma = -1$. If $\xi = \eta = 0$, $\phi' = \Phi$, $-R \leq -S$, $-t \leq -r$, whence $-r \leq -s \leq -t$ gives $r = s = t$, $\phi' = \phi$. For (23), $S = -s$, $T = -r$, ϕ' has $\sigma = -1$, $r' = t$, $s' = s$, $t' = r$, $-r' \leq -t'$, $r = s = t$, $\phi' = \phi$.

Second, let $\sigma = 1$. If $\xi = \eta = 0$, $\phi' = \phi$, $R \leq S$, $t \leq r$, $r = s = t$, $\phi' = \phi$. For (21), $s = t$ by Lemma 3, $S = r-t$, $T = -s$. If $r \neq t$, ϕ' has $\sigma = 1$, $r' = t$, $s' = t-r$, $t' = s$,

$r' > s'$. Hence $r = t$, ϕ' has $\sigma = -1$, $r' = -t$, $s' = 0$, $t' = -s$, $-r' > -s'$. For (22), $r = s = t$ by Lemma 5, $S = -r$, $T = 0$, ϕ' has $\sigma = -1$, $r' = -t$, $s' = -r$, $t' = 0$, $a = -2s'$, an excluded case.

$\{N', Q, P\}$, $a = b = c$. Replace x_1 by z_1 and z_1 by $-x_1$. $R = t$, $S = -s_1$, $T = -r_1$.

First, let $\sigma = -1$. If $\xi = \eta = 0$, ϕ' has $\sigma = -1$, $r' = t$, $s' = s$, $t' = r$, $-r' \leq -t'$, $-t \leq -r$. But $-r \leq -s \leq -t$, whence $r = s = t$, $\phi' = \phi$. For (23), $R = t$, $S = r$, $T = s$, $\phi' = \Phi$, $-R \leq -S$, $r = s = t$, $\phi' = \phi$.

Second, let $\sigma = 1$. If $\xi = \eta = 0$, ϕ' has $\sigma = 1$, $r' = t$, $s' = s$, $t' = r$, $r' \leq t'$, $r \leq s \leq t$, whence $r = s = t$, $\phi' = \phi$. For (21), $s = t$ by Lemma 3, $R = t$, $S = s$, $T = t - r$. If ϕ' has $\sigma = 1$, $\phi' = \Phi$, $R > T$. Hence ϕ' has $\sigma = -1$, $R = -t$, $S = -s$, $T = 0$, $t = r$, $-R > -T$. For (22), $r = s = t$ by Lemma 5, $R = t$, $S = 0$, $T = r$, and ϕ' has $\sigma = -1$, $r' = -t$, $s' = 0$, $-r' > -s'$.

$\{P', N, S$ or $R\}$, according as $\sigma = 1$ or -1, $b = c$, $a = 2\sigma t$. Replace x_1 by $-x_1 - \sigma z_1$, y_1 by z_1, and z_1 by y_1. Then $R = r_1 - \sigma s_1$, $S = t$, $T = -s_1$.

First, let $\sigma = 1$. For $\xi = \eta = 0$, if ϕ' has $\sigma = -1$, then $s' = -t$, $a = -2s'$, contrary to Lemma 3. Hence ϕ' has $\sigma = 1$, $r' = s - r$, $s' = t$, $t' = s$, $a = 2s'$, $s' = t' \leq 2r'$ by Lemma 3, whence $t = s$, $2r \leq s$. But $s \leq 2r$ by (25), whence $s = 2r$, $\phi' = \phi$. For (21), $s = t$, $R = r$, $T = s$, $\phi' = \Phi = \phi$. For (22), $r \geq t$ by $b \geq a$, $R = -r - s + t < 0$, $S = t > 0$, $T = t - s \geq 0$. Hence ϕ' has $\sigma = -1$, $s' = -t$, $a = -2s'$.

Second, let $\sigma = -1$, whence $s = 0$. If $\xi = \eta = 0$, $\phi' = \Phi$, $a = -2S$. This and (21) are excluded by Lemma 3. For (22) or (23), $b = -2r$, $t = 0$ by (26), contrary to $a = -2t$.

$\{S$ or $R, N, P\}$, $a = b = c = 2\sigma t$. Replace x_1 by $z_1 - \sigma x_1$, y_1 by x_1, z_1 by y_1. Then $R = s_1$, $S = -t$, $T = r_1 - \sigma s_1$.

First, let $\sigma = -1$. Then $s = 0$, $r = 0$. Since (21)–(23) are excluded, $\xi = \eta = 0$, ϕ' has $\sigma = -1$, $r' = t' = 0$, $s' = t$, $a = -2s'$, excluded by Lemma 3.

Second, let $\sigma = 1$. If $\xi = \eta = 0$, and $s \neq r$, ϕ' has $\sigma = 1$, $r' = s$, $s' = t$, $t' = s - r$, $a = 2s'$, $s' = t'$ by Lemma 3, $t = s - r < s$, contrary to $s \leq t$. Hence $s = r$, ϕ' has $\sigma = -1$, $r' = -s$, $s' = -t$, $t' = 0$, $a = -2s'$. For (21), $s = t$, $R = -s$, $S = -t$, $T = r$, ϕ' has $\sigma = 1$, $r' = s$, $s' = t$, $t' = r$, $a = 2s'$, $s' = t'$ by Lemma 3, $t = r$, $\phi' = \phi$. For (22), $b = 2r$, $r = s = t$ by Lemma 5, $R = 0$, $S = -t$, $T = -r$, $\phi' = \Phi$, $\sigma = -1$, $a = -2S$, excluded by Lemma 3.

$\{N, P, S$ or $R\}$, $a = b = c = 2\sigma t$. Replace x_1 by $y_1 - \sigma z_1$, y_1 by z_1, z_1 by x_1. Then $R = -t$, $S = r_1 - \sigma s_1$, $T = s_1$. If $\sigma = -1$, then $s = r = 0$, $\xi = \eta = 0$, ϕ' has $\sigma = -1$, $r' = t$, $s' = t' = 0$, $b = -2r'$, excluded by Lemma 5.

Let $\sigma = 1$. If $\xi = \eta = 0$ and $s \neq r$, ϕ' has $\sigma = 1$, $r' = t$, $s' = s - r$, $t' = s$, $b = 2r'$, $s' = t'$ by Lemma 5, contrary to $r > 0$. Hence $s = r$, ϕ' has $\sigma = -1$, $r' = -t$, $s' = 0$, $t' = -s$, $b = -2r'$, excluded by Lemma 5. For (21), $s = t$, $S = r$, $T = -s$,

ϕ' has $\sigma=1$, $r'=t$, $s'=r$, $t'=s$, $b=2r'$, $r'=s'=t'$ by Lemma 5, $\phi'=\phi$. For (22), $r=s=t$ by Lemma 5, $R=-t$, $S=-r$, $T=0$, $\phi'=\Phi$ has $\sigma=-1$, $b=-2R$, excluded by Lemma 5.

$\{N,\ S'\ \text{or}\ R',\ P\}$, $a=b=c=2\sigma t$. Replace x_1 by $z_1+\sigma y_1$, y_1 by $-y_1$, z_1 by x_1. Then $R=t$, $S=s_1$, $T=\sigma s_1-r_1$. If $\sigma=-1$, then $s=r=0$, $\xi=\eta=0$, $\phi'=\Phi$ has $\sigma=-1$, $b=-2R$, excluded by Lemma 5.

Let $\sigma=1$. If $\xi=\eta=0$ and $s\neq r$, $\phi=\Phi$ has $\sigma=1$, $b=2R$, $R=S=T$ by Lemma 5, contrary to $r>0$. Hence $s=r$, ϕ' has $\sigma=-1$ $r'=-t$, $b=-2r'$, excluded by Lemma 5. For (21), $t=s$, $S=-s$, $T=-r$, ϕ' has $\sigma=1$, $r'=t$, $s'=s$, $t'=r$, $b=2r'$, $r'=s'=t'$ by Lemma 5, $\phi'=\phi$. For (22), $r=s=t$ by Lemma 5, $R=t$, $S=0$, $T=r$, ϕ' has $\sigma=-1$, $r'=-t$, $b=-2r'$, excluded by Lemma 5.

$\{S\ \text{or}\ R',\ N,\ Q\}$, $a=b=c=2\sigma t$. Replace x_1 by $-x_1$, y_1 by $z_1+\sigma x_1$, z_1 by y_1. Then $R=r_1$, $S=t$, $T=\sigma r_1-s_1$. If $\sigma=-1$, $s=r=0$, and for either $\xi=\eta=0$ or (23), $R=T=0$, $S=t$, $a=-2S$. Hence $\sigma=1$. If $\xi=\eta=0$, ϕ' has $\sigma=-1$, $s'=-t$, $a=-2s'$. For [1] (21), $s=t$, ϕ' has $\sigma=-1$, $s'=-t$, $a=-2s'$. For (22), $r=s=t$ by Lemma 5, $R=T=-r$, $S=t$, ϕ' has $\sigma=1$, $\phi'=\phi$.

$\{Q,\ N',\ S\ \text{or}\ R'\}$, $a=b=c=2\sigma t$. Replace x_1 by $-z_1$, y_1 by $x_1+\sigma z_1$, z_1 by $-y_1$. Then $R=s_1-\sigma r_1$, $S=t$, $T=-r_1$. The preceding paragraph holds except for (22) and then $R=T=r$, $\phi'=\Phi=\phi$.

$\{N,\ Q,\ S\ \text{or}\ R'\}$, $a=b=c=2\sigma t$. Replace x_1 by $-z_1$, y_1 by $y_1+\sigma z_1$, z_1 by x_1. Then $R=t$, $S=\sigma r_1-s_1$, $T=r_1$. If $\sigma=-1$, $s=r=0$ and for either $\xi=\eta=0$ or (23), $R=t$, $S=T=0$, $b=-2R$. Hence $\sigma=1$. If $\xi=\eta=0$, ϕ' has $\sigma=-1$, $r'=-t$, $b=-2r'$. For [2] (21), $s=t$, ϕ' has $\sigma=-1$, $r'=-t$, $b=-2r'$. For (22), $r=s=t$ by Lemma 5, $S=T=-r$, ϕ' has $\sigma=1$, $\phi'=\phi$.

$\{N',\ S\ \text{or}\ R',\ Q\}$, $a=b=c=2\sigma t$. Replace x_1 by $-y_1$, y_1 by $z_1+\sigma y_1$, z_1 by $-x_1$. Then $R=t$, $S=-r_1$, $T=s_1-\sigma r_1$. The preceding paragraph holds except for (22) and then $S=T=r$, $\phi'=\Phi=\phi$ has $\sigma=1$.

We shall next consider parallelopipeds which involve only N's with given values of ξ and η. We now give the resulting transformation explicitly, without comparing it with (19). It replaces ϕ by a form Φ having the coefficients a, b, c, R, S, T. The transformation which replaces x, y, z by p, q, r is denoted by $[p,\ q,\ r]$.

$\{P',\ N\ \text{or}\ N',\ M\}$, according as $\sigma=1$ or -1, $N=(0,\ -\sigma,\ 1)$ in (22), $b=c=2\sigma r$; $[-x,\ -y,\ \sigma y+z]$, $R=r$, $S=-s$, $T=t-\sigma s$. If $\sigma=-1$, $s=t=0$ by Lemma 3, $\phi'=\Phi=\phi$. If $\sigma=1$, ϕ' has $\sigma=-1$, $r'=-r$, $s'=-s$, $t'=s-t$, $b=-2r'$, $s'=0$, contrary to $s>0$.

[1] $R=r-t\leqq0$, $S=t$, $T=r$.

[2] $S=r$, $T=r-t\leqq0$.

For the next six cases, $a=b=c$, (23), $N=(1, 1, 1)$, ϕ' has $\sigma = -1$, $\phi' = \phi$; proof by (41):

$\{Q, M, N\}$, $[z, x+z, y+z]$, $R=-t$, $S=-s$, $T=r$, $r=s=t$.
$\{Q, N, M'\}$, $[y, x+y, y-z]$, $R=t$, $S=-r$, $T=-s$, $r=s=t$.
$\{M, Q', N\}$, $[z, z-y, x+z]$, $R=s$, $S=-t$, $T=-r$, $r=s=t$.
$\{N, Q, M\}$, $[x, x+y, x+z]$, $R=r$, $S=-t$, $T=-s$, $s=t$.
$\{M, N, Q\}$, $[y, y+z, x+y]$, $R=-s$, $S=r$, $T=-t$, $r=s$.
$\{N, M, Q'\}$, $[x, x-z, x+y]$, $R=-r$, $S=s$, $T=-t$.

For the next six cases, $a=b=c=2r=2s=2t$, $\phi'=\Phi=\phi$, $N=(-1, 0, 1)$ in (21), $\nu=(0, -1, 1)$ in (22), $w=x+y+z$:

$\{M, N, \nu\}$, $[-y, -z, w]$. $\{M, \nu, N\}$, $[z, y, -w]$.
$\{N, M, \nu\}$, $[x, z, -w]$. $\{N, \nu, M\}$, $[-x, -y, w]$.
$\{\nu, M, N\}$, $[-z, -x, w]$. $\{\nu, N, M\}$, $[y, x, -w]$.

For the next four cases, $a=b=c$, (23), $N=(1, 1, 1)$, $\phi'=\phi$; proof by (41):

$\{M', P', N\}$, $[z-y, z, z-x]$, $R=r$, $S=t$, $T=s$, $s=t$.
$\{N', P, M\}$, $[y-x, -x, z-x]$, $R=s$, $S=t$, $T=r$, $r=s=t$.
$\{N, M', P'\}$, $[x-z, x, x-y]$, $R=s$, $S=r$, $T=t$, $r=s$.
$\{M, N', P\}$, $[z-y, -y, x-y]$, $R=r$, $S=s$, $T=t$.

There remain only parallelopipeds which are excluded immediately (and yield no automorphs). They all have $\sigma=+1$. We write $N=(-1, 0, 1)$ in (21) and $\nu=(0, -1, 1)$ in (22).

Two with $b=c=2r$, $a=2s=2t$:

$\{P, N, \nu\}$, $[x-y, -z, y+z]$, $R=r$, $S=0$, $T=-s$; ϕ' has $\sigma=-1$, $r'=-r$, $t'=-s$, $b=-2r'$, $s'=t'=0$ by Lemma 3, contrary to $s>0$.

$\{P, \nu', N\}$, $[x-z, y, z-y]$, $R=-r$, $S=-s$, $T=0$; $\phi'=\Phi$ has $\sigma=-1$, $a=-2S$, excluded by Lemma 3.

Six with $a=b=c=2s=2t$:

$\{Q, M', N\}$, $[-z, x, z-y]$, $R=-s$, $S=r-t$, $T=-r$; $\phi'=\Phi$ has $\sigma=-1$, $-R \leq -S$ or $s \leq 0$.

$\{Q, N, M\}$, $[-y, x, y+z]$, $R=s$, $S=r$, $T=r-t$; ϕ' has $\sigma=-1$, $s'=-r$, $t'=r-t$, $-s' \leq -t'$ or $r \leq 0$.

$\{M, Q, N\}$, $[-z, y, x+z]$, $R=r-t$, $S=s$, $T=r$; ϕ' has $\sigma=-1$, $s'=-s$, $a=-2s'$.

$\{N', Q', M'\}$, $[x, -y, -x-z]$, $R=r$, $S=s$, $T=r-t$; ϕ' has $\sigma=-1$, $s'=-s$, $a=-2s'$.

$\{M', N', Q'\}$, $[y, -z, -x-y]$, $R=r-t$, $S=r$, $T=s$; ϕ' has $\sigma=-1$, $t'=-s$, $a=-2t'$, $s'=-r=0$ by (26).

$\{N, M, Q\}$, $[-x, z, x+y]$, $R=r$, $S=r-t$, $T=s$; ϕ' has $\sigma=-1$, $r'=-r$, $t'=-s$, $a=-2t'$, $s'=r-t=0$ by (26), $-r'\leqq -s'$ or $r\leqq 0$, contrary to $r>0$.

Six with $a=b=c=2s$, $r=s=t$, ϕ' with $\sigma=-1$:

$\{Q, N, \nu\}$, $[-y, x-z, y+z]$, $R=r$, $S=-r$, $T=0$, $s'=-r$, $-s'\leqq t'=0$, contrary to $r>0$.

$\{Q, \nu, N'\}$, $[z, x-y, y-z]$, $R=T=-r$, $S=0$, $-R\leqq -S$, contrary to $r>0$.

$\{N', Q', \nu'\}$, $[x, z-y, -x-z]$, $R=-r$, $S=t$, $T=0$, $r'=-r$, $s'=-t$, $t'=0$, $-r'\leqq -t'$, contrary to $r>0$.

$\{\nu, Q, N\}$, $[-z, y-x, x+z]$, $R=0$, $S=t$, $T=-r$, $s'=-t$, $a=-2s'$.

$\{N, \nu, Q\}$, $[-x, z-y, x+y]$, $R=-r$, $S=0$, $T=t$, $r'=-r$, $-r'\leqq -s'=0$, contrary to $r>0$.

$\{\nu', N', Q'\}$, $[y, x-z, -x-y]$, $R=0$, $S=-r$, $T=t$, $s'=-r$, $a=-2s'$.

Four with $a=b=c=2r$, $r=s=t$, ϕ' with $\sigma=-1$:

$\{M, P, \nu'\}$, $[y, z, x-z]$, $R=0$, $S=-r$, $T=s$, $s'=-r$, $a=-2s'$.

$\{\nu, P, M\}$, $[y, -x, x+z]$, $R=s$, $S=r$, $T=0$, $r'=-s$, $b=-2r'$.

$\{M, \nu, P\}$, $[z, -y, x+y]$, $R=0$, $S=s$, $T=r$, $s'=-s$, $a=-2s'$.

$\{\nu', M', P'\}$, $[-z, x, -x-y]$, $R=s$, $S=0$, $T=r$, $r'=-s$, $b=-2r'$.

Four with $a=b=c=2s$, $r=s=t$, ϕ' with $\sigma=-1$:

$\{N, P, \nu'\}$, $(y-x, z, x-z)$, $R=0$, $S=-r$, $T=-s$, $a=-2S$.

$\{\nu, P, N\}$, $[y-z, -x, x+z]$, $R=-s$, $S=t$, $T=0$, $r'=-s$, $b=-2r'$.

$\{N, \nu, P\}$, $[z-x, -y, x+y]$, $R=0$, $S=-s$, $T=t$, $s'=-s$, $a=-2s'$.

$\{\nu', N', P'\}$, $[y-z, x, -x-y]$, $R=-s$, $S=0$, $T=t$, $r'=-s$, $b=-2r'$.

Six with $a=b=c=2s=2t$, $S=(-1, 1, 0)$, ϕ' with $\sigma=-1$:

$\{S, M', N\}$, $[-x-z, x, z-y]$, $R=-s$, $S=r$, $T=s-r$; $r'=-s$, $b=-2r'$.

$\{S, N, M\}$, $[-x-y, x, y+z]$, $R=s$, $S=r-s$, $T=r$; $r'=-s$, $b=-2r'$.

$\{M, S, N\}$, $[-y-z, y, x+z]$, $R=r$, $S=s$, $T=r-s$, $s'=-s$, $a=-2s'$.

$\{M', N, S\}$, $[-y-z, z, y-x]$, $R=r$, $S=s-r$, $T=-s$, $r'=-r$, $t'=-s$, $a=-2t'$, $s'=0$ by (26), $-r'\leqq -s'$, contrary to $r>0$.

$\{N, S, M'\}$, $[-x-y, y, x-z]$, $R=s-r$, $S=-s$, $T=r$, $s'=-s$, $a=-2s'$.

$\{N, M, S\}$, $[-x-z, z, x+y]$, $R=r-s$, $S=r$, $T=s$, $s'=-r$, $t'=-s$, $a=-2t'$, $s'=0$.

Six with $a=b=c$, $b=2r$, $r=s=t$, ϕ' with $\sigma=-1$:

$\{S', M, \nu\}$, $[x, -x-z, y+z]$, $R=r$, $S=0$, $T=-r$, $r'=-r$, $b=-2r'$.

$\{S, \nu, M\}$, $[-x, x-y, y+z]$, $R=r$, $S=0$, $T=-t$, $r'=-r$, $b=-2r'$.

$\{M, S, \nu\}$, $[-y, y-z, x+z]$, $R=-r$, $S=s$, $T=0$, $s'=-s$, $a=-2s'$.

$\{M', \nu, S\}$, $[-z, z-y, y-x]$, $R=-r$, $S=0$, $T=-t$, $b=-2R$.

$\{\nu, M, S\}$, $[-z, z-x, x+y]$, $R=0$, $S=-s$, $T=t$, $s'=-s$, $a=-2s'$.

$\{\nu, S, M'\}$, $[-y, y-x, x-z]$, $R=0$, $S=-s$, $T=-t$, $a=-2S$.

Since we have employed all possible reduced parallelopipeds, we have proved

Theorem 104. *No two reduced forms in Theorem 103 are equivalent.*

82. Automorphs. For the special form ϕ treated under F_5 in §81, we found a transformation (32) which replaces ϕ by $\phi_5=\phi$, i.e., leaves ϕ unaltered, and is called an *automorph* of ϕ. Since $s=t=0$, we obtain another automorph from (32) by changing the signs of y_1 and z_1.

In the first case under F_1 in § 81, we changed the signs of s_1 and t_1 in ϕ_1 to get ϕ'. Hence in (19) for $\sigma=-1$ and (21), we must change the signs of y_1 and z_1 to obtain the automorph $x=x_1-z_1$, $y=-y_1$, $z=-z_1$.

We obtain all automorphs by mere inspection of all cases $\phi'=\phi$ in § 81, after an occasional adjustment of signs as just explained. We thus obtain

THEOREM 105. *All automorphs, in addition to identity, of a reduced form are listed in the following two tables.*

An automorph which replaces x, y, z by α, β, γ, respectively, is denoted by (α, β, γ).

CASE r, s, t ALL POSITIVE. Write w for $x+y+z$.

Conditions on Form	Automorphs
$a=2s=2t$	$(w, -y, -z)$
$a=2s,\ t=2r$	$(-x-z, -y, z)$
$a=2t,\ s=2r$	$(-x-y, y, -z)$
$b=2r,\ t=2s$	$(-x, -y-z, z)$
$a=b,\ r=s$	$(-y, -x, -z)$
$b=c,\ s=t$	$(-x, -z, -y)$
$b=c,\ a=2s=2t$	$(-w, z, y)$,
$b=c,\ a=2s=2t=4r$	$(x+z, -z, y)$, $(x+y, z, -y)$
$a=b=2r=2s=2t$	$(y, -w, z)$, $(-w, x, z)$, $(-x, w, -z)$
$a=b=c,\ r=s=t$	(z, x, y), (y, z, x), $(-z, -y, -x)$
$a=b=c=2r=2s=2t$	$(-z, w, -y)$, $(-y, -z, w)$, $(z, y, -w)$ $(w, -x, -y)$, $(x, -w, y)$, $(w, -z, -x)$, $(x, z, -w)$, $(-w, y, x)$, $(-x, -y, w)$, $(z, -w, x)$, $(-z, -x, w)$, $(-y, w, -x)$, $(y, x, -w)$

The form in the seventh line has also the automorph in the first line and identity. That in the last line has also the automorphs in the first, fifth, sixth, seventh, ninth, and tenth lines, and identity—24 in all.

Case r, s, t all $\leqq 0$. Write ϵ for $a+b+2r+2s+2t=0$.

Conditions on Form	Automorphs[1]
$a=-2s$, $t=0$	$(x-z,\ -y,\ -z)$
$a=-2t$, $s=0$	$(x-y,\ -y,\ -z)$
$b=-2r$, $t=0$	$(-x,\ y-z,\ -z)$
$a+2s+t=b+2r+t=0$	$(z-x,\ z-y,\ z)$
$a=b$, $r=s$	$(-y,\ -x,\ -z)$
$b=c$, $s=t$	$(-x,\ -z,\ -y)$
$a=b$, ϵ	$(y-z,\ x-z,\ -z)$
$a=b=-2r=-2s$, $t=0$	$(z-y,\ x,\ z),\ (y,\ z-x,\ z)$
$a=b=-2t$, $r=s=0$	$(-y,\ x-y,\ z),\ (x-y,\ x,\ z),\ (-x,\ y-x,\ -z)$
$b=c=-2r$, $s=t=0$	$(x,\ -z,\ y-z),\ (x,\ y-z,\ y),\ (-x,\ -y,\ z-y)$
$b=c$, $s=t$, $b+2r+s=0$, $a=-3s$	$(x-z,\ -z,\ y-z),\ (x-y,\ z-y,\ -y),\ (y-x,\ y,\ y-z)$
$a=b=c$, $r=s=t$	$(z,\ x,\ y),\ (y,\ z,\ x),\ (-z,\ -y,\ -x)$
$a=b=c$, ϵ	$(z-y,\ -y,\ x-y),\ (-x,\ z-x,\ y-x)$
$a=b=c$, ϵ, $r=s$	$(y,\ y-z,\ y-x),\ (x-z,\ x,\ x-y)$
$a=b=c$, ϵ, $s=t$	$(y-z,\ y-x,\ y),\ (z-y,\ z,\ z-x),\ (x,\ x-y,\ x-z)$
$a=b=c=-3s$, $r=s=t$	$\begin{cases}(z;z-x,\ z-y),\ (-y,\ x-y,\ z-y),\ (-z,\ y-z,\ x-z),\\ (x-y,\ x-z,\ x),\ (y-x,\ -x,\ z-x),\ (z-x,\ y-x,\ -x)\end{cases}$

When $a=b=c=-3s$, $r=s=t$, the conditions in the last six lines of the table hold, also those in lines 4, 5, 6, and 7. Including the identity, we have exactly 24 automorphs.

[1] If $r=s=0$, new automorphs are derived by changing the signs of x and y. If $r=t=0$, new ones by changing the signs of x and z. If $s=t=0$, new ones by changing the signs of y and z. If $r=s=t=0$, three new automorphs are derived from each one listed by these changes. This holds if $r=0$, etc., is true, but not listed. From the identity I and the fifth line, we obtain by these changes of signs the 2×4 automorphs of $ax^2+by^2+cz^2$ when $a=b$. From I and the sixth line, we obtain the 8 automorphs when $b=c$. When $a=b=c$ there are 3×4 further automorphs, derived from the twelfth line, and hence 24 in all.

83. Tables of reduced, positive, ternary, quadratic forms.

I. PROPERLY PRIMITIVE, REDUCED, POSITIVE, TERNARY, QUADRATIC FORMS $ax^2+by^2+cz^2+2ryz+2sxz+2txy$ OF DETERMINANT d AND THE NUMBER A OF THEIR AUTOMORPHS. SEPARATE LIST OF[1] $ax^2+by^2+cz^2$.

d	a	b	c	r	s	t	A		d	a	b	c
3	1	2	2	−1	0	0	12		1	1	1	1
5	1	2	3	−1	0	0	4		2	1	1	2
7	1	2	4	−1	0	0	4		3	1	1	3
	2	2	3	1	1	1	6		4	1	1	4
8	1	3	3	−1	0	0	4			1	2	2
	2	2	3	−1	−1	0	8		5	1	1	5
9	1	2	5	−1	0	0	4		6	1	1	6
	2	2	3	0	0	−1	12			1	2	3
10	2	2	3	0	−1	0	4		7	1	1	7
11	1	2	6	−1	0	0	4		8	1	1	8
	1	3	4	−1	0	0	2			1	2	4
12	1	4	4	−2	0	0	12		9	1	1	9
	2	3	3	1	1	1	4			1	3	3
13	1	2	7	−1	0	0	4		10	1	1	10
	2	2	5	1	1	1	6			1	2	5
	2	3	3	−1	0	−1	2		11	1	1	11
14	1	3	5	−1	0	0	2		12	1	1	12
15	1	2	8	−1	0	0	4			1	2	6
	1	4	4	−1	0	0	4			1	3	4
	2	2	5	0	0	−1	12			2	2	3
	2	3	3	0	0	−1	4		13	1	1	13
16	1	4	5	−2	0	0	4		14	1	1	14
	2	2	5	−1	−1	0	8			1	2	7
	2	3	3	−1	0	0	4		15	1	1	15
	3	3	3	−1	−1	−1	24			1	3	5
17	1	2	9	−1	0	0	4		16	1	1	16
	1	3	6	−1	0	0	2			1	2	8
	2	3	4	1	1	1	2			1	4	4
18	2	2	5	0	−1	0	4		17	1	1	17
	2	3	4	−1	0	−1	2		18	1	1	18
19	1	2	10	−1	0	0	4			1	2	9
	1	4	5	−1	0	0	2			1	3	6
	2	2	7	1	1	1	6			2	3	3
	2	3	4	−1	−1	0	2		19	1	1	19
20	1	3	7	−1	0	0	2		20	1	1	20
	1	4	6	−2	0	0	4			1	2	10
	2	3	4	0	0	−1	4			1	4	5
	3	3	3	1	1	1	6			2	2	5
21	1	2	11	−1	0	0	4		21	1	1	21
	1	5	5	−2	0	0	4			1	3	7
	2	2	7	0	0	−1	12					
	2	3	4	0	−1	0	4					
	3	3	3	0	−1	−1	2					
22	2	3	4	−1	0	0	2		22	1	1	22
	2	3	5	1	1	1	2			1	2	11
23	1	2	12	−1	0	0	4		23	1	1	23
	1	3	8	−1	0	0	2					
	1	4	6	−1	0	0	2					
	2	3	5	−1	0	−1	2					

[1] It has 4, 8, or 24 automorphs by the preceding footnote.

d	a	b	c	r	s	t	A		d	a	b	c
24	1	4	7	−2	0	0	4		24	1	1	24
	1	5	5	−1	0	0	4			1	2	12
	2	2	7	−1	−1	0	8			1	3	8
	3	3	3	0	0	−1	4			1	4	6
	3	3	4	−1	−1	−1	4			2	3	4
25	1	2	13	−1	0	0	4		25	1	1	25
	2	2	9	1	1	1	6			1	5	5
	2	3	5	−1	−1	0	2					
	2	3	5	0	0	−1	4					
26	1	3	9	−1	0	0	2		26	1	1	26
	1	5	6	−2	0	0	2			1	2	13
	2	2	7	0	−1	0	4					
27	1	2	14	−1	0	0	4		27	1	1	27
	1	4	7	−1	0	0	2			1	3	9
	1	6	6	−3	0	0	12					
	2	2	9	0	0	−1	12					
	2	3	5	0	−1	0	4					
	2	3	6	1	1	1	2					
	2	4	5	2	1	1	2					
28	1	4	8	−2	0	0	4		28	1	1	28
	2	3	5	−1	0	0	2			1	2	14
	2	3	6	−1	0	−1	2			1	4	7
	2	4	5	−2	−1	0	4			2	2	7
	3	3	4	1	1	1	2					
29	1	2	15	−1	0	0	4		29	1	1	29
	1	3	10	−1	0	0	2					
	1	5	6	−1	0	0	2					
	3	3	4	0	−1	−1	1					
30	2	3	6	0	0	−1	4		30	1	1	30
	3	3	4	−1	−1	0	2			1	2	15
31	1	2	16	−1	0	0	4			1	3	10
	1	4	8	−1	0	0	2			1	5	6
	1	5	7	−2	0	0	2			2	3	5
	2	2	11	1	1	1	6		31	1	1	31
	2	3	6	−1	−1	0	2					
	2	4	5	1	1	1	2					
32	1	3	11	−1	0	0	2		32	1	1	32
	1	4	9	−2	0	0	4			1	2	16
	1	6	6	−2	0	0	4			1	4	8
	2	2	9	−1	−1	0	8					
	2	3	7	1	1	1	2					
	2	4	5	−2	0	0	4					
	3	3	4	0	0	−1	4					
	3	3	5	−1	−1	−1	4					
	3	4	4	2	1	1	2					
33	1	2	17	−1	0	0	4		33	1	1	33
	1	6	7	−3	0	0	4			1	3	11
	2	2	11	0	0	−1	12					
	2	3	6	0	−1	0	4					
	2	3	7	−1	0	−1	2					
	2	4	5	−1	0	−1	2					
	3	3	4	0	−1	0	2					
34	1	5	7	−1	0	0	2		34	1	1	34
	2	2	9	0	−1	0	4			1	2	17

d	a	b	c	r	s	t	A
	2	3	6	−1	0	0	2
	2	4	5	−1	−1	0	2
35	1	2	18	−1	0	0	4
	1	3	12	−1	0	0	2
	1	4	9	−1	0	0	2
	1	6	6	−1	0	0	4
	2	3	7	0	0	−1	4
	2	4	5	0	0	−1	4
	3	4	4	−1	−1	−1	2
36	1	4	10	−2	0	0	4
	1	5	8	−2	0	0	2
	2	4	5	0	−1	0	4
	2	5	5	2	1	1	4
	3	3	5	1	1	1	2
	3	4	4	−2	0	0	12
37	1	2	19	−1	0	0	4
	2	2	13	1	1	1	6
	2	3	7	−1	−1	0	2
	2	3	8	1	1	1	2
	2	5	5	−2	0	−1	2
	3	3	5	0	−1	−1	1
38	1	3	13	−1	0	0	2
	1	6	7	−2	0	0	2
	2	3	8	−1	0	−1	2
	2	4	5	−1	0	0	2
39	1	2	20	−1	0	0	4
	1	4	10	−1	0	0	2
	1	5	8	−1	0	0	2
	1	6	8	−3	0	0	4
	2	2	13	0	0	−1	12
	2	3	7	0	−1	0	4
	3	3	5	−1	−1	0	2
	3	4	4	1	1	1	2
40	1	4	11	−2	0	0	4
	1	7	7	−3	0	0	4
	2	2	11	−1	−1	0	8
	2	3	7	−1	0	0	2
	2	3	8	0	0	−1	4
	2	5	5	1	1	1	4
	3	3	5	0	0	−1	4
	3	3	6	−1	−1	−1	4
	3	4	4	0	−1	−1	2
41	1	2	21	−1	0	0	4
	1	3	14	−1	0	0	2
	1	5	9	−2	0	0	2
	1	6	7	−1	0	0	2
	2	4	7	2	1	1	2
	3	4	4	−1	0	−1	1
42	2	2	11	0	−1	0	4
	2	3	9	1	1	1	2
	2	5	5	−2	0	0	4
	3	3	5	0	−1	0	2

d	a	b	c
35	1	1	35
	1	5	7
36	1	1	36
	1	2	18
	1	3	12
	1	4	9
	1	6	6
	2	2	9
	2	3	6
	3	3	4
37	1	1	37
38	1	1	38
	1	2	19
39	1	1	39
	1	3	13
40	1	1	40
	1	2	20
	1	4	10
	1	5	8
	2	4	5
41	1,	1	41
42	1	1	42
	1	2	21
	1	3	14
	1	6	7

d	a	b	c	r	s	t	A	d	a	b	c
43	1	2	22	−1	0	0	4		2	3	7
	1	4	11	−1	0	0	2	43	1	1	43
	2	2	15	1	1	1	6				
	2	3	8	−1	−1	0	2				
	2	3	9	−1	0	−1	2				
	2	5	5	−1	0	−1	2				
	3	4	5	2	1	1	1				
44	1	3	15	−1	0	0	2	44	1	1	44
	1	4	12	−2	0	0	4		1	2	22
	1	5	9	−1	0	0	2		1	4	11
	1	6	8	−2	0	0	2		2	2	11
	2	4	7	−2	−1	0	4				
	3	3	6	1	1	1	2				
	3	4	4	0	0	−1	2				
	3	4	5	−2	−1	0	2				
	4	4	5	2	2	2	6				
45	1	2	23	−1	0	0	4	45	1	1	45
	1	6	9	−3	0	0	4		1	3	15
	1	7	7	−2	0	0	4		1	5	9
	2	2	15	0	0	−1	12		3	3	5
	2	3	8	0	−1	0	4				
	2	3	9	0	0	−1	4				
	2	4	7	1	1	1	2				
	2	5	5	0	0	−1	4				
	2	5	6	2	1	1	2				
	3	3	6	0	−1	−1	1				
	3	4	4	−1	0	0	4				
46	1	5	10	−2	0	0	2	46	1	1	46
	2	3	8	−1	0	0	2		1	2	23
	2	5	6	−2	0	−1	2				
	3	4	5	−1	−1	−1	1				
47	1	2	24	−1	0	0	4	47	1	1	47
	1	3	6	−1	0	0	2				
	1	4	12	−1	0	0	2				
	1	6	8	−1	0	0	2				
	1	7	8	−3	0	0	2				
	2	3	10	1	1	1	2				
	2	4	7	−1	0	−1	2				
	2	5	6	−2	−1	0	2				
48	1	4	13	−2	0	0	4	48	1	1	48
	1	7	7	−1	0	0	4		1	2	24
	1	8	8	−4	0	0	12		1	3	16
	2	2	13	−1	−1	0	8		1	4	12
	2	3	10	−1	0	−1	2		1	6	8
	2	4	7	−2	0	0	4		2	3	8
	2	5	5	−1	0	0	4		3	4	4
	3	3	6	−1	−1	0	2				
	3	3	6	0	0	−1	4				
	3	3	7	−1	−1	−1	4				
	3	4	5	−2	0	0	4				
	4	4	5	−2	−2	0	8				
	4	4	5	1	2	2	4				
49	1	2	25	−1	0	0	4	49	1	1	49
	1	5	10	−1	0	0	2		1	7	7

d	a	b	c	r	s	t	A		d	a	b	c
	2	2	17	1	1	1	6					
	2	3	9	-1	-1	0	2					
	2	4	7	0	0	-1	4					
	2	5	6	1	1	1	2					
	3	5	5	-2	-1	-1	6					
50	1	3	17	-1	0	0	2		50	1	1	50
	1	6	9	-2	0	0	2			1	2	25
	2	2	13	0	-1	0	4			1	5	10
	2	3	10	0	0	-1	4			2	5	5
	2	4	7	-1	-1	0	2					
	3	4	5	1	1	1	1					

II. IMPROPERLY PRIMITIVE, REDUCED, POSITIVE FORMS.

d	a	b	c	r	s	t	A		d	a	b	c	r	s	t	A
4	2	2	2	1	1	1	24		34	2	2	12	1	1	1	6
6	2	2	2	0	0	-1	12			2	4	6	2	1	1	2
10	2	2	4	1	1	1	6		36	2	2	10	-1	-1	0	8
12	2	2	4	-1	-1	0	8			2	2	12	0	0	-1	12
	2	2	4	0	0	-1	12			2	4	6	-2	-1	0	4
14	2	2	4	0	-1	0	4			4	4	4	1	2	2	8
16	2	2	6	1	1	1	6		38	2	2	10	0	-1	0	4
18	2	2	6	0	0	-1	12			2	4	6	1	1	1	2
20	2	2	6	-1	-1	0	8		40	2	2	14	1	1	1	6
	2	4	4	2	1	1	4			2	4	6	-1	0	-1	2
22	2	2	6	0	-1	0	4		42	2	2	14	0	0	-1	12
	2	2	8	1	1	1	6			2	4	6	-1	-1	0	2
24	2	2	8	0	0	-1	12			2	4	6	0	0	-1	4
	2	4	4	1	1	1	4		44	2	2	12	-1	-1	0	8
26	2	4	4	-1	0	-1	2			2	4	6	0	-1	0	4
28	2	2	8	-1	-1	0	8			4	4	4	1	1	2	2
	2	2	10	1	1	1	6		46	2	2	12	0	-1	0	4
	2	4	4	0	0	-1	4			2	2	16	1	1	1	6
30	2	2	8	0	-1	0	4			2	4	6	-1	0	0	2
	2	2	10	0	0	-1	12		48	2	2	16	0	0	-1	12
	2	4	4	-1	0	0	4			2	4	8	2	1	1	2
										2	6	6	3	1	1	4
									50	4	4	4	-1	-1	-1	6

84. Minimum of positive quadratic forms in four variables.[1]

THEOREM 106. *The minimum of any positive, quaternary, quadratic form* $f(x_1, x_2, x_3, x_4)$ *of determinant d is* $\leq r = \sqrt[4]{4d}$. *Also, r is actually the minimum of*

$$r(x_1^2 + \ldots + x_4^2 + x_1 x_2 + x_1 x_3 + x_1 x_4) ,$$

whose determinant is d.

We may assume that the coefficient a of x_1^2 in f is its minimum. Let $F(X_1, \ldots, X_4)$ denote the adjoint of f. Let the minimum M of $F(O, X_2, X_3, X_4)$ be attained when $X_i = \xi_i (i = 2, 3, 4)$, whence the g.c.d. of the integers ξ_i is 1. By § 9, there exist integers l_i, m_i such that

$$l_3 m_4 - m_3 l_4 = \xi_2 , \qquad l_4 m_2 - l_2 m_4 = \xi_3 , \qquad l_2 m_3 - l_3 m_2 = \xi_4 .$$

[1] Korkine and Zolotareff, *Math. Annalen*, V (1872), 581–83.

There are integral solutions n_i of $n_2\xi_2+n_3\xi_3+n_4\xi_4=1$, whence the determinant $|l_im_in_i|$ is unity. The transformation

$$(42) \qquad x_1=y_1\ , \qquad x_i=l_iy_2+m_iy_3+n_iy_4 \qquad (i=2,\ 3,\ 4)$$

has determinant unity and replaces f by an equivalent form ϕ whose coefficient of y_1^2 is a. Then a is the minimum of ϕ and hence of $\phi(y_1, y_2, y_3, 0)$. Denote the determinant of the latter by Δ. Evidently (42) with $y_4=0$ gives a representation of $\phi(y_1, y_2, y_3, 0)$ by f. But we have[1] $F(0, \xi_2, \xi_3, \xi_4)=\Delta$. Hence $M=\Delta$. The determinant of $F(0, X_2, X_3, X_4)$ is d^2a. By the Corollary in § 79,

$$\Delta \leqq \sqrt[3]{2d^2a}\ , \qquad a \leqq \sqrt[3]{2\Delta}\ .$$

Take the third and ninth powers of these, respectively. Hence $a^8 \leqq 16d^2$.

[1] Jacobi, *Werke*, II, 223. The formula is the case $n=4$ of one on quadratic forms in n variables; Bachmann, *Arithmetik Quad. Formen*, I (1898), 564.

CHAPTER XII

UNIVERSAL, ZERO, QUADRATIC FORMS

85. Summary. It was proved in §14 that every universal, indefinite, ternary, quadratic form is a zero form N. We shall show that N is equivalent to $F = 2^e gaxy + f$, where $f = gby^2 + cyz + gdz^2$, with ga odd, a prime to d, and g prime to c. Let R denote the discriminant of f. Let t denote the largest divisor of a which is prime to g. Then F is universal if and only if R is a quadratic residue to t and one of the following sets of conditions holds: (i) $e = 0$; (ii) c even, $e = 1$, either d is odd, or d is double an odd and b is odd; (iii) c odd, $e \geqq 1$, bd even.

The treatment is an improvement, especially for four variables, on the author's original paper.[1]

86. Reduction to normal form. Let ξ, η, ... be integral values not all zero of the n variables x, y, ... for which the zero form N is zero. Since N is homogeneous, we may assume that ξ, η, ... have no common factor > 1. There exists a square matrix M of determinant unity having ξ, η, ... as elements of the first column and integers elsewhere (for 3-rowed M, see § 10). The linear transformation with the matrix M replaces N by a form P in which the coefficient of x^2 is zero.

The part of P which involves x may be written as Axy', where y' is a linear function of y, z, ..., the g.c.d. of whose coefficients is unity. As noted above there exists a square matrix of determinant unity whose elements are all integers, those of the first row being the coefficients of y'. Let z', w', ... be the linear functions of y, z, ... whose coefficients are the elements of the second, third, ... rows of that matrix. The resulting linear substitution replaces P by an equivalent form Q. After dropping the accents on y', z', ..., we have

$$(1) \qquad Q = Axy + \phi(y, z, w, \ldots) .$$

If $n = 3$, this is of the form (2) with $\psi = z^2$. If $n > 3$, the sum of the terms of ϕ which are linear in y is cyz', where z' is a linear function of z, w, ..., the g.c.d. of whose coefficients is 1. There exist further linear functions

---

[1] *Trans. Amer. Math. Soc.*, XXXI (1929), 164–89. A complete investigation for five variables has been made by R. S. Underwood.

w', . . . such that the determinant of the coefficients in z', w', . . . is 1. Hence Q is equivalent to

$$(2) \qquad h = Axy + By^2 + cyz + \Delta\psi(z, w, \dots) \,,$$

in which the g.c.d. of the coefficients of ψ is 1.

Let $A = 2^e a$, where a is odd. Let g be the g.c.d. of $a = ga$ and $\Delta = gd$. Then c is prime to g. For, if a prime p divides c and g, p is odd and $h \equiv By^2$ (mod p), whence h has at most $\frac{1}{2}(p+1)$ values modulo p and is not universal.

If we replace z by $z + ty$ in h and note that $\Delta \equiv 0$ (mod g), we get a form (1) in which the coefficient of y^2 is $\equiv B + ct$ (mod g). This is divisible by g when t is suitably chosen. Hence we may take $B = gb$ in (2).

THEOREM 107. *Every universal, zero, quadratic form in three or more variables is equivalent to a form*

$$(3) \qquad F = 2^e gaxy + f \,, \qquad f = gby^2 + cyz + gd\psi(z, w, \dots) \,,$$

where g and a are odd, a is prime to d, c is prime to g, and the g.c.d. of the coefficients of ψ is unity.

CASE OF THREE VARIABLES

87. Problem reduced to a congruence. Here $f = gby^2 + cyz + gdz^2$. Under specified conditions on the coefficients of f, we shall prove that to every G corresponds an odd integer y such that $f \equiv G$ (mod gay) has a solution $z = Z$. To illustrate our method, take the simplest case $e = 0$. Then $f = G + gayQ$, where Q is an integer. Hence $F = G$ when $x = -Q$, $z = Z$, and y has the chosen value.

Note that we employ a modulus which is not a constant, but a multiple of the variable y.

Let t be the largest divisor of a which is prime to g, and let r be the largest divisor of g which is prime to a. We may write

$$(4) \quad \begin{cases} g = qr, \ a = st, \ q \text{ and } s \text{ have the same distinct prime factors, } r \text{ and } t \\ \text{are prime to each other and to both } q \text{ and } s. \end{cases}$$

LEMMA 1. *If G and y are any assigned integers such that y is prime to sg, $f \equiv G$ (mod sg) is solvable for z.*

It suffices to prove that $f \equiv G$ is solvable with respect to the relatively prime moduli sq and r whose product is sg. Since c and y are prime to g, $f \equiv cyz \equiv G$ (mod g) has a solution z. This disposes of modulus r. It has a solution z_1 modulo q; let $cyz_1 = G + qM$. Every solution modulo q is given by $z=z_1+\zeta q$. Insert this z into $f\equiv G$ (mod sq), cancel G, and delete the common factor q. We get

$$rby^2+cy\zeta+M+rd(z_1+\zeta q)^2\equiv 0 \quad (\text{mod } s) .$$

If s is a product of powers p^n of distinct primes, it suffices to prove that the same congruence modulo p^n is solvable. Let p^m be the highest power of p which divides q. Then $m\geq 1$ since p divides s and therefore q. Write $S=cy$, $-k=rby^2+M+rdz_1^2$, and transpose the latter. The congruence becomes

$$(5) \qquad\qquad S\zeta+p^m\phi(\zeta)\equiv k \quad (\text{mod } p^n) ,$$

where $\phi(\zeta)$ is a quadratic function. Since c is prime to g, it is prime to q and hence to s. Hence S is not divisible by p.

If $m\geq n$, (5) is $S\zeta\equiv k$ and is solvable.

Next, let $n>m$. Then (5) implies $S\zeta\equiv k$ (mod p^m), which has a solution ζ', whence $\zeta=\zeta'+Zp^m$, $S\zeta'=k+Np^m$. Cancellation of k from (5) and division by p^m gives

$$N+SZ+\phi(\zeta'+Zp^m)\equiv 0, \text{ or } SZ+p^mP(Z)\equiv k' \quad (\text{mod } p^{n-m}) ,$$

where $k'=-N-\phi(\zeta')$ is independent of Z. If $n-m\leq m$, this becomes $SZ\equiv k'$ and is solvable. If $n-m>m$, we repeat the process and reduce the problem to a congruence modulo p^{n-2m}.

To proceed by induction on h, suppose the problem has been reduced to

$$(6) \qquad\qquad Su+p^m\psi(u)\equiv K \quad (\text{mod } p^{n-hm}), \; n>hm .$$

Since this is evidently solvable if $n-hm\leq m$, let $n-hm>m$. Evidently (6) has a solution u' modulo p^m, whence

$$u=u'+vp^m , \qquad Su'=K+p^mQ .$$

Cancellation of K from (6) and division by p^m gives

$$Q+Sv+\psi(u'+vp^m)\equiv 0, \text{ or } Sv+p^mH(v)\equiv K' \quad (\text{mod } p^{n-hm-m}) .$$

Since the latter is of type (6) with h replaced by $h+1$, the induction is complete. Ultimately we reach a congruence (6) with h so large that $0\leq n-hm\leq m$, which is therefore solvable.

88. Solution modulo ty. Let t be a product of powers p^n of distinct primes. Each $p>2$. We have $4gdf=Z^2-Ry^2$, where $Z=2gdz+cy$ and R is defined in (8). But $4gd$ is prime to t. If $R \equiv 0 \pmod{p}$, then $4gdF \equiv Z^2$ (mod p) and F takes only $\frac{1}{2}(p+1)$ values incongruent modulo p and is not universal. Also, $f \equiv G \pmod{p^n}$ is equivalent to

$$(7) \qquad\qquad Z^2 - Ry^2 \equiv k \pmod{p^n}, \qquad k = 4gdG .$$

If R is a quadratic non-residue of p, take $G \equiv 0 \pmod{p}$. Then $y \equiv 0$, $Z \equiv 0$, $z \equiv 0 \pmod{p}$, and F is divisible by p^2 and is not universal.

Thus R is a quadratic residue of p and hence of p^n (by induction on n) and therefore of t. Hence if F is universal,

$$(8) \qquad\qquad R = c^2 - 4g^2bd \text{ is a quadratic residue of } t .$$

Then $R\delta^2 \equiv 1 \pmod{p^n}$ has a solution δ. Multiply (7) by δ^2 and write $u = \delta Z$, $K = \delta^2 k$. We get

$$(9) \qquad\qquad u^2 - y^2 \equiv K \pmod{p^n} .$$

Except in the case

$$(10) \qquad\qquad p = 3, \ K \equiv 1 \pmod 3 ,$$

$u^2 - y^2 \equiv K \pmod{p}$ has a solution with y prime to p. Take any integer a prime to p and determine β so that $a\beta \equiv 1 \pmod{p}$. Then $2y \equiv a - K\beta \pmod{p}$ determines an integer y, which is not divisible by p if $a^2 \not\equiv K \pmod{p}$. Since at most three residues a are excluded, we can choose a suitable a if $p > 3$. In case $p = 3$ and $K \equiv 0$ or $2 \pmod 3$, only $a \equiv 0$ is excluded. Take $u = y - a$. Then $y + u \equiv -K\beta$, $u^2 - y^2 \equiv Ka\beta \equiv K \pmod{p}$.

Except in case (10), congruence (9) has a solution with y prime to p. To proceed by induction from $n = m$ to $n = m+1$, let

$$u^2 - Y^2 = K + Sp^m, \ Y \text{ prime to } p .$$

Then $2Y\eta \equiv S \pmod{p}$ has a solution η, and (9) holds modulo p^{m+1} for $y = Y + \eta p^m$. From u and y we get Z and then z.

Hence except in case (10), $f \equiv G \pmod{p^n}$ has a solution with y prime to p. We are now ready to prove

LEMMA 2. *Assume* (8) *and exclude case* (10). *Then to each G corresponds an odd prime π not dividing adg such that, when $y = \pi$, $f \equiv G \pmod{ty}$ has a solution z.*

Write $t = \tau T$, $\tau = p_1^{n_1} \ldots p_j^{n_j}$, where no one of the distinct primes $p_i (i = 1, \ldots, j)$ divides G, while each prime factor of T divides G. We proved that $f \equiv G$ (mod $p_i^{n_i}$) has a solution y_i, z_i with y_i prime to p_i. But there exist integers Y and Z satisfying

$$Y \equiv y_1, \ Z \equiv z_1 \ (\text{mod } p_1^{n_1}), \ \ldots, \qquad Y \equiv y_j, \ Z \equiv z_j \quad (\text{mod } p_j^{n_j}) .$$

Hence Y, Z satisfy $f \equiv G$ (mod τ) and Y is prime to τ.

Write D for gdG. We saw that gd is prime to t. Hence D is prime to τ. The divisor τ of a is odd. Let $q_1, \ldots, q_h$ be the distinct odd primes which occur in D with odd exponents. The system of congruences

$$\pi \equiv Y \ (\text{mod } \tau), \ \pi \equiv 1 \ (\text{mod } 8), \ \pi \equiv 1 \ (\text{mod } q_i) \qquad (i = 1, \ldots, h)$$

has a solution $\pi \equiv V$ (mod M), where V is prime to $M = 8\tau q_1 \ldots q_h$. There are infinitely many primes of the form $V + Mw$. Let π be one of them which does not divide $2adg$. We shall prove that Lemma 2 holds for this π. For Jacobi symbols,

$$(q_i | \pi) = (\pi | q_i) = 1 , \qquad (2 | \pi) = 1 ,$$

whence $(D | \pi) = 1$, since D is the product of $q_1 \ldots q_h$, a power of 2, and a square. For $y = \pi$, $f \equiv G$ (mod y) is equivalent to $(gdz)^2 \equiv D$ (mod π), which has a solution $z = z'$.

Finally, $f \equiv G$ (mod T) has a solution $z = Z'$ when $y = \pi$. Let p^n be a highest power of a prime dividing T. Thus p divides G. Since π is not a divisor of a and hence not of T, $p \neq \pi$. Since p^n is the highest power of p which divides t, $f \equiv G$ (mod p^n) was proved equivalent to (9), where now K is divisible by p. We readily prove that (9) has a solution u when y has any assigned value (say π) not divisible by p. If $n = 1$, take $u = y$. To proceed by induction, let $U^2 - y^2 = K + Qp^m$. Then (9) holds modulo p^{m+1} when $u = U + Sp^m$, if $2SU + Q \equiv 0$ (mod p), which is satisfied by choice of S.

Determine z so that $z \equiv Z$ (mod τ), $z \equiv z'$ (mod π), $z \equiv Z'$ (mod T). Then z is the number desired in Lemma 2.

89. Theorem 108. *Let* (8) *hold, where t is the largest divisor of a which is prime to g. Then to every G corresponds an odd integer y such that $f \equiv G$ (mod agy) has a solution z.*

This follows from Lemmas 1 and 2 except in case (10), since sg and ty are relatively prime.

In case (10), $k \equiv \delta^2 \equiv R \equiv 1$ (mod 3), and (7) requires $y \equiv 0$ (mod 3). For each prime factor $p_i \neq 3$ of τ, we saw that $f \equiv G$ (mod $p_i^{n_i}$) has a solution y_i, z_i with y_i prime to p_i. Choose Y so that Y is prime to 3 and $3Y \equiv y_i$ (mod $p_i^{n_i}$) for each such p_i. Take $y = 3Y$. Now $k + 9RY^2$ is a quadratic residue of 3 and hence of 3^{n+1}. Hence as in (7), $f \equiv G$ (mod 3^{n+1}) has a solution z for $y=3Y$. The same was just proved for each $p_i^{n_i}$ as modulus. Hence $f \equiv G \pmod{3\tau}$ has a solution $z=Z$ for $y=3Y$, where Y is prime to τ. Since $3\pi \equiv 3Y \pmod{3\tau}$, this holds also if we replace y by 3π for π determined as in the proof of Lemma 2.

For $y=3\pi$, $f \equiv G \pmod{\pi}$ is equivalent to $(gdz)^2 \equiv D \pmod{\pi}$, which has a solution z since $(D|\pi)=1$. Hence for $y=3\pi$, there is a solution z of $f \equiv G$ modulo $3\tau\pi = \tau y$, as well as modulo T (by the proof of Lemma 2), and hence modulo ty.

By the first remark in § 87, we now have

THEOREM 109. *If $e=0$, F is universal in case* (8).

90. Classic, universal, ternary, quadratic forms. Consider the classic forms F in which all coefficients of products of different variables are even:

Theorem 110. *When $e \geq 1$ and c is even, F is universal if and only if* (8) *holds and*

$$(11) \qquad e=1; \text{ either } d \text{ is odd, or } d \equiv 2 \pmod{4} \text{ and } b \text{ is odd } .[1]$$

Write $F=2^e Axy+f$, $f=By^2+2Cyz+Dz^2$, where A is odd. Let F be universal. Then B and D are not both even. If B is even and D is odd, we replace z by $z+y$ in F and obtain a like form in which $B'=B+2C+D$ is odd. Hence we may take B odd.

First, let $e \geq 3$. Since F represents a complete set of residues modulo 8, the same is true of

$$BF \equiv Y^2+hz^2 \pmod{8}, \qquad Y=y+BCz .$$

If h is even, Y^2+hz^2 evidently has at most six values modulo 8. Hence h is odd, and it has at most seven residues: $0, 1, 4, 5, h, h+1, h+4$.

Second, let $e=2$, C odd. Then

$$\phi=BF \equiv 4xy+y^2 \pm 2yz+dz^2 \pmod{8}$$

and we may choose the upper sign. The residues of ϕ modulo 4 are $0, 1, d$, $d+3$, whence $d=4k+3$. Consider odd values of ϕ. Then $y+z$ is odd and

$$F \equiv 4xy+(y+z)^2+(4k+2)z^2 \equiv 4x(z+1)+1+(4k+2)z^2 \pmod{8} .$$

For z even, $F \equiv 4x+1 \equiv 1$ or 5; for z odd, $F \equiv 4k+3$. Hence F represents only three of the four odd residues modulo 8.

[1] Hence an indefinite, classic, ternary ϕ is universal if and only if $\Omega = \mp 1$, Δ is odd or double an odd, and $(\psi|p)=(-\Omega|p)$ for each odd prime factor p of Δ, where ψ is reciprocal to ϕ. Oppenheim deduced also a like theorem for non-classic forms.

Third, let $e=2$, C even. If $A\equiv3$ (mod 4), we change the sign of x. Hence let $A\equiv1$ (mod 4). Then $F\equiv4xy+f$ (mod 16). Replacing x by $x+ky+sz$, we obtain a like form having $B'\equiv B+4k$, $2C'\equiv2C+4s$, $D'\equiv D$, whence we may take $B\equiv\pm1$, $2C\equiv0$ (mod 16). If $B\equiv-1$, we employ the universal form $-F$ with y changed in sign. Hence it suffices to treat $F\equiv 4xy+y^2+Dz^2$ (mod 16). By the residues 0, 1, D, $D+1$ modulo 4, we have $D=4k+2$. When F is even, $y=2Y$ and $F=2h$, $h\equiv4xY+2Y^2+mz^2$ (mod 8), $m=2k+1$. If h is odd, then z is odd and $h\equiv m$, $m+2$, or $m+6$ (mod 8). Hence $F\not\equiv2$ $(m+4)$ (mod 16).

Hence $e=1$ in a universal F. We employ the notation (3). Here c is even. Let d be even. Since F is not always even, gb is odd. If $d\equiv0$ (mod 4) and F is even, then y is even and $F\equiv0$ (mod 4), whence $F\equiv2$ (mod 4) is impossible.

Conversely, the conditions in Theorem 110 imply that F is universal. If d is odd, this follows from Theorem 108 since, for any assigned odd y, $F\equiv gby^2+z^2\equiv G$ (mod 2), has a solution z, whence $F\equiv G$ (mod $P=2gay$) is solvable. As in § 87, $F=G$ is solvable.

Next, let $d\equiv2$ (mod 4) and b be odd. If y and G are any assigned odd integers, F is odd and $F\equiv G$ (mod 2) for every z, whence F represents all odd G. Finally, let G be even. Take $y=2Y$. Then $F=4gaxY+4gbY^2+2cYz+gdz^2$ and $F\equiv2z^2\equiv G$ (mod 4) has a solution z. This F is derived from (3) by replacing e by 2, b by $4b$, c by $2c$, y by Y, and has the same g, a, d, x, z. The conditions in Theorem 107 hold also here, while R in (8) is multiplied by 4. Using also Theorem 108, we conclude that there exists an odd Y such that $F\equiv G$ has a solution z both modulo 4 and agY and hence modulo $4gaY$. Thus $F=G$ is solvable as in § 87.

91. Theorem 111. *When c is odd, $e\geq1$, F is universal if and only if (8) holds and bd is even.*

I. Let d be even. Assign an odd value to y and write k for the odd integer cy. Then $F\equiv gby^2+\phi$ (mod 2^e), where $\phi=kz+gdz^2$. Then ϕ ranges with z over a complete set of residues modulo 2^e. For, $\phi\equiv kZ+gdZ^2$ implies

$$(z-Z)[k+gd\ (z+Z)]\equiv0\quad(\text{mod }2^e)\ .$$

Since the second factor is odd, $z\equiv Z$ (mod 2^e). Hence if G is arbitrary, $F\equiv G$ (mod 2^e) has a solution z. Hence F is universal if (8) holds.

II. Let d be odd. If b is odd, $F\equiv y+yz+z$ (mod 2) and F is even only when y and z are both even, whence $F\not\equiv2$ (mod 4). Hence for a universal F, b is even.

Assign a fixed odd value to y. If $f(y,\ z)\equiv f(y,\ Z)$ (mod 2^e), then

$(z-Z)L \equiv 0$, where $L = cy + gd(z+Z)$. If $z - Z$ is even, L is odd and $z \equiv Z$ (mod 2^e). Hence if z ranges over the 2^{e-1} even integers

$$(12) \qquad\qquad 0, 2, 4, \ldots, 2^e - 2 ,$$

f take 2^{e-1} even values incongruent modulo 2^e, which are therefore congruent to the numbers (12) rearranged. In other words, when G is any assigned even integer, $F \equiv G$ (mod 2^e) has a solution z. Then by Theorem 108 and § 87, $F = G$ is solvable.

Next, let G be any odd integer. If n is arbitrary, $F \equiv G$ (mod 2^n) has a solution with $x = 0$, y even. Write $y = 2Y$, $k = gdG$. Then k is odd. Multiplication by gd yields the equivalent congruence $Z^2 - RY^2 \equiv k$ (mod 2^n), where $Z = gdz + cY$. Now $R \equiv 1$ (mod 8) and $Z^2 - Y^2$ takes the values 0, 1, 3, 4, 5, 7 modulo 8. Hence our congruence is solvable if $n = 3$. To proceed by induction, let $\zeta^2 - R\eta^2 = k + Q2^m$, $m \geq 3$. Since ζ and η are not both even,

$$(\zeta + u2^{m-1})^2 - R(\eta + v2^{m-1})^2 \equiv k + 2^m(Q + \zeta u - R\eta v) \equiv k \qquad (\text{mod } 2^{m+1}) ,$$

by choice of u and v modulo 2.

Take $n = 2e + 2$, and write $H = Z^2 - RY^2$. If in a solution of $H \equiv k$ (mod 2^n), Y is divisible by $u = 2^{e+1}$, then $Z^2 \equiv k$, whence $H \equiv k$ (mod 2^n) has a solution in which Y is an arbitrary multiple of u, and hence a solution with $Y = u$. Next, let there be no solution having Y divisible by u. Then in every solution, Y is the product of 2^s by an odd integer where $s \leq e$. In both cases there is a solution with $Y = 2^p\eta$, where η is odd and $p \leq e + 1$. Then $y = 2^h\eta$, $h \leq e + 2$. Since $e + h \leq n$, we see that $F \equiv G$ (mod 2^{e+h}) has a solution with $x = 0$, $y = 2^h\eta$.

For this y let F become F_1. We see that F_1 can be derived from F by replacing y by η, e by $e + h$, b by $2^{2h}b$, and c by $2^h c$, and not altering x, z, g, a, d. The R for F_1 is the product of R in (8) by 2^{2h}. Also F_1 satisfies the conditions in Theorem 107. As just proved, $F_1 \equiv G$ (mod 2^{e+h}) has a solution with η odd. Hence by Theorem 108 and § 87, $F_1 = G$ and hence also $F = G$ is solvable.

92. Case of four variables. In (3), let $\psi = hz^2 + jzw + lw^2$. The replacement of w by $w + vz$ yields a like form with $h' = h + jv + lv^2$. We can choose v so that h' is not divisible by any assigned odd prime p, since $h' \equiv 0$ (mod p) has at most two roots. Hence we may assume that h is prime to ga.

We employ the discriminants N and R of ψ and $f_{w=0}$, and the determinant $-gdJ/h$ of f. Thus

$$(13) \qquad N = j^2 - 4hl , \quad R = c^2 - 4g^2bdh , \qquad J = c^2j^2 - NR .$$

Theorem 112. *F is not universal in any of the cases*:

$$(14) \qquad \begin{cases} J \equiv 0 \ (mod \ p), \quad (N \,|\, p) = -1 \ ; \\ N \equiv 0, \ cj \equiv 0 \ and \ either \ R \equiv 0 \ (mod \ p) \ or \ (R \,|\, p) = -1 \ , \end{cases}$$

where p is any prime dividing a but not g. Except in these cases, to every G corresponds an odd integer y such that $F \equiv G$ (mod gay) has solutions z, w. If also $F \equiv G$ (mod 2^e) is solvable for z and w, F is universal.

The proof of Lemma 1 holds also here if we take $w = 0$ and replace d by dh. Hence it remains only to show that $F \equiv G$ (mod ty) is solvable. For modulus t, multiplication by $4gdh$, which is prime to t, yields the equivalent congruence

$$(15) \qquad 4g^2 dh by^2 + 4gdh cyz + g^2 d^2 (\zeta^2 - Nw^2) \equiv 4gdhG \quad (mod \ t) \ ,$$

where $\zeta = 2hz + jw$.

Let t be a product of powers p^n of distinct primes.

Case N not divisible by p. The product of (15) by N gives

$$(16) \qquad Nu^2 - v^2 + Jy^2 \equiv k \quad (mod \ p^n) \ ,$$

where $u = gd\zeta + cy$, $v = Ngdw + cjy$, $k = 4NgdhG$.

(i) $J \not\equiv 0$ (mod p). For $n = 1$, $y = 1$, (16) has a solution u_1, v_1. By induction on n, (16) has a solution $u = u_1$, $v = v_1$, $y = Y$, where $Y \equiv 1$ (mod p). There exist infinitely many primes of the form $Y + \xi p^n$. Hence there exists an odd prime y not dividing $agdhN$ such that $F \equiv G$ (mod t) has solutions z, w. Determine m by $gdm \equiv 1$ (mod y). Multiplication of $F \equiv gd\psi \equiv G$ (mod y) by $4mh$ yields the equivalent congruence $\zeta^2 - Nw^2 \equiv 4mhG$ (mod y), which has solutions ζ, w and hence z, w.

(ii) Let N be a quadratic residue of p. Then (16) has solutions $y = 1$, u and v not both divisible by p.

(iii) Let $J \equiv 0$ (mod p), $(N \,|\, p) = -1$. Consider multiples G of p. Then $k = pK$. Write $J = pT$. Then (16) requires $u \equiv v \equiv 0$ (mod p). By its origin,

$$4gdhN(F - G) = Nu^2 - v^2 + Jy^2 - k \ .$$

The second member is $\equiv pM$ (mod p^2), where $M = Ty^2 - K$. We can choose K so that M is prime to p for every y. To each K corresponds a single G. Hence F is never congruent modulo p^2 to certain multiples G of p. Thus F is not universal.

Case $N \equiv 0$ (mod p). Write $N = p\epsilon$.

I. Let $jc \not\equiv 0$ (mod p). We can solve $\zeta \equiv 0$ (mod p^n) for z. Take $y = 1$ and write $\mu = 2gdcj$, $\nu = g^2d^2\epsilon$, $k = 4g^2dhb - 4gdhG$. Then (15) for $t = p^n$ is equivalent to

$$(17) \qquad \mu w + \nu p w^2 \equiv k \pmod{p^n}, \qquad \mu \not\equiv 0 \pmod{p}.$$

Since this has a solution w' modulo p, write $w = w' + \omega p$, $\mu w' = k + \gamma p$. Then (17) is equivalent to

$$\mu \omega + \gamma + \nu(w' + \omega p)^2 \equiv 0, \text{ or } \mu \omega + p\phi(\omega) \equiv K \pmod{p^{n-1}}.$$

Suppose we have similarly reduced the solution of (17) to

$$(18) \qquad \mu u + p\psi(u) \equiv L \pmod{p^{n-m}}.$$

This has a solution u' modulo p, whence $\mu u' = L + \delta p$. Write $u = u' + vp$. Then (18) is equivalent to

$$\mu v + \delta + \psi(u' + vp) \equiv 0, \text{ or } \mu v + pP(v) \equiv L' \pmod{p^{n-m-1}}.$$

This is of type (18) with m replaced by $m+1$. But (18) is solvable when $m = n-1$. Hence $F \equiv G \pmod{p^n}$ is solvable with $y = 1$.

II. Let $j \equiv 0$ (mod p). Then (15) gives

$$(19) \quad Z^2 - Ry^2 \equiv k \pmod{p}, \qquad Z = 2gdhz + cy, \qquad k = 4gdhG.$$

Since this is of type (7), R is not divisible by p. Next, if R is a quadratic non-residue of p, and if $G \equiv 0$ (mod p), then $y \equiv 0$, $Z \equiv 0$, $z \equiv 0$ (mod p), $F \equiv gdlw^2$ (mod p^2). But $p\epsilon = N \equiv -4hl$ (mod p^2). Hence $4hF \equiv \tau pw^2$ (mod p^2), where $\tau = -gd\epsilon$. Also, h is prime to p. Hence F represents only those multiples mp of p for which $4hm \equiv \tau w^2$ (mod p). Hence m has at most $\frac{1}{2}(p+1)$ values modulo p. Thus F is not universal.

Hence R must be a quadratic residue of p and therefore of t. Theorem 108 shows that there is an odd y such that $f \equiv G \pmod{agy}$ has a solution z, $w = 0$.

III. Let $c \equiv 0$, $j \not\equiv 0$ (mod p). In (15) write Z for $gd(2hz + jw)$. We get the congruence (19). As in II, R must be a quadratic residue of p, and our theorem follows as before by taking $w = 0$.

THEOREM 113. *If* $e = 0$, F *is universal except in cases* (14).

Let F be a classic form, whence $e \geq 1$, c and dj are even.

THEOREM 114. *Let $e = 1$ and exclude cases* (14). *Then F is universal when d is odd, but when $d = 2D$ if and only if bD is odd.*

For, if d is odd, h and l are not both even. When y has any assigned odd value, $F \equiv b + hz + lw \equiv G \pmod 2$ is solvable.

Let $d = 2D$. Since F is not always even, b is odd. If G is odd, $F \equiv y^2 \equiv D \pmod 2$ holds for y odd. Next, let $G = 2\gamma$. Then $y = 2Y$, $F = 2\phi$, $\phi = 2gaxY + 2gbY^2 + cYz + gD\psi$. Since ϕ shall take odd values, D is odd. Since $\psi \equiv 0$ or $1 \pmod 2$ is solvable, $\phi \equiv \gamma \pmod 2$ is solvable when Y and γ are arbitrary. Now ϕ is derived from F by replacing y, b, d by Y, $2b$, $\frac{1}{2}d$, respectively. Then N, R, J are unaltered. Hence $\phi = \gamma$ is solvable by Theorem 112.

The author (*l.c.*) determined all the universal forms when $e > 1$, d and l are odd, and c and j are even. F. E. Sparks is treating all remaining cases.

CHAPTER XIII

NUMBER OF REPRESENTATIONS AS A SUM
OF 5, 6, 7, OR 8 SQUARES

93. Historical note. Let $r_s(n)$ denote the number of representations of the positive integer n as a sum of s integral squares. We shall ignore asymptotic formulas, and restrict our attention to exact formulas for $r_s(n)$ in terms of familiar arithmetical functions.

For $s = 2, 4, 6,$ or 8, Jacobi[1] found $r_s(n)$ in terms of the divisors of n by using expansions of elliptic functions.

For $s = 3, 5,$ or 7, the formulas involve quadratic and non-residues. Gauss[2] expressed $r_3(n)$ as a multiple of the number of classes, in the principal genus, of the properly primitive, binary, quadratic forms of determinant $-n$.

Eisenstein[3] published without proof formulas for $r_5(n)$ and $r_7(n)$ in terms of Jacobi's symbols when n is odd and without square factor. Smith[4] removed the restrictions on n, but gave no proof.

The Paris Academy of Sciences proposed its Grand Prix for 1882 on representation as a sum of five squares. Equal prizes were awarded to Smith[5] and Minkowski,[6] then 18 years of age. Their proofs depend on the arithmetic of quadratic forms in m variables, and are (in Mordell's opinion) examples of the most delicate and intricate demonstrations to be found in the whole range of analysis.

Mordell[7] noted that the problem of finding $r_s(n)$ is equivalent to finding the series in q giving the expansion of the sth power of

$$\vartheta = 1 + 2q + 2q^4 + 2q^9 + \ldots .$$

By the theory of modular functions, ϑ^s can be expressed as a sum of a finite number of modular invariants. For an even s, he constructed all these in-

[1] *Fund. Nova Funct. Ellipt.*, 1829, 103, 106–7, 184, 188. See the author's *History of the Theory of Numbers*, II, 235, 285, 305.

[2] *Disq. Arith.*, 1801, Art. 291. *History*, 262.

[3] *Jour. für Math.*, XXXV (1847), 368; XXXIX (1850), 180–82. *History*, 305.

[4] *Proc. Roy. Soc. London*, XVI (1867), 207; *History*, 308–9.

[5] *Mém. Savans Etr. Paris Acad. Sc.*, (ser. 2), XXIX (1887), No. 1; Smith's *Coll. Math. Papers*, II (1894), 623–80.

[6] *Ibid.*, No. 2. *Gesamm. Abh.*, I (1911), 3–144. *History*, 312.

[7] *Quar. Jour. Math.*, XLVIII (1917), 93–104.

variants. But for an odd s, there was one, denoted by χ, which he was unable to construct.

About the same time, Hardy, Littlewood, and Ramanujan developed a powerful method for dealing with Waring's problem to find the number of representations of n as a sum of s positive kth powers. Using the idea of the singular series, Hardy[1] showed how to construct this invariant χ for any s, and gave the actual formulas when s is 5 or 8. Next, employing Mordell's ideas, Hardy proved that $r_s(n)$ is identical with the singular series $\rho_s(n)$ in (9) for $s = 5$ or 8. Finally, he gave general rules for the calculation of the singular series and carried out the work for $s = 5$ and $s = 8$.

From Hardy's result for $s = 5$, Mordell[2] obtained the general expression for χ when s is odd.

The present version follows Hardy's paper in the main. The following variations are due to A. Oppenheim (a former pupil of Hardy), who prepared the manuscript of §§ 94–100, and the last part of § 103 beginning with (111). He remodeled the proof of $r_s(n) = \rho_s(n)$, carrying out the proof uniformly for $s \geq 5$ and introducing the condition $s \leq 8$ only where compelled in the crucial Lemma 11. Incidentally he proved also Theorem 116 for the number of representations as a sum of s odd squares, $5 \leq s \leq 8$.

Gordon Pall prepared the manuscript of §§ 101, 102, and the first parts of § 95 and § 103. He incorporated and checked Miss Stanley's[3] calculations for $s = 7$, corrected an error in the proof of rule of multiplication for $A(k)$ and other errors of detail.

94. Outline of the method. The generating function for $r_s(n)$, the number of representations of n as a sum of s squares, is

$$(1) \qquad f(q) = 1 + \sum_{n=1}^{\infty} r_s(n) q^n = \left(\sum_{-\infty}^{\infty} q^{n^2} \right)^s = \{\vartheta_3(0 \,|\, \tau)\}^s = \vartheta^s \,,$$

where $q = \exp \pi i \tau$ and $I(\tau) > 0$, the radius of convergence of the series being plainly unity. By Cauchy's theorem we have

$$(2) \qquad r_s(n) = \frac{1}{2\pi i} \int_C \frac{f(q)}{q^{n+1}} \, dq$$

where C is the circle $|q| = r < 1$ described counterclockwise.

[1] *Trans. Amer. Math. Soc.*, XXI (1920), 255–84; XXIX (1927), errata supplied by G. K. Stanley. Some errors when dealing with ϑ^5 were corrected by Pall.

[2] *Trans. Cambridge Phil. Soc.*, XXII (1919), 361–72.

[3] *Jour. London Math. Soc.*, II (1927), 91–96.

The natural method of evaluating a contour integral, $\int \phi(q)dq$, where $\phi(q)$ is an analytic function of q, is to deform the contour of integration by means of Cauchy's theorem and to apply the necessary corrections when we cross singularities of the integrand. This method can be used, for example, when $\phi(q)$ has no essential singularities in the finite part of the plane and tends to zero sufficiently rapidly when $|q| \to \infty$. In our case, however, this procedure is foredoomed to failure; for, the function $f(q)$ defined by (1) does not exist in the sense of the theory of functions of a complex variable outside the unit circle. The circle $|q| = 1$ is a natural boundary for $f(q)$.

To meet this difficulty, which crops up in more acute form in many problems of analytic number theory, such as the representation of numbers by sums of cubes, kth powers, or primes, Hardy, Littlewood, and Ramanujan have devised and successfully exploited a method which we proceed to explain.

Although every point $e^{\pi u i}$ (u real) on the unit circle is a singularity of $f(q)$, there is a certain set of them which, so to speak, stand out or dominate the rest. This set is composed of the so-called rational points, given by $u = 2h/k$ where h and k are integers. We may suppose that $0 \leq h < k$ and $(h, k) = 1$, where (h, k) denotes the g.c.d. of h and k.

We now try to construct a power series

$$(3) \qquad f_{h,\,k}(q) = \sum c_{h,\,k,\,n} q^n$$

which is to simulate $f(q)$ near $q = \exp(2h\pi i/k)$, that is to say, we want $f_{h,\,k}(q)$ to behave as much like $f(q)$ as possible when $q \to \exp(2h\pi i/k)$. Plainly it is also desirable that $f_{h;\,k}(q)$ should be as simple and natural as we can make it. We hope now that by replacing $f(q)$ in (2) by $\sum f_{h,\,k}(q)$, which imitates $f(q)$ fairly closely in the neighborhood of the unit circle, we may obtain a fairly close approximation to $r_s(n)$ by means of the sum

$$(4) \qquad \rho_s(n) = \sum_{h,\,k}{}' c_{h,k,n} \;,$$

which arises formally from this substitution.

In our problem, as we shall see, the appropriate auxiliary function (3) is

$$(5) \qquad f_{h,\,k}(q) = \frac{\pi^{\frac{1}{2}s}}{\Gamma(\frac{1}{2}s)} \left(\frac{S(h,\,k)}{k} \right)^s F_s(qe^{-2h\pi i/k}) \;,$$

where

$$(6) \qquad F_s(q) = \sum_{n=1}^{\infty} n^{\frac{1}{2}s-1} q^n \;,$$

and

$$(7) \qquad S(h, k) = \sum_{j=1}^{k} e^{2j^2 h \pi i/k} .$$

We try therefore

$$(8) \qquad c_{h, k, n} = \frac{\pi^{\frac{1}{2}s} n^{\frac{1}{2}s-1}}{\Gamma(\frac{1}{2}s)} \left(\frac{S(h, k)}{k} \right)^s e^{-2nh\pi i/k} ,$$

and

$$(9) \qquad \rho_s(n) = \sum_{h, k} c_{h, k, n} = \frac{\pi^{\frac{1}{2}s} n^{\frac{1}{2}s-1}}{\Gamma(\frac{1}{2}s)} \sum_{1}^{\infty} A(k) = \frac{\pi^{\frac{1}{2}s} n^{\frac{1}{2}s-1}}{\Gamma(\frac{1}{2}s)} S ,$$

where

$$(10) \qquad A(1) = 1 , \qquad A(k) = k^{-s} \sum_{h} S^s(h, k) e^{-2nh\pi i/k} ,$$

the summation extending over all positive values of h less than and prime to k. The series (9) is called the *singular series*. Its construction has been quite formal and it remains, therefore, (i) to investigate more rigorously its bearing on the solution of our problem, and (ii) to find its sum.

In the present problem we do not substitute for $f(q)$ in the integral (2), but study directly (after Hardy and Mordell) the properties of the function

$$(11) \qquad \Theta_s(q) = 1 + \sum_{h, k} f_{h, k}(q) .$$

For $s = 5$, 6, 7, or 8, the answer to (i) is contained in
THEOREM 115. *If $s = 5$, 6, 7 or 8, then*

$$(12) \qquad \Theta_s(q) \equiv \vartheta^s(0, q) = f(q)$$

and therefore

$$(13) \qquad \rho_s(n) = r_s(n) \qquad (n = 1, 2, \dots) .$$

We obtain (Lemmas 6, 7, 8) certain identities which, combined with the theta-function formula, show that, for $s \geq 5$, Θ_s/f is invariant under the substitutions of the modular subgroup Γ_3 (Lemma 10). From another identity (Lemma 9), we shall see that, if $s \leq 8$, Θ_s/f is bounded throughout the fundamental polygon, G_3, of Γ_3 (Lemma 11). From Lemmas 9, 10, and 1 (a classical result in the theory of modular functions) it follows that, for $5 \leq s \leq 8$, Θ_s/f is a constant, and hence Theorem 115.

Actually we prove more. Let $R_s(n)$ denote the number of representations of n as a sum of s *odd* squares. Its generating function is

$$(14) \qquad g(q) = \sum R_s(n) q^{\frac{1}{4}n} = \left\{ \sum_{-\infty}^{\infty} q^{\frac{1}{4}(2n+1)^2} \right\}^s = \{\vartheta_2(0, q)\}^s = \vartheta_2^s \; .$$

Write

$$(15) \qquad\qquad s \equiv s' \pmod 8 \; , \qquad 0 < s' \leqq 8 \; , \qquad 8r = s' \; ,$$

$$(16) \qquad\qquad G_s(q) = \sum_{l=0}^{\infty} (l+r)^{\frac{1}{2}s-1} q^{2l+2r} \; ,$$

$$(17) \qquad\qquad W(h, k) = \sum_{j=1}^{k} e^{(j-\frac{1}{2})^2 h \pi i / k} \qquad (k \text{ odd, positive}) \; ,$$

$$(18) \qquad\qquad \Phi_s(q) = \frac{(2\pi)^{\frac{1}{2}s}}{\Gamma(\frac{1}{2}s)} \sum_{h, k} k^{-s} W^s(h, k) G_s(q e^{-h\pi i/k}) \; ,$$

over $k = 1, 3, 5, \ldots$, $0 \leqq h < k$ and $(h, k) = 1$; and

$$(19) \qquad P_s(n) = \frac{(2\pi)^{\frac{1}{2}s}}{\Gamma(\frac{1}{2}s)} \left(\frac{n}{8}\right)^{\frac{1}{2}s-1} \sum_{h, k} k^{-s} W^s(h, k) e^{-\frac{1}{4}nh\pi i/k}$$

over the same range. Then the analysis which proves Theorem 115 proves also

Theorem 116. *If $s = 5, 6, 7$, or 8, then*

$$(20) \qquad\qquad \Phi_s(q) \equiv \vartheta_2^s(0, q) = g(q)$$

and, therefore,

$$(21) \qquad\qquad R_s(n) = P_s(n) \text{ or } 0 \; ,$$

according as n is congruent or incongruent to s, modulo 8.

We have still to find the sum of the singular series $\rho_s(n)$. Following Hardy, we give in § 101 general rules for its calculation for any value of s. In particular we carry out the calculations for $s = 5$ and $s = 7$. The results are stated in Theorem 117. For $s = 6$ or 8, the details are considerably easier.

95. Modular functions, theta functions. A group of transformations is a set of transformations which contains the inverse of any transformation in the set and the product of any two transformations in the set.

A single-valued analytic function of a complex variable which is unaltered by a group of linear transformations of the variable is called an automorphic function. One example is given by elliptic functions in which the group of transformations is generated by the two transformations $z' = z + \omega_1$, $z' = z + \omega_2$, ω_1/ω_2 imaginary. The next simplest and most important examples are the modular functions in which the transformations are of the form

$$(22) \qquad \tau' = \frac{a\tau + b}{c\tau + d} ,$$

where a, b, c, d are integers such that $ad - bc = 1$, and τ, τ' are complex numbers.

The set of all such linear transformations (22) forms a group G. It is generated by the two transformations $\tau' = \tau + 1$, $\tau' = -1/\tau$.

The subgroup of G which is generated by the two transformations

$$(23) \qquad \tau' = \tau + 2 , \qquad \tau' = -1/\tau$$

is denoted by Γ_3. It is of importance in the sequel.

By the index of a subgroup G_0 of G we understand the least number m of transformations $T_1, T_2, \ldots, T_m$ of G such that every transformation of the group G can be expressed as a product of a transformation of the subgroup G_0 by one of these m transformations. In symbols, $G = G_0 T_1 + G_0 T_2 + \ldots + G_0 T_m$. For example the group Γ_3 is of finite index 3 under G.

The analytic function $f(\tau)$ is said to be a *modular function* when it is not a constant, is defined for[1] $I(\tau) > 0$, and has the following three properties:

I. Is invariant under the modular group or a subgroup thereof of finite index:

$$f\left(\frac{a\tau + b}{c\tau + d}\right) = f(\tau) .$$

II. Is regular or has at most a pole at any finite point.

III. Considered as a function of $q = \exp \pi i \tau$, it has no essential singularity at $q = 0$.

Fundamental polygon. It is plain that (22) transforms the real axis into itself, the upper half-plane into the upper half-plane, and the lower half-plane into the lower half-plane. We say that the points τ and τ' are equivalent relative to a sub-group G_0 of G if they can be transformed into each other by transformations of G_0. A region R of points τ in the upper half-plane such that every point of the upper half-plane is equivalent to one and

---

[1] We write $I(\tau)$ for imaginary part of τ, $R(\tau)$ for real part of τ.

but one point of the region R relative to the subgroup G_0 is called a *fundamental polygon* of G_0.

Let $\tau = x + iy$. A fundamental polygon, G_3, of the modular subgroup Γ_3 is the region in the upper half-plane bounded by the straight lines and circle

$$x = \pm 1 , \qquad x^2 + y^2 = 1 , \qquad y \geqq 0 ,$$

only the right hand half of the boundary being counted as part of the fundamental polygon.

LEMMA 1. *A function which is analytic, satisfies conditions* I, II, *and* III, *but is bounded in the fundamental polygon of the group in* I, *is a constant.*[1]

Theta-functions. These functions were first introduced into analysis by Jacobi. The two theta-functions we require are defined by the series

$$(24) \qquad \vartheta(x, q) = \vartheta_3(x, q) = \vartheta_3(x \mid \tau) = \sum_{-\infty}^{\infty} q^{n^2} \cos 2nx ,$$

$$(25) \qquad \vartheta_2(x, q) = \vartheta_2(x \mid \tau) = \sum_{-\infty}^{\infty} q^{\frac{1}{4}(2n+1)^2} \cos (2n+1)x ,$$

where $q = \exp \pi i \tau$, $I(\tau) > 0$ so that $|q| < 1$, and x is arbitrary.

For any x, ϑ and ϑ_2 are analytic functions of τ (or q) regular in the half-plane $I(\tau) > 0$ (or the circle $|q| < 1$). We require the following properties[2] of $\vartheta(0, q)$ and $\vartheta_2(0, q)$:

$$(26) \quad \vartheta(0 \mid \tau \pm 2) = \vartheta(0 \mid \tau) , \qquad \vartheta\left(0 \mid -\frac{1}{\tau}\right) = \sqrt{-i\tau} \, \vartheta(0 \mid \tau) ,$$

$$\vartheta\left(0 \mid 1 - \frac{1}{\tau}\right) = \sqrt{-i\tau} \, \vartheta_2(0 \mid \tau),$$

where I (τ) *and* R $(\sqrt{-i\tau})$ *are positive.*

Further, $\vartheta(0 \mid \tau)$ *has no zeros in the half-plane* $I(\tau) > 0$.

96. The symbols[3] O, o **and** ∞. Let $f(z)$ and $g(z)$ be two functions of z defined at a set of points of which $z = a$ is a limiting point. The functions are not necessarily defined at a. By $z \to a$ we mean that z tends to a through points of the set.

If $|f/g| < k$ whenever $|z - a| < \epsilon$, where k is independent of z, we say that $f(z)$ is *of the order of* $g(z)$ and we write $f(z) = O\{g(z)\}$.

[1] L. R. Ford, *Automorphic Functions*, 1929, p. 94, Theorem 10.

[2] Whittaker and Watson, *Modern Analysis*, chap. xxi.

[3] An account may be found in Hardy, *Orders of Infinity*.

If $\lim (f/g) = 0$ when $z \to a$, we say that f *is of lower order than* g and we write $f(z) = o\{g(z)\}$.

Thus $O\{g(z)\}$ represents any function of the order of $g(z)$, and $o\{g(z)\}$ represents any function of lower order than $g(z)$.

Finally if $\lim (f/g) = 1$, we say that f is *asymptotic* to g, and we write $f(z) \backsim g(z)$.

It may be observed that the assertions

$$f \backsim g , \qquad f = g\{1 + o(1)\} , \qquad f = g + o(g)$$

are equivalent.

Examples. Let x be real. Then

$$\sin (1/x) = O(1) , \qquad \sin (1/x) = o(1/x) , \qquad \sin x \backsim x$$

when $x \to 0$. But $\sin (1/x) \neq o(1)$ when $x \to 0$.

97. Gaussian sums, convention for amplitudes, Lipschitz's formula.
LEMMA[1] 2. *Let h and k be positive integers.* (i) *If $(h, k) = 1$, then*

$$(27) \qquad\qquad S^4(h, k) = \eta_k k^2$$

where $\eta_k = +1$, 0, or -4, according as k is odd, double an odd integer, or divisible by 4.

(ii) *If h and k are of opposite parity, then*

$$(28) \qquad \sum_{j=1}^{k} e^{j^2 h \pi i / k} = e^{\frac{1}{4}\pi i}(k/h)^{\frac{1}{2}} \sum_{j=1}^{h} e^{-j^2 k \pi i / h} .$$

(iii) *If k is odd, then*

$$(29) \qquad W(h, k) = \sum_{j=1}^{k} e^{(j-\frac{1}{2})^2 h \pi i / k} = e^{\frac{1}{4}\pi i}(k/h)^{\frac{1}{2}} \sum_{j=1}^{h} (-)^j e^{-j^2 k \pi i / h} .$$

Note that from (28) and (29) two formulas conjugate to these may be derived by changing the sign of i.

Convention about amplitudes. The amplitude of the non-zero complex number z is determined to within an integral multiple of 2π by the equations

$$\cos \mathrm{am}\, z = x/r , \qquad \sin \mathrm{am}\, z = y/r , \qquad r = |z| > 0 ,$$

---

[1] For (i) see Bachmann's *Analytische Zahlentheorie*, 1894, chap. vii. (ii) and (iii) are contained in formula (17b), p. 243, of a memoir by G. Landsberg, "Zur Theorie der Gausschen Summen und der linearen Transformation der Thetafunktionen," *Jour. für Math.*, CXI (1893), 234–53.

where x and y are the real and imaginary parts of z. These equations have a unique solution ϕ such that $-\pi < \phi \leq \pi$. We write $\phi = \text{Am } z$ and agree to take throughout this value for am z. The following results are immediate:

$$(30)[1] \quad \begin{cases} -\tfrac{1}{2}\pi < \phi < \tfrac{1}{2}\pi & \text{if } x > 0 \; ; \quad\quad \phi = \tfrac{1}{2}\pi(\text{sign } y) \quad \text{if } x = 0 \; ; \\ 0 < \phi < \pi & \text{if } y > 0 \; ; \quad\quad \phi = \tfrac{1}{2}\pi(1 - \text{sign } x) \quad \text{if } y = 0 \; . \end{cases}$$

We define z^s by the equation

$$(31) \qquad\qquad z^s = \exp\left[s \log |z| + is \text{ Am } z \right] ,$$

where Am z has the value just assigned.

LEMMA 3. *If $z_1 \neq 0$, $z_1 = z_2 z_3$, $x_1 \geq 0$, $x_2 \geq 0$ and $y_3 > 0$, then*

$$(32) \qquad\qquad \text{Am} z_1 = \text{Am} z_2 + \text{Am} z_3 \; , \qquad z_1^s = z_2^s z_3^s$$

for any s.

For, $\phi_1 = \phi_2 + \phi_3 + 2l\pi$, where l is an integer. The hypothesis of the lemma and (30) show that $|2l\pi| < \tfrac{1}{2}\pi + \tfrac{1}{2}\pi + \pi = 2\pi$. Hence $l = 0$. The second part follows from (31).

LEMMA[2] 4. *Let $R(t) > 0$ and either $0 < u < 1$, $g > 0$ or $u = 1$, $g > 1$. Then*

$$(33) \qquad \frac{(2\pi)^g}{\Gamma(g)} \sum_{l=0}^{\infty} (l+u)^{g-1} e^{-2\pi t(l+u)} = \sum_{n=-\infty}^{\infty} e^{2nu\pi i}(t+ni)^{-g} ,$$

where the many-valued functions are defined by (31) and, therefore, by (30) their amplitudes lie between $-\tfrac{1}{2}\pi$ and $\tfrac{1}{2}\pi$.

In particular therefore from (6), (15), and (16),

$$(34) \quad \pi^{\frac{1}{2}s} F_s(q) = \pi^{\frac{1}{2}s} \sum_{n=1}^{\infty} n^{\frac{1}{2}s-1} q^n = \Gamma(\tfrac{1}{2}s) \sum_{n=-\infty}^{\infty} \left\{ (2n-\tau)i \right\}^{-\frac{1}{2}s} \qquad (s \geq 3) ,$$

$$(35) \quad (2\pi)^{\frac{1}{2}s} G_s(q) = (2\pi)^{\frac{1}{2}s} \sum_{l=0}^{\infty} (l+r)^{\frac{1}{2}s-1} q^{2l+2r} = \Gamma(\tfrac{1}{2}s) \sum_{n=-\infty}^{\infty} \left\{ (n-\tau)i \right\}^{-\frac{1}{2}s}$$

$$(s \geq 3) ,$$

where, as usual, $q = \exp \pi i \tau$ and $I(\tau) > 0$, so that $|q| < 1$.

We obtain (34) by taking $u = 1$, $t = -\tfrac{1}{2}i\tau$, $g = \tfrac{1}{2}s > 1$ in (33); and (35) by taking $u = r$ of (15), $t = -i\tau$, $g = \tfrac{1}{2}s > 1$ in (33).

---

[1] We omit the relation $-\pi < \phi < -\tfrac{1}{2}\pi$ if $x < 0$ and $y < 0$, since we do not use it.

[2] R. Lipschitz, "Untersuchung der Eigenschaften einer Gattung von unendlichen Reihen," *Jour. für Math.*, CV (1889), 127-56.

A deduction from (34) will be useful. Let $\tau = iy$, where y is positive, so that $q = e^{-\pi y}$ is real. Then

$$\sum_{-\infty}^{\infty} \{(2n - \tau)i\}^{-\frac{1}{2}s} = y^{-\frac{1}{2}s} + \sum_{n \neq 0} (2ni + y)^{-\frac{1}{2}s} = y^{-\frac{1}{2}s} + O(1)$$

as $y \to 0$, so that

$$(36) \qquad F_s(q) = \Gamma(\tfrac{1}{2}s) \left(\log \frac{1}{q} \right)^{-\frac{1}{2}s} + O(1) \qquad (s \geqq 3)$$

when $0 \leqq q < 1$ and $q \to 1$.

We sketch a proof[1] of Lemma 4 valid for $g > 1$, which is the only case we need. With the point t as center draw a circle C of large enough radius $N + \frac{1}{2}$, where N is a positive integer, to cut the negative real axis at the point P. Let D be a contour starting from P and going counter-clockwise once around the origin back to P. Since $R(t) > 0$ we may suppose that D lies entirely to the left of the line $R(z) = R(t)$, that is to say, uniformly on D we have $R(z) \leqq R(t) - \delta$, where δ is a (small) positive number. The function

$$w(z) = -2\pi z^{-g} e^{2\pi u(z-t)} / \{1 - e^{2\pi(z-t)}\}$$

is regular throughout the domain bounded by C and D, save for simple poles at the points $z = t + ni$ $(n = 0, \pm 1, \ldots, \pm N)$. When $N \to \infty$, the sum of the residues of $w(z)$ at these poles is the series on the right of (33) provided that $g > 1$.

Now if $g > 1$ it is easily verified that the integral around C tends to zero when $N \to \infty$ (and, moreover, uniformly in any bounded domain of values of t on the right of the imaginary axis). Hence the series on the right of (33) is equal to $1/2\pi i$ times $\int w(z)dz$ taken around a contour starting from $-\infty$ and going once positively around the origin back to $-\infty$. Since, on this contour, $R(z) \leqq R(t) - \delta$, we have

$$\{1 - e^{2\pi(z-t)}\}^{-1} = \sum_{l=0}^{\infty} e^{2l\pi(z-t)}.$$

The integration term by term is permissible. Employing Hankel's well known integral for the Gamma-function,[2] we obtain the series on the left of (33), whence Lemma 4, provided that $g > 1$, $0 < u \leqq 1$.

That it holds for $0 < u < 1$, $g > 0$, follows by analytic continuation.

[1] For an analysis of a similar problem, see Whittaker and Watson, *loc. cit.*, pp. 266, 268–69.

[2] *Ibid.*, p. 245.

98. Behavior of ϑ^s; transformations of Θ_s.

LEMMA 5. *If* $q = Qe^{2h\pi i/k}$, *where* h *and* k *are integers such that* $0 \leq h < k$, $(h, k) = 1$, *and* $0 \leq Q < 1$, *then, when* $Q \to 1$,

$$(37) \qquad f(q) \sim \frac{\pi^{\frac{1}{2}s}}{\Gamma(\frac{1}{2}s)} \left(\frac{S(h, k)}{k} \right)^s F_s(Q) \qquad (s \geq 3) ,$$

unless $S(h, k)$ *is zero (which, by Lemma 4, can happen if and only if* $k \equiv 2$ *(mod 4)), and then*

$$(38) \qquad f(q) = o\{F_s(Q)\} .$$

[It is this result (37) which justifies the choice (5) for $f_{h, k}$.]

We have

$$\vartheta_3(0, q) = 1 + 2 \sum_1^\infty Q^{n^2} e^{2n^2 h \pi i/k} = 1 + 2 \sum_{j=1}^k \sum_{l=0}^\infty Q^{(lk+j)^2} e^{2(lk+j)^2 h \pi i/k}$$

$$(39) \qquad = 1 + 2 \sum_{j=1}^k e^{2j^2 h \pi i/k} \sum_{l=0}^\infty Q^{(lk+j)^2} ,$$

the rearrangement being permissible since the double series is absolutely convergent. Now the first product in (40) is the sum for $n = 1$ to ∞ of $a_n Q^n$, where a_n is the number of integers $l \geq 0$ such that $(lk+j)^2 \leq n$. Plainly $a_n = k^{-1} n^{\frac{1}{2}} + O(1)$, so that

$$(40) \qquad (1-Q)^{-1} \sum_{l=0}^\infty Q^{(lk+j)^2} = k^{-1} \sum_1^\infty n^{\frac{1}{2}} Q^n + O \sum_1^\infty Q^n$$

$$= \Gamma(\tfrac{3}{2}) k^{-1} \{\log (1/Q)\}^{-\frac{3}{2}} + O(1) + O\{1/(1-Q)\}$$

from (36). Since $(1-Q)^{-1} \sim \log (1/Q)$ and $\Gamma(3/2) = \frac{1}{2}\sqrt{\pi}$, we deduce from (39) and (40) that

$$(41) \qquad \vartheta \sim \sqrt{\pi} k^{-1} S(h, k)(\log (1/Q))^{-\frac{1}{2}}$$

unless $S(h, k)$ is zero, when

$$(41') \qquad \vartheta = o\{\log (1/Q)\}^{-\frac{1}{2}} .$$

And Lemma 5 follows from $f = \vartheta^s$, (41), (41'), and (36).

LEMMA 6. *The function* Θ_s *defined by*

$$(42) \quad \Theta_s(q) = 1 + \frac{\pi^{\frac{1}{2}s}}{\Gamma(\frac{1}{2}s)} \sum_{h, k} k^{-s} S^s(h, k) F_s(qe^{-2h\pi i/k}) \qquad (0 < h < k, (h, k) = 1) ,$$

*is an analytic function of q, regular in the domain $|q|<1$, if $s\geqq 5$. Also, for
every n, the singular series $\rho_s(n)$ of (9) is absolutely convergent if $s\geqq 5$.*

If $|q|\leqq r<1$, we have, on substituting for F_s from (34), a triple series
the sum of the moduli of whose terms does not exceed

$$(43) \qquad A_1(s)\sum_{h,\,k,\,n} k^{-s}k^{\frac12 s}n^{\frac12 s-1}r^n < A_2(r,\,s)\sum_k k^{1-\frac12 s}\,,$$

since, by (27), $S(h,k)=O(k^{\frac12})$, and h has at most k values. In (43), A_1 and
A_2 are positive numbers depending only on the numbers indicated. Plainly
the simple series in (43) is convergent if $\frac12 s-1>1$ or, since s is integral, if
$s\geqq 5$.

We suppose therefore from now on that

$$(44) \qquad s=4a+b\geqq 5\,,$$

where a and b are integers, $a\geqq 1$, $b\geqq 0$.

The triple series, being absolutely convergent, may be summed in any
manner and so may be arranged as a power series in q, the coefficient of q^n
being an absolutely convergent double series. But this coefficient is $\rho_s(n)$,
which proves the second part of Lemma 6.

Again, since the triple series is also a uniformly convergent series of
analytic functions in the domain $|q|\leqq r<1$, it follows by a theorem of
Weierstrass that $\Theta_s(q)$ is analytic and regular in the domain $|q|<1$. And
this completes the proof of Lemma 6.

LEMMA 7. *Let $s=4a+b\geqq 5$, $a\geqq 1$, $b\geqq 0$,*

$$(45) \qquad c=c_{2a}=1+3^{-2a}+5^{-2a}+7^{-2a}+\cdots\,,$$

$$(46) \qquad T(h,\,k)=\sum_{j=1}^{k}{}' e^{i^2h\pi i/k} \quad (k>0)\,.$$

Then

$$(47) \qquad \chi(\tau)=c\Theta_s(q)=c+\sum(-)^{ah}k^{-\frac12 b}T^b(h,\,k)\{(h-k\tau)i\}^{-\frac12 s}\,,$$

*where, as usual, $q=\exp \pi i\tau$ and $I(\tau)>0$, and the summation extends over all
integral values of h and k of opposite parity save that $k\geqq 1$.*

Replace τ in (34) by $\tau - 2hk^{-1}$. Substitute the resulting series for $F_s(qe^{-2h\pi i/k})$ in (42). We find that

$$\Theta_s(q) = 1 + \sum_{h,\,k} k^{-\frac{1}{2}b}\eta_k^a S^b(h,\,k) \sum_{\nu=-\infty}^{\infty} \{(2(\nu k + h) - k\tau)i\}^{-\frac{1}{2}s},$$

by use of (27). The triple series is absolutely convergent and so may be summed in any way we please. It follows that

$$(48) \qquad \Theta_s(q) = 1 + \sum_{h,\,k} k^{-\frac{1}{2}b}\eta_k^a S^b(h,\,k)\{(2h - k\tau)i\}^{-\frac{1}{2}s},$$

where now $k = 1, 2, 3, \ldots$ and h takes *all* values prime to k.

If k is odd, then $2h = H$ is even and prime to k, and $S(h, k) = T(H, k)$; if $k \equiv 0 \pmod 4$, then $k = 2K$, K even, h is odd and prime to K, and $S(h, k) = 2T(h, K)$; if $k \equiv 2 \pmod 4$, $\eta_k = 0$. We obtain from (48)

$$(49) \qquad \Theta_s(q) = 1 + \psi(\tau),$$

for $\psi(\tau)$ in (51), where now $k = 1, 2, 3, \ldots$, and h assumes all values of opposite parity and prime to k.

To remove the restriction that h is prime to k, multiply the absolutely convergent series (49) by the absolutely convergent series (45). The series resulting is also absolutely convergent and so may be summed in any way. Observing that for m odd and positive,

$$(-)^{mah} = (-)^{ah}, \qquad T^b(mh,\,mk) = m^b T^b(h,\,k),$$

$$(mk)^{-\frac{1}{2}b}\{(mh - mk\tau)i\}^{-\frac{1}{2}s} = m^{-2a-b}k^{-\frac{1}{2}b}\{(h - k\tau)i\}^{-\frac{1}{2}s},$$

we obtain (47), which proves Lemma 7.

LEMMA 8. *We have*

$$(50) \qquad \chi_s(\tau) = \psi(\tau) + (-\tau i)^{-\frac{1}{2}s}\psi(-1/\tau),$$

where

$$(51) \qquad \psi(\tau) = \sum (-)^{ah}k^{-\frac{1}{2}b}T^b(h,\,k)\{(h - k\tau)i\}^{-\frac{1}{2}s},$$

the summation extending over integers $k \geq 1$ and $h \geq 0$ of opposite parity.

The sum in (47) may be divided into two parts, one from $h \geq 0$ which yields the term $\psi(\tau)$ in (50), and the other from $h < 0$.

Now, if $h < 0$, we have, by Lemma 3,

$$(52) \qquad \left\{ \left(k - \frac{h}{\tau} \right) i \right\}^{-\frac{1}{2}s} = \left\{ (h - k\tau)i \right\}^{-\frac{1}{2}s} \left(-\frac{1}{\tau} \right)^{-\frac{1}{2}s} ,$$

and, by (46) and (28),

$$(53) \qquad T(h, k) = e^{-\frac{1}{4}\pi i}(k/|h|)^{\frac{1}{2}}T(k, -h) .$$

Hence that part of the sum in (47) which arises from $h < 0$ is equal to

$$(54) \qquad \sum (-)^{ah}e^{-\frac{1}{4}b\pi i}(-h)^{-\frac{1}{2}b}T^b(k, -h)\left(-\frac{1}{\tau} \right)^{\frac{1}{2}s}\left\{ \left(k - \frac{h}{\tau} \right)i \right\}^{-\frac{1}{2}s}$$

summed over $k = 1, 2, \ldots$ and $-h = 1, 2, \ldots$, h and k of opposite parity so that $(-)^{ah} = (-)^{ak}e^{-a\pi i}$. Replace in (54) $-h$ by K, k by H, and note that by Lemma 3, $i^{\frac{1}{2}s} = (-\tau i)^{\frac{1}{2}s}(-1/\tau)^{\frac{1}{2}s}$. Then (54) becomes

$$(55) \qquad (-\tau i)^{-\frac{1}{2}s}\sum (-)^{aH}K^{-\frac{1}{2}b}T^b(H, K)\left\{ \left(H + \frac{K}{\tau} \right)i \right\}^{-\frac{1}{2}s}$$

over all positive integers H and K of opposite parity. The term c in (47) added to (55) makes the contribution of the sum arising from $h < 0$ equal to $(-\tau i)^{-\frac{1}{2}s}\psi(-1/\tau)$, the second term on the right of (50).

Lemma 8 is therefore proved.

LEMMA 9. *If* $s \geq 5$, $\tau = 1 - 1/T$, $Q = e^{\pi iT}$, *then*

$$(56) \qquad \chi_s\left(1 - \frac{1}{T} \right) = c(-iT)^{\frac{1}{2}s}\Phi_s(Q) ,$$

where, as usual, $I(\tau) > 0$ *so that* $I(T) > 0$ *and* $|Q| < 1$.

Writing $h = H - K$, $k = H$ in (47), we have

$$(57) \quad \chi\left(1 - \frac{1}{T} \right) = c + \sum (-)^{aH-a}H^{-\frac{1}{2}b}T^b(H-K, H)\left\{ \left(-K + \frac{H}{T} \right)i \right\}^{-\frac{1}{2}s} ,$$

where $H = 1, 2, 3, \ldots$ and K ranges over all odd integers.

Now

$$(58) \quad T(H-K, H) = \sum_{j=1}^{H}(-)^{j}ie^{-j^2K\pi i/H} = e^{-\frac{1}{4}\pi i\epsilon}(H/|K|)^{\frac{1}{2}}W(H\epsilon, |K|) ,$$

where $\epsilon = \text{sign } K$, by (29), since $K\epsilon = |K|$.

Also, from (52) with $h=-K$, $k=H$, $\tau=-1/T$ if $K>0$, and with $k=-K$, $h=-H$, $\tau=T$ if $K<0$, we obtain two formulas which may be combined into

$$(59) \quad \left\{\left(-K+\frac{H}{T}\right)i\right\}^{-\frac{1}{2}s} = T^{\frac{1}{2}s}e^{-\frac{1}{4}\pi is(1-\epsilon)}L , \qquad L=\{(H\epsilon-T|K|)i\}^{-\frac{1}{2}s} .$$

Combining (58) and (59), we see that the general term in (57) is equal to

$$(-)^{aH-a}H^{-\frac{1}{2}b}|K|^{-\frac{1}{2}b}H^{\frac{1}{2}b}T^{\frac{1}{2}s}e^{d}W^{b}(H\epsilon, |K|)L$$

$$(60) \qquad = e^{-\frac{1}{4}s\pi i}T^{\frac{1}{2}s}|K|^{-\frac{1}{2}b}(-)^{aH}W^{b}(H\epsilon, |K|)L ,$$

for L as in (59) and $d=-\frac{1}{4}b\epsilon\pi i-\frac{1}{4}\pi is(1-\epsilon)$.

The series on the right of (57) is obtained by summing (60) over the ranges $H=1, 2, 3, \ldots$ and $K=$ all odd integers. But the form of (60) shows that precisely the same result is obtained by summing over the ranges $H=\pm 1, \pm 2, \pm 3, \ldots$ and $K=$ all positive odd integers. We arrive therefore at the identity

$$(61) \qquad \chi_s\left(1-\frac{1}{T}\right) = (-iT)^{\frac{1}{2}s} \sum_{K=1,3,5,\ldots} \sum_{H=-\infty}^{\infty} \frac{(-)^{aH}W^{b}(H, K)}{K^{\frac{1}{2}b}\{(H-KT)i\}^{\frac{1}{2}s}} ,$$

the terms arising from $H=0$ accounting for the term c in (57).

Since the series in (61) is merely a rearrangement of the absolutely convergent series (47), it also is absolutely convergent. Hence the subseries obtained by restricting H to be prime to K is also absolutely convergent and we obtain [compare the argument from (49) to (47)]

$$(62) \qquad \chi_s\left(1-\frac{1}{T}\right) = (-iT)^{\frac{1}{2}s}c_{2a}\sum \frac{(-)^{ah}W^{b}(h, k)}{k^{\frac{1}{2}b}\{(h-kT)i\}^{\frac{1}{2}s}} ,$$

summed over $k=1, 3, 5, \ldots$ and all h prime to k, since for m positive and odd, $(-)^{mah}=(-)^{ah}$, $W(mh, mk)=mW(h, k)$.

Now write $h=nk+H$, $0\leq H<k$, $(H, k)=1$. Plainly as h takes all values congruent to H (mod k), n takes all values. Since

$$W(nk+H) = e^{\frac{1}{2}n\pi i}W(H, k) ,$$

we obtain on replacing H by h,

$$(63) \qquad \chi_s\left(1-\frac{1}{T}\right) = c(-iT)^{\frac{1}{2}s}\sum \frac{(-)^{an+ah}e^{\frac{1}{2}bn\pi i}W^{b}(h, k)}{k^{\frac{1}{2}b}\{(nk+h-kT)i\}^{\frac{1}{2}s}}$$

summed over $k = 1, 3, 5, \ldots,$ $0 \le h < k$, $(h, k) = 1$, and all integers n, the triple series being absolutely convergent. (Compare the argument in Lemma 6.) We may therefore write

$$(64) \quad \chi_s\left(1 - \frac{1}{T}\right) = c(-iT)^{\frac{1}{2}s} \sum_{h,\,k} \frac{(-)^{ah} W^b(h,\,k)}{k^{2a+b}} \sum_{n=-\infty}^{\infty} \frac{e^{\frac{1}{2}sn\pi i}}{\{(n - T + h/k)i\}^{\frac{1}{2}s}},$$

summed over $k = 1, 3, 5, \ldots,$ $0 \le h < k$, $(h, k) = 1$.

Now $s \equiv 8r \pmod 8$ by (15). Therefore if we replace in (35) τ by $T - h/k$, the series with respect to n in (64) is equal to $(2\pi)^{\frac{1}{2}s} G_s(Qe^{-h\pi i/k})/\Gamma(\frac{1}{2}s)$. Observing that $W^4(h, k) = (-)^h k^2$ for $0 \le h < k$, $(h, k) = 1$, k odd, we obtain from (64)

$$(65) \qquad \chi_s\left(1 - \frac{1}{T}\right) = c(-iT)^{\frac{1}{2}s} \frac{(2\pi)^{\frac{1}{2}s}}{\Gamma(\frac{1}{2}s)} \sum_{h,\,k} k^{-s} W^s(h, k) G_s(Qe^{-h\pi i/k})$$

summed over $k = 1, 3, 5, \ldots,$ $0 \le h < k$, $(h, k) = 1$. But, by (18), this is (56), which proves Lemma 9.

99. The function[1] $\eta(\tau)$.

LEMMA 10. *If* $s \ge 5$, *the function* $\eta(\tau)$ *defined by*

$$(66) \qquad \eta(\tau) = \eta_s(\tau) = \chi_s(\tau)/\vartheta^s = c\Theta_s/\vartheta^s$$

is an analytic function of τ, *regular for* $I(\tau) > 0$, *and is invariant under the substitutions of the modular subgroup* Γ_3.

By Lemma 6, if $s \ge 5$, $\chi(\tau) = c\Theta_s(e^{\pi i\tau})$ is regular for $I(\tau) > 0$. By the remark below (26), $\vartheta(0 \mid \tau)$ is regular and has no zeros in $I(\tau) > 0$. The first part of Lemma 10 follows immediately.

Again from (47) and Lemma 8, we deduce

$$(67) \qquad \chi(\tau + 2) = \chi(\tau), \qquad \chi\left(-\frac{1}{\tau}\right) = (-i\tau)^{\frac{1}{2}s}\chi(\tau).$$

From (66), (67), and (26), we obtain

$$\eta(\tau + 2) = \eta(\tau), \qquad \eta(-1/\tau) = \eta(\tau),$$

which proves the second part of Lemma 10, since the transformations $\tau' = \tau + 2$, $\tau' = -1/\tau$ generate the modular subgroup Γ_3.

---

[1] The terms used in this section are explained in § 95.

LEMMA 11. *For $s = 5$, 6, 7, or 8, the function $\eta_s(\tau)$ of (66) is bounded throughout the fundamental polygon G_3 of Γ_3.*

This Lemma is the crucial one.

The region G_3 is defined by

$$\tau = x + iy , \qquad |\tau| \geqq 1 , \qquad -1 \leqq x \leqq 1 , \qquad y \geqq 0$$

only the right-hand half of the boundary being counted as part of G_3. The only frontier points G_3 has in common with the real axis are the points $\tau = \pm 1$.

Now by the first part of Lemma 10, if $s \geqq 5$, $\eta(\tau)$ is regular for $I(\tau) > 0$. Hence $\eta(\tau)$ is bounded throughout G_3 if we exclude the neighborhoods of the points $\tau = \pm 1$. It remains therefore to consider the behavior of $\eta(\tau)$ when τ approaches one or other of the points $\tau = \pm 1$ from inside G_3.

Since the transformation $\tau' = \tau + 2$ is a translation of two units to the right along the x-axis, it is sufficient to consider the behavior of $\eta(\tau)$ when $\tau \to 1$ subject to the conditions

$$(68) \qquad |\tau| \geqq 1 , \qquad |\tau - 2| \geqq 1 , \qquad I(\tau) > 0 .$$

For this purpose, following Mordell and Hardy, we write

$$\tau = 1 - T^{-1} , \qquad T = X + iY , \qquad Q = \exp \pi iT ,$$

so that when $\tau \to 1$ subject to (68), $Y \to \infty$ and $|Q| \to 0$.

Now from Lemma 9, (10) and (18), we see that near $Q = 0$, $\chi_s(1 - 1/T)$ behaves like a constant multiple of

$$(69) \qquad (-iT)^{\frac{1}{4}s} Q^{2r} \qquad (r \text{ defined by (15))} .$$

But from (26) and (25),

$$(70) \quad \vartheta^s(0 \,|\, 1 - T^{-1}) = (-iT)^{\frac{1}{2}s} \vartheta_2^s(0 \,|\, T) = (-iT)^{\frac{1}{2}s} Q^{\frac{1}{4}s} 2^s (1 + Q^2 + \ldots)^s .$$

From (69) and (70) it is clear that *to insure the boundedness of $\eta(\tau) = \chi(\tau)/\vartheta^s$ when $\tau \to 1$ subject to (68), it is sufficient that*

$$(71) \qquad 2r \geqq \tfrac{1}{4}s , \qquad s \leqq 8r = s' \leqq 8 . \qquad \text{(from (15))} .$$

Lemma 11 is now proved.

LEMMA 12. *For $s = 5$, 6, 7, or 8, $\eta(\tau)$ is a constant. And in fact*

$$\eta_s(\tau) = c_{2a} .$$

By Lemmas 10 and 11, $\eta(\tau)$ satisfies the conditions of Lemma 1 if $s=$ 5, 6, 7, or 8. Therefore by Lemma 1, $\eta(\tau) = \chi(\tau)/\vartheta^s$ must be a constant for these values of s. Since $\vartheta^s = 1$, $\Theta_s = 1$ when $q = 0$ and $\chi(\tau) = c_{2a}\Theta_s$, the constant must be c_{2a}.

100. Proof of Theorems 115, 116. From Lemma 12, since $\eta(\tau) = c_{2a}\Theta_s/\vartheta^s$, we have

$$(12) \qquad \Theta_s(q) = \vartheta^s(0, q) \quad (s = 5, 6, 7, 8) .$$

and therefore

$$(13) \qquad \rho_s(n) = r_s(n) \quad (5 \leq s \leq 8) ,$$

which is Theorem 115. From (56), (25), and (12), we deduce

$$(20) \qquad \Phi_s(Q) = \vartheta_2^s(0, Q) \quad (s = 5, 6, 7, 8)$$

and therefore Theorem 116.

101. General rules for summing the singular series. Values of the Gaussian sum (7). We assume that $(h, k) = 1$. We have

$$(72) \qquad \text{If } (k, l) = (h, l) = 1, \text{ then } S(h, kl) = S(hl, k)S(hk, l) .$$

We therefore need consider only the cases $k = 2^u$ and $k = p^u$, where p is an odd prime.

$$(73) \qquad S(h, 2) = 0 .$$

$$(74) \qquad \text{If } k = 2^u, \ u = 2v+1 > 1, \ S(h, k) = 2^{v+1}e^{\frac{1}{4}h\pi i} .$$

$$(75) \qquad \text{If } k = 2^u, \ u = 2v > 0, \ S(h, k) = 2^{v+1} \cos \tfrac{1}{4}h\pi \cdot e^{\frac{1}{4}h\pi i} .$$

$$(76) \qquad S(h, p) = (h \,|\, p)i^{\frac{1}{4}(p-1)^2}\sqrt{p} .$$

$$(77) \qquad \text{If } k = p^u, \ u = 2v+1 > 1, \ S(h, k) = p^v S(h, p) .$$

$$(78) \qquad \text{If } k = p^u, \ u = 2v > 0, \ S(h, k) = p^v .$$

We can now evaluate $S(h, k)$ for all relatively prime h and k.

If n is not divisible by the odd prime p, the sum

$$\sigma = \sum_{h=1}^{p-1} (h \,|\, p)e^{-2nh\pi i/p}$$

may be evaluated in terms of (76). Evidently

$$\sigma = \sum_R e^{-2nR\pi i/p} - \sum_N e^{-2nN\pi i/p} = \sum_1 - \sum_2 ,$$

where R runs over a complete set of quadratic residues and N a complete set of non-residues of p. Clearly $2\sum_1 + 1 = S(-n, p)$, while $\sum_1 + \sum_2 = -1$. Hence

$$(79) \qquad \sigma = -(\sum_2 + \sum_1 - 2\sum_1) = S(-n, p)$$

$$= i^{-\frac{1}{4}(p-1)^2}(n \mid p)\sqrt{p} .$$

For $A(k)$ defined in (10), we shall prove

$$(80) \qquad A(kk') = A(k)A(k') \quad \text{if } (k, k') = 1 , \qquad k > 0 , \ k' > 0 .$$

Let h run over a reduced set of residues modulo k (i.e., over the positive integers less than and prime to k). Let h' run over a reduced set of residues modulo k'. Then $H = hk' + h'k$ runs over a reduced set of residues modulo kk'. By (10),

$$(81) \qquad (kk')^s A(k)A(k') = \sum P^s e^{-2n\pi i H/kk'} ,$$

summed for h and h', where $P = S(h, k)S(h', k')$. By (7), P is the sum for $j = 1, \ldots, k$ and $j' = 1, \ldots, k'$ of e with the exponent $2j^2\pi ih/k + 2j'^2\pi ih'/k'$, which we may replace by $2J^2\pi iH/kk'$, since $J = jk' + j'k$ runs over a complete set of residues modulo k (or k') simultaneously with j (or j'). Hence $P = S(H, kk')$. By (10), the second member of (81) is now $(kk')^s A(kk')$. This proves (80).

It follows that, if $s \geq 5$,

$$(82) \qquad S = A(1) + A(2) + \cdots = 1 + A(2) + \cdots = \Pi\chi(p) ,$$

where p ranges over all primes ≥ 2, and

$$(83) \qquad \chi(p) = 1 + A(p) + A(p^2) + A(p^3) + \cdots .$$

For, by Lemma 6, S is absolutely convergent for $s \geq 5$ so that the product $\Pi\chi(p)$ is also absolutely convergent.

Calculation of $A(2^u)$

By (73), we have $A(2) = 0$.

LEMMA 13. *If u is odd and >1, $A(2^u)=0$ unless*

(84) 2^{u-3} *divides n, and 4 divides $\nu - s$, where $\nu = n/2^{u-3}$.*

But if (84) *holds*,

(85) $$A(2^u) = 2^{-(\frac{1}{2}s-1)(u-1)}e^{-\frac{1}{4}(\nu-s)\pi i} .$$

Let $u = 2v + 1 > 1$. By (74),

$$S(h,\, 2^u) = 2^{v-1}S(h,\, 8) .$$

Write $h = 8z + m$. When $z = 0,\, 1,\, \ldots ,\, 2^{u-3}-1$ and $m = 1,\, 3,\, 5,\, 7$, h runs over a reduced set of residues modulo 2^u. Hence

$$A(2^u) = \sum_h 2^{-s(v+2)}S^s(h,\, 8)e^{-2nh\pi i/2^u}$$

$$= \sum_m 2^{-s(v+2)}S^s(m,\, 8)e^{-2nm\pi i/2^u}\sum_z e^{-2nz\pi i/2^{u-3}} .$$

The inner sum is zero unless 2^{u-3} divides n.

If $n = 2^{u-3}\nu$, the inner sum is 2^{u-3}, and

$$A(2^u) = 2^{u-3-s(v+2)}\sum_m 2^{2s}e^{\frac{1}{4}sm\pi i}e^{-\frac{1}{4}\nu m\pi i} .$$

This sum is zero unless $s-\nu$ is divisible by 4, and is then a sum of four terms each equal to $2^{2s}\exp\frac{1}{4}(s-\nu)\pi i$. This gives (85).

LEMMA 14. *If u is even and >1, $A(2^u)=0$ unless 2^{u-2} divides n, and then*

(86) $A(2^u) = 2^{-(\frac{1}{2}s-1)(u-1)}\cos\left(\frac{1}{2}\nu\pi - \frac{1}{4}s\pi\right) ,$ $\nu = n/2^{u-2} .$

Write $u = 2v$. By (75), $S(h,\, 2^u) = 2^{v-1}S(h,\, 4)$. Write $h = 4z + m$, where $z = 0,\, 1,\, \ldots ,\, 2^{u-2}-1$ and $m = 1,\, 3$. Then

$$A(2^u) = 2^{-s(v+1)}\sum_h S^s(h,\, 4)e^{-2nh\pi i/2^u}$$

$$= 2^{-s(v+1)}\sum_m S^s(m,\, 4)e^{-2nm\pi i/2^u}\sum_z e^{-2nz\pi i/2^{u-2}} .$$

The inner sum is zero unless 2^{u-2} divides n. But if $n = 2^{u-2}\nu$,

$$A(2^u) = 2^{2v-2-s(u+1)}\sum_m S^s(m,\, 4)e^{-\frac{1}{2}\nu m\pi i} .$$

By (75), this sum is

$$2^{2s}\{(\cos \tfrac{1}{4}\pi)^s e^{\frac{1}{4}s\pi i - \frac{1}{2}\nu\pi i} + (\cos \tfrac{3}{4}\pi)^s e^{\frac{3}{4}s\pi i - \frac{3}{2}\nu\pi i}\}$$

$$= 2^{2s - \frac{1}{2}s}\{e^{(\frac{1}{4}s - \frac{1}{2}\nu)\pi i} + (-1)^s e^{-(\frac{1}{4}s - \frac{1}{2}\nu)\pi i} e^{s\pi i - 2\nu\pi i}\}$$

$$= 2^{\frac{3}{2}s+1} \cos (\tfrac{1}{2}\nu\pi - \tfrac{1}{4}s\pi) \ .$$

This proves (86).

Calculation of $A(p^u)$

Lemma 15. *If p is not a divisor of n,*

$$A(p) = -p^{-\frac{1}{2}s}, \quad s \equiv 0 \ (mod \ 4) \ ; \quad A(p) = (n \,|\, p) p^{-\frac{1}{2}(s-1)}, \quad s \equiv 1 \ (mod \ 4) \ ;$$

$$A(p) = -(-1)^{\frac{1}{4}(p-1)} p^{-\frac{1}{2}s}, \quad s \equiv 2 \ (mod \ 4) \ ;$$

$$A(p) = (-1)^{\frac{1}{4}(p-1)} (n \,|\, p) p^{-\frac{1}{2}(s-1)} \ , \quad s \equiv 3 \ (mod \ 4) \ .$$

But if p divides n,

$$A(p) = (p-1) p^{-\frac{1}{2}s}, \quad s \equiv 0 \ (mod \ 4) \ ; \quad A(p) = 0 \ , \quad s \equiv 1, 3 \ (mod \ 4) \ ;$$

$$A(p) = (-1)^{\frac{1}{4}(p-1)} (p-1) p^{-\frac{1}{2}s} \ , \quad s \equiv 2 \ (mod \ 4) \ .$$

By (76),

$$A(p) = i^{\frac{1}{4}s(p-1)^2} p^{-\frac{1}{2}s} \sum, \quad \sum = \sum_{h=1}^{p-1} (h \,|\, p)^s e^{-2nh\pi i/p} \ .$$

If s is even, Σ is -1 or $p-1$, according as p is not or is a divisor of n, while $\frac{1}{4}s(p-1)^2 \equiv \frac{1}{2}s(p-1) \ (mod \ 4)$. This proves Lemma 15 when s is even.

Let s be odd. If p divides n, $\Sigma = 0$ since there are as many quadratic residues of p as non-residues. But if p is not a divisor of n, (79) applies.

Lemma 16. *If u is odd and > 1, $A(p^u) = 0$ unless p^{u-1} divides n;*

(87) $\qquad A(p^u) = p^{-(\frac{1}{2}s-1)(u-1)} A(p, \nu) \quad$ *if $n = p^{u-1}\nu$,* $\quad \nu \not\equiv 0 \ (mod \ p)$,

where $A(p, \nu)$ denotes the value of $A(p)$ when $n = \nu$. If p^u divides n,

(88) $\qquad \begin{cases} A(p^u) = (p-1) p^{u-1-\frac{1}{2}su} \ , & s \equiv 0 \ (mod \ 4) \ ; \\ A(p^u) = 0 \ , & s \equiv 1, 3 \ ; \\ A(p^u) = (-1)^{\frac{1}{4}(p-1)} (p-1) p^{u-1-\frac{1}{2}su} \ , & s \equiv 2 \ . \end{cases}$

Let $u = 2v+1 > 1$. By (77), $S(h, p^u) = p^v S(h, p)$. Write $h = pz+m$. The following summations are for $z = 0, 1, \ldots, p^{u-1}-1$ and $m = 1, \ldots, p-1$. Then

$$A(p^u) = p^{-s(v+1)} \sum_h S^s(h, p) e^{-2nh\pi i/p^u}$$

$$= p^{-s(v+1)} \sum_m S^s(m, p) e^{-2nm\pi i/p^u} \sum_z e^{-2nz\pi i/p^{u-1}} .$$

The inner sum vanishes unless p^{u-1} divides n. But if $n = p^{2v}\nu$,

$$A(p^u) = p^{2v-s(v+1)} \sum_m S^s(m, p) e^{-2\nu m\pi i/p} .$$

If p is not a divisor of ν, this is $p^{2v-sv}A(p, \nu)$, which proves (87). Next, let p divide ν. The sum is

$$\sum_m S^s(m, p) = i^{ts} p^{\frac12 s} \sum_m (m \,|\, p)^s , \qquad t = \tfrac14(p-1)^2 .$$

The final sum is 0 or $p-1$, according as s is odd or even. This proves (88).

LEMMA 17. *If u is even and > 1,*

(89) $A(p^u) = 0$ *if p^{u-1} is not a divisor of n ;*

(90) $A(p^u) = -p^{u-1-\frac12 su}$ *if $n = p^{u-1}\nu$,* $\nu \not\equiv 0 \pmod{p}$;

(91) $A(p^u) = (p-1)p^{u-1-\frac12 su}$ *if p^u divides n .*

Let $u = 2v$. By (78), $S(h, p^u) = p^v$. Hence

$$A(p^u) = p^{-sv} \sum_m e^{-2nm\pi i/p^{2v}} \sum_z e^{-2nz\pi i/p^{2v-1}} .$$

The inner sum vanishes unless p^{2v-1} divides n. If $n = p^{2v-1}\nu$,

$$A(p^u) = p^{2v-1-sv} \sum_m e^{-2\nu m\pi i/p} .$$

This sum is -1 or $p-1$, according as p is not or is a divisor of ν.

VALUE OF $\chi(2)$ WHEN s IS ODD

First, let n be not divisible by 4. Then (84_1) holds only when $u = 3$, while 2^{u-2} divides n only when $u = 2$. Hence $A(2^u) = 0$ if $u \geqq 4$. If $u = 3$, (84_2) fails unless $n \equiv s \pmod 4$. Hence

$$A(8) = 0 \text{ if } n \not\equiv s , \qquad A(8) = (-1)^{\frac14(n-s)} 2^{2-s} \text{ if } n \equiv s \pmod 4 .$$

By (86) with $u=2$,

$$A(4) = 2^{-(\frac{1}{2}s-1)}a , \qquad a = \cos\left(\tfrac{1}{2}n\pi - \tfrac{1}{4}s\pi\right) .$$

Thus a is -1 to the power

$$\tfrac{1}{8}[(2n+7s)^2 - 1] \equiv \tfrac{1}{8}(s^2-1) + \tfrac{1}{2}n(n-s) \pmod 2 .$$

$$a = (2\,|\,s)(-1)^{\frac{1}{2}n(n-s)} .$$

Since n is not divisible by 4, while $A(2)=0$,

$$(92) \qquad \begin{aligned} \chi(2) &= 1 + (2\,|\,s)2^{-\frac{1}{2}(s-1)} + (-1)^{\frac{1}{2}(n-s)}2^{2-s} \quad \text{if } n \equiv s \pmod 4 , \\ \chi(2) &= 1 - (2\,|\,s)2^{-\frac{1}{2}(s-1)} \quad \text{if } n \not\equiv s \pmod 4 . \end{aligned}$$

In the general case, write $n = 2^c N$, N odd, $c \geq 2$.

If u is odd and $>c+3$, or even and $>c+2$, $A(2^u)=0$ by the first cases in Lemmas 13 and 14.

Let $u = c+3$ be odd. Then (84_2) fails and $A(2^u)=0$ unless $N \equiv s \pmod 4$. In the latter case, (85) gives

$$A(2^{c+3}) = (-1)^{\frac{1}{4}(N-s)}2^{-\frac{1}{2}(s-2)(c+2)} .$$

If u is odd, $1 < u < c+3$, then $\nu - s$ is odd and (84_2) fails, whence $A(2^u)=0$.

Finally, let u be even, $2 \leq u \leq c+2$. Then (86) gives

$$\begin{aligned} A(2^{c+2}) &= (2\,|\,2N+7s)2^{-\frac{1}{2}(s-2)c - \frac{1}{2}(s-1)} \qquad (c+2 \text{ even}) , \\ A(2^{c+1}) &= (2\,|\,4+7s)2^{-\frac{1}{2}(s-2)(c-1) - \frac{1}{2}(s-1)} \qquad (c+1 \text{ even}) , \\ A(2^u) &= (2\,|\,s)2^{-\frac{1}{2}(s-2)(u-2) - \frac{1}{2}(s-1)} \qquad (u < c+1) . \end{aligned}$$

Write $c = 2l$ or $c = 2l+1$, according as c is even or odd. Hence

$$(93) \qquad 2^{(s-2)l}\chi(2) = 2^{(s-2)l} + (2\,|\,s)\sum_{j=1}^{l} 2^{j(s-2) - \frac{1}{2}(s-1)} + \kappa ,$$

where κ is independent of l, being $-(2\,|\,s)2^{-\frac{1}{2}(s-1)}$ unless $N \equiv s \pmod 4$ and $c = 2l$, and then

$$\kappa = (2\,|\,s)2^{-\frac{1}{2}(s-1)} + (-1)^{\frac{1}{4}(N-s)}2^{2-s} .$$

VALUE OF $\chi(p)$ WHEN $p>2$ AND s IS ODD

First, let n be free of square factors.

If p is not a divisor of n, the first cases of Lemmas 16 and 17 give $A(p^2)=0$, $A(p^3)=0$, ..., while Lemma 15 gives

$$A(p)=(n'\,|\,p)p^{-\frac{1}{2}(s-1)}\ ,\qquad n'=(-1)^{\frac{1}{2}(s-1)}n\ .$$

Thus

(94) $$\chi(p)=1+(n'\,|\,p)p^{-\frac{1}{2}(s-1)}\qquad\text{if }n\not\equiv 0\ (\mathrm{mod}\ p)\ .$$

If p divides n, Lemmas 15–17 give $A(p)=0$, $A(p^3)=A(p^4)=\ldots=0$. By (90), $A(p^2)=-p^{1-s}$. Hence

(95) $$\chi(p)=1-p^{1-s}\qquad\text{if}\qquad n\equiv 0\ (\mathrm{mod}\ p)\ .$$

In general, write

(96) $$n=2^c N=2^c\omega^a\omega'^{a'}\ldots\qquad(c\geqq 0\ ,\qquad a>0\ ,\qquad a'>0,\ldots)\ .$$

We again have (94). If $p=\omega$ and $a=1$, $\chi(p)$ is given by (95). Let $p=\omega$, $a>1$. By Lemmas 16 and 17, we obtain the following results.

If $a=2b+1$, then

$$A(\omega^{2k+1})=0\quad(k\geqq 0)\ ,\quad A(\omega^{2k})=(\omega-1)\omega^{2k-1-ks}\quad(1\leqq k\leqq b)\ ;$$
$$A(\omega^{2b+2})=-\omega^{2b+1-(b+1)s}\ ,\qquad A(\omega^{2k})=0\qquad(k>b+1)\ .$$

If $a=2b$, the values of $A(\omega^m)$, $m\leqq 2b$ or $m\geqq 2b+3$, are the same as before, while

$$A(\omega^{2b+1})=(\nu'\,|\,\omega)\omega^{-(s-2)b-\frac{1}{2}(s-1)}\ ,\qquad A(\omega^{2b+2})=0\ ,$$

where $\nu'=(-1)^{\frac{1}{2}(s-1)}\nu$, $\nu=n/\omega^a$. Hence

(97) $$\chi(\omega)=\frac{(1-\omega^{1-s})(1-\omega^{(2-s)(b+1)})}{1-\omega^{2-s}}\qquad(a=2b+1)\ ,$$

(98) $$\chi(\omega)=\frac{(1-\omega^{1-s})(1-\omega^{(2-s)b})}{1-\omega^{2-s}}+\omega^{2b-bs}(1+(\nu'\,|\,\omega)\omega^{-\frac{1}{2}(s-1)})\ ,\qquad(a=2b)\ .$$

102. Sum of the singular series when n contains no odd square factor. Now $\chi(p)$ is given by (94) and (95), where p is any odd prime, and $\chi(2)$ is given by (92) or (93). Hence

$$S=\chi(2)\Pi(1-p_1^{1-s})\Pi\{1+(n'\,|\,p_2)p_2^{-\frac{1}{2}(s-1)}\}\ ,$$

where p_1 ranges over the odd primes which divide n, and p_2 over those which do not divide n. Since $1-p^{1-s}$ is the product of $1\pm(n'|p)p^{-\frac{1}{2}(s-1)}$, we have

$$(99) \qquad S = \chi(2)\Pi(1-p^{1-s})\Pi\gamma_{p_2}(n') \ ,$$

$$(100) \qquad \gamma_p(k) = [1-(k|p)p^{-\frac{1}{2}(s-1)}]^{-1} \ .$$

If $s \geq 4$, the product is absolutely convergent and

$$\Pi\gamma_{p_2}(n') = \sum(n'|m)m^{-\frac{1}{2}(s-1)} \ ,$$

where m ranges over all positive odd integers prime to n. Hence if s is odd and >4, (9) and (99) give

$$(101) \qquad \rho_s(n) = C\pi^{-\frac{1}{2}(s-1)}n^{\frac{1}{2}s-1}\sum(n'|m)m^{-\frac{1}{2}(s-1)} \ ,$$

where

$$(102) \qquad C = [\pi^{s-\frac{1}{2}}\chi(2)\Pi(1-p^{1-s})]/\Gamma(\tfrac{1}{2}s) \ .$$

For $s = 5$ or 7, (101) gives $r_s(n)$. If $s = 5$,

$$\Pi_{p>2}(1-p^{1-s}) = (1-2^{-4})^{-1}\Pi_{p\geq 2}(1-p^{-4})$$

$$= \frac{16}{15}\Big(1+\frac{1}{2^4}+\frac{1}{3^4}+\cdots\Big)^{-1} = \frac{96}{\pi^4} \ ,$$

$$(103) \quad \begin{cases} C=160 \text{ if } n\equiv 2, 3, 6, 7, \quad C=112 \text{ if } n\equiv 5, \quad C=80 \text{ if} \\ \quad n\equiv 1 \text{ (mod 8) ;} \\ C=100 \text{ if } n\equiv 12 \text{ (mod 16) ;} \quad C=90 \text{ if } n\equiv 4, \quad C=94 \text{ if} \\ \quad n\equiv 20 \text{ (mod 32) .} \end{cases}$$

If $s = 7$,

$$\Pi(1-p^{1-s}) = 960/\pi^6 \qquad (p>2) \ ,$$

$$(104) \quad \begin{cases} C=448 \text{ if } n\equiv 1, 2, 5, 6, \quad C=592 \text{ if } n\equiv 7, \quad C=560 \text{ if} \\ \quad n\equiv 3 \text{ (mod 8) ;} \\ C=574 \text{ if } n\equiv 4 \text{ (mod 16) ;} \quad C=\frac{1}{2}1157 \text{ if } n\equiv 28, \\ \quad C=\frac{1}{2}1155 \text{ if } n\equiv 12 \text{ (mod 32) .} \end{cases}$$

103. The main theorem. According as the g.c.d. of x_1, ..., x_s is 1 or >1, the representation $n = x_1^2 + \cdots + x_s^2$ is called *primitive* or *imprimitive*.

Let $r(n)$ denote the number of all representations of $n > 0$ as a sum of $s = 5$ or 7 squares, and $R(n)$ the number of primitive representations of n. Then

$$r(n) = \sum R(n/d^2) ,$$

where d^2 ranges over all square divisors of n.

Let $r'(n)$ denote the number of representations of n as a sum of s squares with no common odd divisor >1. Then

$$r(n) = \sum r'(n/d^2) ,$$

where d^2 ranges over all *odd* squares dividing n.

Theorem 117. *Let $s = 5$ or 7. For C in (102), the sum of the series (101) is $r'(n)$. If n is not divisible by 4, $R(n) = r'(n)$ and C is given by (103) and (104). If n is divisible by 4, $R(n)$ has the value (101) with $C = 80$ when $s = 5$ and $C = 560$ when $s = 7$.*

The proof requires

LEMMA 18. *If, for every n,*

$$(105) \qquad\qquad r(n) = \sum \phi(n/d^2) ,$$

where d^2 ranges over all odd square divisors of n, then $\phi(n) = r'(n)$.

This is true since (105) was seen to hold for $\phi = r'$ and since (105) uniquely determines the value of $\phi(k)$ for $k = 1, 2, \ldots$:

$$\phi(1) = r(1) , \quad \phi(2) = r(2) , \ldots, \quad \phi(9) + \phi(1) = r(9) ,$$
$$\phi(10) = r(10) , \ldots, \quad \phi(81) + \phi(9) + \phi(1) = r(81), \ldots .$$

Let Ω^2 be the largest square dividing n. Write $D = n/\Omega^2$. All odd primes fall into the following four classes:

I. q not a divisor of n. By (94),

$$(106) \qquad\qquad \chi(q) = 1 + (n'|q)q^{-\frac{1}{2}(s-1)} .$$

II. ω_1 a divisor of D, but not of Ω. By (95),

$$(107) \qquad\qquad \chi(\omega_1) = 1 - \omega_1^{1-s} .$$

III. ω_2 a divisor of Ω, but not of D. Let $2b_2$ be the exponent of the highest power of ω_2 which divides n. By (98),

$$(108) \quad \chi(\omega_2) = (1 - \omega_2^{1-s})[1 + \omega_2^{2-s} + \cdots + \omega_2^{(b_2-1)(2-s)} + \gamma_{\omega_2}(\nu')\omega_2^{b_2(2-s)}] \ .$$

IV. ω_3 divides neither Ω nor D. Let $2b_3 + 1$ be the exponent of the highest power of ω_3 which divides n. By (97),

$$(109) \quad \chi(\omega_3) = (1 - \omega_3^{1-s})[1 + \omega_3^{2-s} + \cdots + \omega_3^{b_3(2-s)}] \ .$$

Hence

$$(110) \quad S = \chi(2)\,\Pi\chi(q)\,\Pi\chi(\omega_1)\,\Pi\chi(\omega_2)\,\Pi\chi(\omega_3) \ .$$

We perform the multiplications segregating the second factors of $\chi(\omega_2)$ and $\chi(\omega_3)$. We get

$$(111) \quad n^{\frac{1}{2}s-1}S = \chi(2)P(n)\,\Pi(1 - p^{1-s}) \ ,$$

$$(112) \quad P(n) = n^{\frac{1}{2}s-1}\Pi\gamma_q(n')\,\Pi\Sigma\lambda_u(\omega_2)\omega_2^{(2-s)u}\,\Pi\Sigma\omega_3^{(2-s)v} \ ,$$

where the products extend over all q, ω_2, ω_3, respectively; and in the summations, $u \leq b_2$, $v \leq b_3$. Also, $\lambda_u(\omega_2) = 1$ if $u < b_2$,

$$\lambda_u(\omega_2) = \gamma_{\omega_2}(\nu') \ , \qquad \nu' = (-1)^{\frac{1}{2}(s-1)}\omega_2^{-2b_2}n \ , \quad \text{if} \quad u = b_2 \ .$$

Let $\pi_1, \ldots, \pi_r$ be the distinct primes of type ω_2. Let the corresponding u's be $u_1, \ldots, u_r$. Let $p_1, \ldots, p_t$ be the distinct primes of type ω_3, and $v_1, \ldots, v_t$ the corresponding v's. The general term of (112) is

$$(113) \quad n^{\frac{1}{2}s-1}\Pi\gamma_q(n') \cdot \lambda_{u_1}(\pi_1) \ldots \lambda_{u_r}(\pi_r)[\pi_1^{2u_1} \ldots \pi_r^{2u_r}p_1^{2v_1} \ldots p_t^{2v_t}]^{1-\frac{1}{2}s}$$
$$= (n/d^2)^{\frac{1}{2}s-1}\Pi\gamma_q(n'/d^2) \ ,$$

where the last product extends over the odd primes q not dividing n/d^2, while $d^2 = \Pi\pi_i^{2u_i}\Pi p_j^{2v_j}$ is a typical odd square divisor of n, and $\lambda_u(\omega_2)$ supplies the necessary additional factor to the last product whenever $u = b_2$.

Since d^2 ranges over all odd square divisors of n,

$$(114) \quad r(n) = \rho(n) = \sum\psi(n/d^2) \ ,$$

where $\psi(n)$ is the function on the right of (101), whence

$$(115) \quad \psi(n) = C\pi^{-\frac{1}{2}(s-1)}n^{\frac{1}{2}s-1}\Pi\gamma_q(n') \ ,$$

the product extending over the odd primes q not dividing n. Hence by Lemma 18, $r'(n) = \psi(n)$, which proves the first part of Theorem 117.

Next, let $4^l (l \geqq 1)$ be the highest power of 4 which divides n. Evidently

$$(116) \qquad r'(n) = \mathrm{R}(n) + \mathrm{R}(n/4) + \cdots + \mathrm{R}(n/4^l) \,,$$

whence

$$(117) \qquad \mathrm{R}(n) = r'(n) - r'(n/4) = \psi(n) - \psi(n/4) \,.$$

But $\psi(n)$ and $\psi(n/4)$ differ only as to the factor $\chi(2)$ in (102) and the outside power of n in (101). Hence $\psi(n) - \psi(n/4)$ is the product of

$$(118) \qquad \frac{\pi^{\frac{1}{2}s}}{\Gamma(\frac{1}{2}s)} \Pi(1 - p^{1-s}) n^{\frac{1}{2}s-1} \sum (n' \,|\, m) m^{-\frac{1}{2}(s-1)} \,,$$

summed for the positive odd m prime to n, and

$$(119) \qquad \chi(2, \ n) - 2^{2-s} \chi(2, \tfrac{1}{4}n) \,.$$

By (93), (119) has the value

$$(120) \qquad V = 1 + (2 \,|\, s) 2^{-\frac{1}{2}(s-1)} - 2^{2-s} \,.$$

Hence

$$(121) \qquad \mathrm{R}(n) = B\pi^{-\frac{1}{2}(s-1)} n^{\frac{1}{2}s-1} \sum (n' \,|\, m) m^{\frac{1}{2}(s-1)} \,,$$

$$(122) \qquad B = \pi^{s-\frac{1}{2}} [\Gamma(\tfrac{1}{2}s)]^{-1} V \Pi(1 - p^{1-s}) \,, \quad B(5) = 80 \,, \quad B(7) = 560 \,.$$

The last part of Theorem 117 follows from (117)–(122).

Similar results may be obtained more simply when s is 6 or 8. We can also sum the singular series for $R_s(n)$ obtained in Theorem 117 when $5 \leqq s \leqq 8$.

The explicit formulas for $R_s(n)$ may be derived by elementary arguments from those for $r_s(n)$. But we cannot so obtain the singular series.

INDEX

INDEX

Adjoint, 4
Associated form, 108, 136
Asymtotic, 205
Automorph, 34, 179
Automorphic function, 203

Binary form; see Characters, Duplication, Genus, Indefinite, Numbers, Positive, Proper, Reduced, Represent, Representation

Characters: of binary, 37, 44, 55
of ternary, 51
Cofactor, 3
Continued fraction, 80, 81, 97
Contragredient transformation, 6
Conventions of sign for Ω, Δ, 10

Definite form, 10
Derived set, 88
Determinant, 3 n.
Diophantine equations, 68–76
$ax^2+by^2+cz^2=0$, 19
$ax+by+cz=0$, 24
$ax^2+by^2+cz^2+du^2+cv^2=0$, 68
$ax^2+by^2+cz^2+du^2=0$, 70
$x^2+y^2+z^2=3xyz$, 101–6
quadratic in $n \geqq 5$ variables, 70
system, $x_2y_3-x_3y_2=Z_1$, etc., 11
see Pellian
Divisor of form, 7
Duplication of binary forms, 61

Equivalence, 6
sufficient conditions for, 54–60
test for, 28
Equivalent forms, 6, 25, 28, 54–60
in relation to minima, 79, 80, 92, 99, 106, 108, 112, 124, 141, 144, 146

Form; see Binary, Character, Duplication, Equivalence, Equivalent, Genus, Indefinite, Lower bound, Minima, Numbers, Positive, Proper, Reduced, Representation, Simultaneous, Sum of

squares, Table, Ternary, Universal, Zero
Fundamental identities, 9
parallelogram, 156
reduced, 158–59
parallelopiped, 162
reduced, 163
polygon, 203

Genus of binary forms, 44
existence, 63
principal, 47, 61–63
Genus of ternary forms, 52
case each contains a single class, 54
existence, 67

Improperly primitive, 7, 59
Indefinite binary: minimum of, 79–107
notations, 80, 92, 93, 107
periods, 93
Indefinite form, 10
Indefinite quaternary: minimum of, 134–46
ternary associated, 136
whose lower bound is not attained, 146
Indefinite ternary: minimum of, 108–36
whose lower bound is not attained, 130
Infinitude of primes represented: by a primitive linear form, 44
by a quadratic and linear form, 48
Integral transformation, 6
Invariants of a form, 6, 7
Ω and Δ, 7
Inverse transformation, 6

Lattice, 156, 162
Linear transformation, 4
contragredient, 6
integral, 6
inverse, 6
transpose of, 5
Lower bound, 77, 81, 89
not attained, 130, 146

Markoff numbers, 100–06

Minima of indefinite forms, 77–146
   positive quaternary, 185
   positive ternary, 164
   see Indefinite
Modular function, 203

Negative form, 10
Numbers represented: by binary, 51
   by sum of squares, 198
   by ternary, 14, 33, 63–66
   see Proper, Representation of Numbers

Order of function, 204–5

Pellian equation, 35–44
   summary, 43
Positive; *see* Minima, Ternary
Positive binary: reduced, 159–60
   represented by lattice, 156–57
Positive form, 10
Prime; *see* Infinitude
Primitive binary, 32
Primitive form, 7, 8
Primitive representation, 223
Primitive set, 11
Proper representation: of binary by ter-
   nary, 25–34, 63
   of numbers, 8, 14, 33, 63–66
Properly primitive, 7

Quadratic form; *see* Form
Quaternary; *see* Indefinite, Minima

Reciprocal of a form, 7
Reciprocity principle, 8
Reduced binary, 118–19, 159–60
Represent a binary, 25
   number, 8
Representation of a binary by a ternary,
   25–34, 63
   sufficient conditions for, 29
   when binary is primitive, 32
Representation of all binaries of a genus
   by a ternary, 44–51
Representation of numbers, 8, 77
   as sum of squares, 198
   by binary, 51
   by indefinite ternary, 63–66
   by ternary, 14, 33
Representation, proper, 12
   simultaneous, 12

Reverse set, 81
Root of system of congruences, 27
   representative of, 27

Sign of Ω, Δ, 10
Signature, 138
Simultaneous representation by a form
   and its reciprocal, 12–17
Singular series, 201, 215
Sum of squares, number of representations, 198–225
Symbols
   Ω, Δ, 7
   $f(\delta) = \delta x^2 - a d y^2$, 37
   $I(\tau)$, $R(\tau)$, 203
   $L(f)$, 77
   $O, o, \sim, \rightarrow$, 204
   $r(n)$, $R(n)$, 223
   $r_s(n)$, 198
   S, 138
   2_j, 81
   $(f(u)|p)$, 52
   (a, t, b), 25
   $(g_1, g_2, \ldots)$, 80
   $(a; b; \ldots)$, 93
   $[a, b, c] = a x^2 + b x y + c y^2$, 109
   $\{A, B, C\}$, 162
Symmetrical point, 157

Table of automorphs, 179–80
Table of positive ternary, 181–85
Table of reduced ternary which are indefinite, but not zero forms, 147–51
Ternary forms, 9–67
   binary associated with, 108
   classic, 17
   positive, minimum of, 164
     reduced, 155–85
   see Genus, Indefinite, Numbers, Proper,
     Representation, Table, Universal,
     Zero
Theta functions, 204
Transformation; *see* Linear

Universal forms, 17–23
Universal zero forms, 187–97

Zero forms include all:
   indefinite, universal, ternary, 17–23
   quadratics in n variables, $n \geqq 5$, 70
   see Universal

[PRINTED IN U·S·A]

CHELSEA

SCIENTIFIC

BOOKS

KREIS UND KUGEL
By W. BLASCHKE

Isoperimetric properties of the circle and sphere, the (Brunn-Minkowski) theory of convex bodies, and differential-geometric properties (in the large) of convex bodies. A standard work.

—x + 169 pp. 5½x8½. [59] Cloth **$3.50**
[115] Paper **$1.50**

VORLESUNGEN ÜBER INTEGRAL-GEOMETRIE. Vols. I and II
By W. BLASCHKE
EINFÜHRUNG IN DIE THEORIE DER SYSTEME VON DIFFERENTIAL-GLEICHUNGEN
By E. KÄHLER

—222 pp. 5½x8½. [64] Three Vols. in One **$4.50**

VORLESUNGEN ÜBER FOURIERSCHE INTEGRALE
By S. BOCHNER

"A readable account of those parts of the subject useful for applications to problems of mathematical physics or pure analysis."
—*Bulletin of the A. M. S.*

—1932. 237 pp. 5½x8½. Orig. pub. at $6.40. [42] **$3.50**

ALMOST PERIODIC FUNCTIONS
By H. BOHR

Translated by H. Cohn. From the famous series *Ergebnisse der Mathematik und ihrer Grenzgebiete*, a beautiful exposition of the theory of Almost Periodic Functions written by the creator of that theory.

—1951. 120 pp. 6x9. Lithotyped. German edition was $4.50.
[27] **$2.50**

LECTURES ON THE CALCULUS OF VARIATIONS
By O. BOLZA

A standard text by a major contributor to the theory.

—Ready June or July, 1961. Corr. repr. of first ed. xi + 267 pp. 5⅜x8. [145] Cloth **$3.25**
[152] Paper **$1.19**

THEORIE DER KONVEXEN KÖRPER
By T. BONNESEN and W. FENCHEL

"Remarkable monograph."
—*J. D. Tamarkin, Bulletin of the A. M. S.*

—1934. 171 pp. 5½x8½. Orig. publ. at $7.50 [54] **$3.95**

THE CALCULUS OF FINITE DIFFERENCES
By G. BOOLE

A standard work on the subject of finite differences and difference equations by one of the seminal minds in the field of finite mathematics.

Some of the topics covered are: *Interpolation, Finite Integration, Summation of Series, General Theory of Difference and Differential Equations of First Order, Linear DEqns with Variable Coefficients, Linear DEqns, Geometrical Applications.* Numerous exercises with answers.

—Fourth edition. 1958. xii + 336 pp. 5x8. [121] Cloth **$3.95**
[148] Paper **$1.39**

A TREATISE ON DIFFERENTIAL EQUATIONS
By G. BOOLE·

Including the Supplementary Volume.

—Fifth edition. 1959. xxiv + 735 pp. 5¼x8. [128] **$6.00**

THEORY OF FUNCTIONS
By C. CARATHÉODORY

Translated by F. STEINHARDT. The recent, and already famous textbook, *Funktionentheorie.*

Partial Contents: **Part One.** Chap. I. Algebra of Complex Numbers. II. Geometry of Complex Numbers. III. Euclidean, Spherical, and Non-Euclidean Geometry. **Part Two.** Theorems from Point Set Theory and Topology. Chap. I. Sequences and Continuous Complex Functions. II. Curves and Regions. III. Line Integrals. **Part Three.** Analytic Functions. Chap. I. Foundations. II. The Maximum-modulus principle. III. Poisson Integral and Harmonic Functions. IV. Meromorphic Functions. **Part Four.** Generation of Analytic Functions by Limiting Processes. Chap. I. Uniform Convergence. II. Normal Families of Meromorphic Functions. III. Power Series. IV. Partial Fraction Decomposition and the Calculus of Residues. **Part Five.** Special Functions. Chap. I. The Exponential Function and the Trigonometric Functions. II. Logarithmic Function. III. Bernoulli Numbers and the Gamma Function.

Vol. II.: **Part Six.** Foundations of Geometric Function Theory. Chap. I. Bounded Functions. II. Conformal Mapping. III. The Mapping of the Boundary. **Part Seven.** The Triangle Function and Picard's Theorem. Chap. I. Functions of Several Complex Variables. II. Conformal Mapping of Circular-Arc Triangles. III. The Schwarz Triangle Functions and the Modular Function. IV. Essential Singularities and Picard's Theorems.

"A book by a master . . . Carathéodory himself regarded [it] as his finest achievement . . . written from a catholic point of view."—*Bulletin of A.M.S.*

—Vol. I. Second edition. 1958. 310 pp. 6x9. [97] **$4.95**
—Vol. II. Second edition. 1960. 220 pp. 6x9. [106] **$4.95**

ALGEBREN
By M. DEURING

—(Ergeb. der Math.) 1935. v + 143 pp. 5½x8½. Orig. pub. at $6.60.　　　　　　　　　　　　　　　　[50]　**$3.95**

HISTORY OF THE THEORY OF NUMBERS
By L. E. DICKSON

"**A monumental work** . . . Dickson always has in mind the needs of the investigator . . . The author has [often] expressed in a nut-shell the main results of a long and involved paper *in a much clearer way than the writer of the article did himself.* The ability to reduce complicated mathematical arguments to simple and elementary terms is highly developed in Dickson."—*Bulletin of A. M. S.*

—Vol. I (Divisibility and Primality) xii + 486 pp. Vol. II (Diophantine Analysis) xxv + 803 pp. Vol. III (Quadratic and Higher Forms) v + 313 pp.　　[86]　Three vol. set　**$19.95**

STUDIES IN THE THEORY OF NUMBERS
By L. E. DICKSON

A systematic exposition, starting from first principles, of the arithmetic of quadratic forms, chiefly (but not entirely) ternary forms, including numerous original investigations and correct proofs of a number of classical results that have been stated or proved erroneously in the literature.

—1930. viii + 230 pp. 5⅜x8.　　　　　　[151]　**In prep.**

THE INTEGRAL CALCULUS
By J. W. EDWARDS

A leisurely, immensely detailed, textbook of over 1,900 pages, rich in illustrative examples and manipulative techniques and containing much interesting material that must of necessity be omitted from less comprehensive works.

There are forty large chapters in all. The earlier cover a leisurely and a more-than-usually-detailed treatment of all the elementary standard topics. Later chapters include: Jacobian Elliptic Functions, Weierstrassian Elliptic Functions, Evaluation of Definite Integrals, Harmonic Analysis, Calculus of Variations, etc. Every chapter contains many exercises (with solutions).

—2 vols. 1,922 pp. 5x8. Originally published at $31.50 the set. [102], [105]　Each volume　**$7.50**

AUTOMORPHIC FUNCTIONS
By L. R. FORD

"Comprehensive . . . remarkably clear and explicit."—*Bulletin of the A. M. S.*

—2nd ed. (Cor. repr.) x + 333 pp. 5⅜x8.　　[85]　**$4.95**

ASYMPTOTIC SERIES
By W. B. FORD

TWO VOLUMES IN ONE: *Studies on Divergent Series and Summability* and *The Asymptotic Developments of Functions Defined by MacLaurin Series.*

PARTIAL CONTENTS: I. MacLaurin Sum-Formula; Introduction to Study of Asymptotic Series. II. Determination of Asymptotic Development of a Given Function. III. Asymptotic Solutions of Linear Differential Equations. . . . V. Summability, etc. *I.* First General Theorem. . . . *III.* MacLaurin Series whose General Coefficient is Algebraic. . . . *VII.* Functions of Bessel Type. *VIII.* Asymptotic Behavior of Solution of Differential Equations of Fuchsian Type. Bibliography.

—1916; 1936-60. x + 341 pp. 6x9. [143] Two vols. in one.
$6.00

THE CALCULUS OF EXTENSION
By H. G. FORDER

Partial Contents: I. Plane Geometry. II. Geometry in Space. III. Applications to Projective Geometry. . . . VIII. Applications to Systems of Linear Equations and Determinants. XII. Oriented Circle and Systems of Circles. XIII. The General Theory of Matrices . . . XV. Algebraic Products.

—1941-60. xvi + 490 pp. 5⅜x8. [135] **$4.95**

RUSSIAN MATHEMATICAL BIBLIOGRAPHY
By G. E. FORSYTHE

A bibliography of Russian Mathematics Books for the past quarter century. Supplements may be issued. Added subject index.

—1956. 106 pp. 5x8. [111] **$3.95**

CURVE TRACING
By P. FROST

This much-quoted and charming treatise gives a very readable treatment of a topic that can only be touched upon briefly in courses on Analytic Geometry. Teachers will find it invaluable as supplementary reading for their more interested students and for reference. The Calculus is not used.

Seventeen plates, containing over 200 figures, illustrate the discussion in the text.

—5th (unaltered) ed. 1960. 210 pp. + 17 fold-out plates. 5⅜x8. [140] **$3.50**

ARITHMETISCHE UNTERSUCHUNGEN
By C. F. GAUSS

The German translation of his *Disquisitiones Arithmeticae*.
—Repr. of 1st German ed. 860 pp. 5⅜x8.   [150]   **In prep.**

THEORY OF PROBABILITY
By B. V. GNEDENKO

Translated from the second Russian edition, with additions and revisions by Prof. Gnedenko.

Partial Contents: I. The Concept of Probability (Different approaches to the definition. Field of events. Geometrical Probability. Statistical definition. Axiomatic construction . . .). II. Sequences of Independent Trials. III. Markov Chains. IV. Random Variables and Distribution Functions (Continuous and discrete distributions. Multidimensional d. functions. Functions of random variables. Stieltjes integral). V. Numerical Characteristics of Random Variables (Mathematical expectation. Variance . . . Moments). VI. Law of Large Numbers (Mass phenomena. Tchebychev's form of law. Strong law of large numbers . . .). VII. Characteristic Functions (Properties. Inversion formula and uniqueness theorem. Helly's theorems. Limit theorems. Char. functs. for multidimensional random variables . . .). VIII. Classical Limit Theorem (Liapunov's theorem. Local limit theorem). IX. Theory of Infinitely Divisible Distribution Laws. X. Theory of Stochastic Processes (Generalized Markov equation. Continuous S. processes. Purely discontinuous S. processes. Kolmogorov-Feller equations. Homogeneous S. processes with independent increments. Stationary S. process. Stochastic integral. Spectral theorem of S. processes. Birkhoff-Khinchine ergodic theorem). XI. Elements of Statistics (Some problems. Variational series and empirical distribution functions. Glivenko's theorem and Kolmogorov's compatibility criterion. Two-sample problem. Critical region. Comparison of two statistical hypotheses . . . Confidence limits). TABLES. BIBLIOGRAPHY.

—Ready, 1961-1962. About 400 pp. 6x9. [132] Prob. **$6.50**

LES INTÉGRALES DE STIELTJES et leurs Applications aux Problèmes de la Physique Mathématique
By N. GUNTHER
—1932. 498 pp. 5½x8.   [63]   **$5.95**

LEÇONS SUR LA PROPAGATION DES ONDES ET LES ÉQUATIONS DE L'HYDRODYNAMIQUE

By J. HADAMARD

"[Hadamard's] unusual analytic proficiency enables him to connect in a wonderful manner the physical problem of propagation of waves and the mathematical problem of Cauchy concerning the characteristics of partial differential equations of the second order."—*Bulletin of the A. M. S.*

—viii + 375 pp. 5½x8½. [58] **$4.95**

REELLE FUNKTIONEN. Punktfunktionen

By H. HAHN

—426 pp. 5½x8½. Orig. pub. at $12.80. [52] **$4.95**

LECTURES ON ERGODIC THEORY

By P. R. HALMOS

CONTENTS: Introduction. Recurrence. Mean Convergence. Pointwise Convergence. Ergodicity. Mixing. Measure Algebras. Discrete Spectrum. Automorphisms of Compact Groups. Generalized Proper Values. Weak Topology. Weak Approximation. Uniform Topology. Uniform Approximation. Category. Invariant Measures. Generalized Ergodic Theorems. Unsolved Problems.

"Written in the pleasant, relaxed, and clear style usually associated with the author. The material is organized very well and painlessly presented. A number of remarks ranging from the serious to the whimsical add insight and enjoyment to the reading of the book."

—*Bulletin of the Amer. Math. Soc.*

—1960. (Repr. of 1956 ed.) viii + 101 pp. 5¼x8. [142] **$2.95**

INTRODUCTION TO HILBERT SPACE AND THE THEORY OF SPECTRAL MULTIPLICITY

By P. R. HALMOS

Prof. Halmos' recent book gives a clear, readable introductory treatment of Hilbert Space. The multiplicity theory of continuous spectra is treated, for the first time in English, in full generality.

—1957. 2nd ed. (c. repr. of 1st ed.). 120 pp. 6x9. [82] **$3.25**

RAMANUJAN:
Twelve Lectures on His Life and Works

By G. H. HARDY

The book is somewhat more than an account of the mathematical work and personality of Ramanujan; it is one of the very few full-length books of "shop talk" by an important mathematician.

—viii + 236 pp. 6x9. [136] **$3.95**

GRUNDZÜGE DER MENGENLEHRE
By F. HAUSDORFF

Some of the topics in the Grundzüge omitted from later editions:

Symmetric Sets—Principle of Duality—most of the "Algebra" of Sets—most of the "Ordered Sets"—Partially Ordered Sets—Arbitrary Sets of Complexes—Normal Types—Initial and Final Ordering—Complexes of Real Numbers—General Topological Spaces—Euclidean Spaces —the Special Methods Applicable in the Euclidean plane—Jordan's separation Theorem—The Theory of Content and Measure—The Theory of the Lebesgue Integral.

—First edition. 484 pp. 5½x8¼.   [61] **$4.95**

SET THEORY
By F. HAUSDORFF

Now for the first time available in English, Hausdorff's classic text-book has been an inspiration and a delight to those who have read it in the original German. The translation is from the Third (latest) German edition.

"We wish to state without qualification that this is an indispensable book for all those interested in the theory of sets and the allied branches of real variable theory."—*Bulletin of A. M. S.*

—1957. 352 pp. 6x9.   [119] **$6.00**

VORLESUNGEN ÜBER DIE THEORIE DER ALGEBRAISCHEN ZAHLEN
By E. HECKE

"An elegant and comprehensive account of the modern theory of algebraic numbers."
                    —*Bulletin of the A. M. S.*

"A classic."—*Mathematical Gazette.*

—1923. 264 pp. 5½x8½.   [46] **$3.95**

INTEGRALGLEICHUNGEN UND GLEICHUNGEN MIT UNENDLICHVIELEN UNBEKANNTEN
By E. HELLINGER and O. TOEPLITZ

"Indispensable to anybody who desires to penetrate deeply into this subject."—*Bulletin of A.M.S.*

—With a preface by E. Hilb. 1928. 286 pp. 5¼x8. [89] **$4.50**

Grundzüge Einer Allgemeinen Theorie der
LINEAREN INTEGRALGLEICHUNGEN
By D. HILBERT

—306 pp. 5½x8¼.   [91]   **$4.50**

PRINCIPLES OF MATHEMATICAL LOGIC
By D. HILBERT and W. ACKERMANN

The famous *Grundüge der Theoretischen Logik*
translated into English, with added notes and revisions by PROF. R. E. LUCE.

"The best textbook in a Western European
language for a student wishing a fairly thorough
treatment."—*Bulletin of the A. M. S.*

—1950-59. xii + 172 pp. 6x9.   [69]   **$3.75**

GEOMETRY AND THE IMAGINATION
By D. HILBERT and S. COHN-VOSSEN

The theme of this book is *insight*. Not merely
proofs, but proofs that offer *insight*—intuitive
understanding—into *why they are true*. Not
merely properties of the hyperboloid or of Pascal's
hexagon, but insight into *why they have these
properties*. In this wide-ranging survey, one of the
world's greatest and most original mathematicians
uses insight as both his technique and his aim.
Both the beginner and the mature mathematician
will learn much from this fascinating treatise.

Translated from the German by P. NEMENYI.

CHAPTER HEADINGS: I. The Simplest Curves and
surfaces. II. Regular Systems of Points. III. Projective Configurations. IV. Differential Geometry.
V. Kinematics. VI. Topology.

"A mathematical classic . . . The purpose is to
make the reader *see* and *feel* the proofs."—*Science.*

"A fascinating tour of the 20th-century mathematical zoo."—*Scientific American.*

"Students . . . will experience the sensation of
being taken into the friendly confidence of a great
mathematician and being shown the *real signifi-
cance* of things."—*Science Progress.*

"A glance down the index (*twenty-five columns
of it*) reveal the breadth of range:—

"Annulus; Atomic structure; Automorphic functions; Bubble, soap; Caustic Curve; Color problem;
Density of packing, of circles; Four-dimensional
space; Gears, hyperboloidal; Graphite; Lattices;
Mapping; "Monkey Saddle"; Table salt; Zinc.

"*These are but a few of the topics* . . . The title
evokes the imagination and the text must surely
capture it."—*Math. Gazette.*

—1952. 358 pp. 6x9.   [87]   **$6.00**

THEORIE DER ENDLICHEN UND UNENDLICHEN GRAPHEN

By D. KÖNIG

"Elegant applications to Matrix Theory . . . Abstract Set Theory . . . Linear Forms . . . Electricity . . . Basis Problems . . . Logic, Theory of Games, Group Theory."—*L. Kalmar, Acta Szeged.*

—1936. 269 pp. 5¼x8¼. Orig. publ. at $7.20. [72] **$4.50**

DIOPHANTISCHE APPROXIMATIONEN

By J. F. KOKSMA

—(Ergeb. der Math.) 1936. 165 pp. 5½x8½. Orig. publ. at $7.25. [66] **$3.50**

FOUNDATIONS OF THE THEORY OF PROBABILITY

By A. KOLMOGOROV

Translation edited by N. MORRISON. With a bibliography and notes by A. T. BHARUCHA-REID.

Almost indispensable for anyone who wishes a thorough understanding of modern statistics, this basic tract develops probability theory on a postulational basis.

—2nd ed. 1956. viii + 84 pp. 6x9. [23] **$2.50**

EINFÜHRUNG IN DIE THEORIE DER KONTINUIERLICHEN GRUPPEN

By G. KOWALEWSKI

—406 pp. 5¼x8¼. Orig. publ. at $10.20. [70] **$4.95**

DETERMINANTENTHEORIE EINSCHLIESSLICH DER FREDHOLMSCHEN DETERMINANTEN

By G. KOWALEWSKI

PARTIAL CONTENTS: Definition and Simple Properties . . . Systems of Linear Equations . . . Symmetric, Skew-symmetric, Orthogonal Determinants . . . Resultants and Discriminants . . . Linear and Quadratic Forms . . . Functional, Wronskian, Gramian determinants . . . Geometrical applications . . . Linear Integral Equations . . . Theory of Elementary Divisors.
"A classic in its field."—*Bulletin of the A. M. S.*

—Third edition. 1942. 328 pp. 5½x8. [39] **$4.95**

IDEALTHEORIE
By W. KRULL
—(Ergeb. der Math.) 1935. 159 pp. 5½x8½. Orig. publ.
(paper bound) at $7.00.   [48] Cloth, **$3.95**

GROUP THEORY
By A. KUROSH

Translated from the second Russian edition and
with added notes by PROF. K. A. HIRSCH.

A complete rewriting of the first, and already
famous, Russian edition.

Partial Contents: PART ONE: The Elements of
Group Theory. Chap. I. Definition. II. Subgroups
(Systems, Cyclic Groups, Ascending Sequences of
Groups). III. Normal Subgroups. IV. Endomor-
phisms and Automorphisms. Groups with Opera-
tors. V. Series of Subgroups. Direct Products.
Defining Relations, etc. PART TWO: Abelian Groups.
VI. Foundations of the Theory of Abelian Groups
(Finite Abelian Groups, Rings of Endomorphisms,
Abelian Groups with Operators). VII. Primary
and Mixed Abelian Groups. VIII. Torsion-Free
Abelian Groups. Editor's Notes. Bibliography.

Vol. II. PART THREE: Group-Theoretical Con-
structions. IX. Free Products and Free Groups
(Free Products with Amalgamated Subgroup,
Fully Invariant Subgroups). X. Finitely Generated Groups. XI. Direct Products. Lattices (Modular, Complete Modular, etc.). XII. Extensions of
Groups (of Abelian Groups, of Non-commutative
Groups, Cohomology Groups). PART FOUR: Solvable and Nilpotent Groups. XIII. Finiteness Conditions, Sylow Subgroups, etc. XIV. Solvable
Groups (Solvable and Generalized Solvable Groups,
Local Theorems). XV. Nilpotent Groups (Generalized, Complete, Locally Nilpotent Torsion-Free,
etc.). Editor's Notes. Bibliography.

—Vol. I. 2nd ed. 1959. 271 pp. 6x9.   [107] **$4.95**
—Vol. II. 2nd ed. 1960. 308 pp. 6x9.   [109] **$4.95**

DIFFERENTIAL AND INTEGRAL CALCULUS
By E. LANDAU

Landau's sparkling *Einführung* in English translation. Completely rigorous, completely self-
contained, borrowing not even the fundamental
theorem of algebra (of which it gives a rigorous
elementary proof), it develops the entire calculus
including Fourier series, starting only with the
properties of the number system. A masterpiece of
rigor and clarity.
—2nd ed. 1960. 372 pp. 6x9.   [78] **$6.00**

ELEMENTARE ZAHLENTHEORIE
By E. LANDAU

"Interest is enlisted at once and sustained by the
accuracy, skill, and enthusiasm with which Landau
marshals ... facts and simplifies ... details."
          —*G. D. Birkhoff, Bulletin of the A. M. S.*
—1927. vii + 180 + iv pp. 5½x8¼.   [26] **$3.50**

FOUNDATIONS OF ANALYSIS

By E. LANDAU

"Certainly no clearer treatment of the foundations of the number system can be offered. . . . One can only be thankful to the author for this fundamental piece of exposition, which is alive with his vitality and genius."—*J. F. Ritt, Amer. Math. Monthly.*

—2nd ed. 1960. 6x9.   [79] **$3.50**

HANDBUCH DER LEHRE VON DER VERTEILUNG DER PRIMZAHLEN

By E. LANDAU

To Landau's monumental work on prime-number theory there has been added, in this edition, two of Landau's papers and an up-to-date guide to the work: an Appendix by Prof. Paul T. Bateman.

—2nd ed., 1953. 1,028 pp. 5½x8½. [96]   **$13.95**

UEBER ANALYSIS

By E. LANDAU, B. RIEMANN, and H. WEYL

—See: Weyl-Landau-Riemann.

MEMOIRES SUR LA THEORIE DES SYSTEMES DES EQUATIONS DIFFERENTIELLES LINEAIRES, Vols. I, II, III

By J. A. LAPPO-DANILEVSKIĬ

THREE VOLUMES IN ONE.

Some of the chapter titles are: General theory of functions of matrices; Analytic theory of matrices; Problem of Poincaré; Systems of equations in neighborhood of a pole; Analytic continuation; Integral equations and their application to the theory of linear differential equations; Riemann's problem; etc.

"The theory of [systems of linear differential equations] is treated with elegance and generality by the author, and his contributions constitute an important addition to the field of differential equations."—*Applied Mechanics Reviews.*

—3 volumes bound as one. 689 pp. 5¼x8¼.   [94] **$10.00**

TOPOLOGY

By S. LEFSCHETZ

CONTENTS: I. Elementary Combinatorial Theory of Complexes. II. Topological Invariance of Homology Characters. III. Manifolds and their Duality Theorems. IV. Intersections of Chains on a Manifold. V. Product Complexes. VI. Transformations of Manifolds, their Coincidences, Fixed Points. VII. Infinite Complexes. VIII. Applications to Analytical and Algebraic Varieties.

—2nd ed. (Corr. repr. of 1st ed.). x + 410 pp. 5¼x8¼.
[116] **$4.95**

VORLESUNGEN ÜBER ZAHLENTHEORIE
By E. LANDAU

The various sections of this important work (Additive, Analytic, Geometric, and Algebraic Number Theory) can be read independently of one another.

—Vol. I, Pt. 2. ✻(Additive Number Theory) xii + 180 pp. Vol. II. (Analytical Number Theory and Geometrical Number Theory) viii + 308 pp. Vol. III. (Algebraic Number Theory and Fermat's Last Theorem) viii + 341 pp. 5¼x8¼. ✻(Vol. I, Pt. 1 is issued as **Elementary Number Theory**.)   Originally publ. at $26.40
[32]   Three vols. in one **$14.00**

ELEMENTARY NUMBER THEORY
By E. LANDAU

The present work is a translation of Prof. Landau's famous *Elementare Zahlentheorie*, with added exercises by Prof. Paul T. Bateman.

PART ONE. Foundations of Number Theory. I. Divisors. II. Prime Numbers, Prime Factorization. III. G.C.D. IV. Number-theoretic Functions. V. Congruences. VI. Quadratic Residues. VII. Pell's Equation. PART TWO. Brun's Theorem and Dirichlet's Theorem. PART THREE. Decomposition into Two, Three, and Four Squares. I. Farey Fractions. II. Dec. into 2 Squares. III. Dec. into 4 Squares. IV. Dec. into 3 Squares. PART FOUR. Class Numbers of Binary Quadratic Forms. II. Classes of Forms. III. Finiteness of Class Number. IV. Primary Representation... VI. Gaussian Sums... IX. Final Formulas for Class Number.

EXERCISES for Parts One, Two, and Three.
—1958. 256 pp. 6x9.   [125]   **$4.95**

EINFÜHRUNG IN DIE ELEMENTARE UND ANALYTISCHE THEORIE DER ALGEBRAISCHE ZAHLEN UND DER IDEALE
By E. LANDAU
—2nd ed. vii + 147 pp. 5½x8.   [62]   **$2.95**

GRUNDLAGEN DER ANALYSIS
By E. LANDAU

The student who wishes to study mathematical German will find Landau's famous *Grundlagen der Analysis* ideally suited to his needs.

Only a few score of German words will enable him to read the entire book with only an occasional glance at the Vocabulary! [A COMPLETE German-English vocabulary, prepared with the novice especially in mind, has been appended to the book.]

—3rd ed. 1960. 173 pp. 5⅜x8.   [24]   Cloth   **$3.50**
[141]   Paper   **$1.95**

CHELSEA SCIENTIFIC BOOKS

ELEMENTS OF ALGEBRA
By HOWARD LEVI

"This book is addressed to beginning students of
mathematics. . . . The level of the book, however, is
so unusually high, mathematically as well as peda-
gogically, that it merits the attention of professional mathematicians (as well as of professional
pedagogues) interested in the wider dissemina-
tion of their subject among cultured people . . . **a
closer approximation to the right way to teach
mathematics to beginners than anything else now
in existence.**"—*Bulletin of the A. M. S.*

—Third ed. 1960. xi + 161 pp. 5⅜x8.   [103] **$3.25**

LE CALCUL DES RÉSIDUS
By E. LINDELÖF

Important applications in a striking diversity of
mathematical fields: statistics, number theory, the
theory of Fourier series, the calculus of finite
differences, mathematical physics and advanced
calculus, as well as function theory itself.

—151 pp. 5½x8½.   [34] **$3.25**

THE THEORY OF MATRICES
By C. C. MacDUFFEE

"No mathematical library can afford to be without
this book."—*Bulletin of the A. M. S.*

—(Ergeb. der Math.) 2nd edition. 116 pp. 6x9. Orig. publ.
at $5.20.   [28] **$2.95**

  MACMAHON, "Introduction . . ." see Klein

COMBINATORY ANALYSIS, Vols. I and II
By P. A. MACMAHON

TWO VOLUMES IN ONE.

A broad and extensive treatise on an important
branch of mathematics.

—xx + 300 + xx + 340 pp. 5⅜x8. [137] Two vols. in one.
        $7.50

FORMULAS AND THEOREMS FOR THE FUNCTIONS OF MATHEMATICAL PHYSICS
By W. MAGNUS and F. OBERHETTINGER

Gathered into a compact, handy and well-arranged
reference work are thousands of results on the
many important functions needed by the physicist,
engineer and applied mathematician.

  Translated by J. WERMER.

—1954. 182 pp. 6x9. German edition was $7.00. [51] **$3.90**

THE DEVELOPMENT OF MATHEMATICS IN CHINA AND JAPAN
By Y. MIKAMI

A scholarly work.

—First ed. 1913. viii + 347 pp. 5⅜x8. Summer, '61.
[149]   **$3.95**

GEOMETRIE DER ZAHLEN
By H. MINKOWSKI
—viii + 256 pp. 5½x8¼.   [93]   **$4.50**

DIOPHANTISCHE APPROXIMATIONEN
By H. MINKOWSKI

"Since the author has given an elementary, entertaining, account, both in geometric and arithmetic language, of some important original results as well as the salient features of a classic theory, but presented in a novel manner, his work is deserving of the attention of the very widest circle of readers."--*L. E. Dickson.*

—viii + 235 pp. 5¼x8¼.   [118]   **$4.50**

MORDELL, "Fermat's Last Theorem," see *Klein*

INVERSIVE GEOMETRY
By F. MORLEY and F. V. MORLEY

CHAPTER HEADINGS: I. Operations of Elementary Geometry. II. Algebra. III. The Euclidean Group. IV. Inversions. V. Quadratics. VI. The Inversive Group of the Plane. VII. Finite Inversive Groups. VIII. Parabolic, Hyperbolic, and Elliptic Geometries. IX. Celestial Sphere. X. Flow. XI. Differential Geometry. XII. The Line and the Circle. XIII. Regular Polygons. XIV. Motions. XV. The Triangle. XVI. Invariants under Homologies. XVII. Rational Curves. XVIII. Conics. XIX. Cardioid and Deltoid. XX. Cremona Transformations. XXI. The n-Line.

—xi + 273 pp. 5¼x8¼.   [101]   **$3.95**

LEHRBUCH DER KOMBINATORIK
By E. NETTO

The standard work on the fascinating subject of Combinatory Analysis.

—Second edition. viii + 348 pp. 5x8 in.   [123]   **$4.95**

VORLESUNGEN ÜBER DIFFERENZENRECHNUNG
By N. H. NÖRLUND
—ix + 551 pp. 5x8. Orig. publ. at $11.50.   [100]   **$5.95**

DIOPHANTISCHE GLEICHUNGEN
By T. SKOLEM

"This comprehensive presentation . . . should be warmly welcomed. We recommend the book most heartily."—*Acta Szeged.*

—(Ergeb. der Math.) 1938. ix + 130 pp. 5½x8½. Cloth. Orig. publ. at $6.50. [75] **$3.50**

ALGEBRAISCHE THEORIE DER KOERPER
By E. STEINITZ

"Epoch-making."—*A. Haar, Aca Szeged.*
—177 pp. including two appendices. 5¼x8¼. [77] **$3.25**

INTERPOLATION
By J. F. STEFFENSEN

"A landmark in the history of the subject.

"Starting from scratch, the author deals with formulae of interpolation, construction of tables, inverse interpolation, summation of formulae, the symbolic calculus, interpolation with several variables, in a clear, elegant and rigorous manner . . . The student . . . will be rewarded by a comprehensive view of the whole field. . . . A classic account which no serious student can afford to neglect."—*Mathematical Gazette.*

—1950. 2nd ed. 256 pp. 5¼x8¼. Orig. $8.00. [71] **$4.95**

A HISTORY OF THE MATHEMATICAL THEORY OF PROBABILITY
By I. TODHUNTER

Introduces the reader to *almost every process and every species of problem which the literature of the subject can furnish.* Hundreds of problems are solved in detail.

—640 pp. 5¼x8. Previously publ. at $8.00. [57] **$6.00**

SET TOPOLOGY
By R. VAIDYANATHASWAMY

In this text on Topology, the first edition of which was published in India, the concept of partial order has been made the unifying theme.

Over 500 exercises for the reader enrich the text.

CHAPTER HEADINGS: I. Algebra of Subsets of a Set. II. Rings and Fields of Sets. III. Algebra of Partial Order. IV. The Closure Function. V. Neighborhood Topology. VI. Open and Closed Sets. VII. Topological Maps. VIII. The Derived Set in T_1 Space. IX. The Topological Product. X. Convergence in Metrical Space. XI. Convergence Topology.

—2nd ed. 1960. vi + 305 pp. 6x9. [139] **$6.00**

LECTURES ON THE GENERAL THEORY OF INTEGRAL FUNCTIONS
By G. VALIRON
—1923. xii + 208 pp. 5¼x8.   [56]   **$3.50**

GRUPPEN VON LINEAREN TRANSFORMATIONEN
By B. L. VAN DER WAERDEN
—(Ergeb. der Math.) 1935. 94 pp. 5½x8½.   [45]   **$2.50**

LEHRBUCH DER ALGEBRA
By H. WEBER

The bible of classical algebra, still unsurpassed for its clarity and completeness. Much of the material on elliptic functions is not available elsewhere in connected form.

PARTIAL CONTENTS: *VOL. I.* CHAP. I. Rational Functions. II. Determinants. III. Roots of Algebraic Equations. V. Symmetric Functions. V. Linear Transformations. Invariants. VI. Tchirnhaus Transformation. VII. Reality of Roots. VIII. Sturm's Theorem. X. Limits on Roots. X. Approximate Computation of Roots. XI. Continued Fractions. XII. Roots of Unity. XIII. Galois Theory. XIV. Applications of Permutation Group to Equations. XV. Cyclic Equations. XVI. Kreisteilung. XVII. Algebraic Solution of Equations. XVIII. Roots of Metacyclic Equations.

VOL. II. CHAPS. I.-V. Group Theory. VI.-X. Theory of Linear Groups. XI.-XVI. Applications of Group Theory (General Equation of Fifth Degree. The Group G_{168} and Equations of Seventh Degree . . .). XVII.-XXIV. Algebraic Numbers. XXV. Transcendental Numbers.

VOL. III. CHAP. I. Elliptic Integral. II. Theta Functions. III. Transformation of Theta Functions. IV. Elliptic Functions. V. Modular Function. V. Multiplication of Elliptic Functions. Division. VII. Equations of Transformation. VIII. Groups of the Transformation Equations and the Equation of Fifth Degree . . . XI.-XVI. Quadratic Fields. XVII. Elliptic Functions and Quadratic Forms. XVIII. Galois Group of Class Equation. XIX. Computation of Class Invariant . . . XII. Cayley's Development of Modular Function. XXIII. Class Fields. XXIV.-XXVI. Algebraic Functions. XXVII. Algebraic and Abelian Differentials.

—Ready, Fall, '61. 3rd ed. (C. repr. of 2nd ed.). 2,345 pp. 5x8.
[144]   Three vol. set.   Probably   **$19.50**

DATE DUE

MAY 3 0 1970		
MAY 28 1970		
GAYLORD		PRINTED IN U.S.A